ION EXCHANGE AND SOLVENT EXTRACTION

Volume 5

ION EXCHANGE AND SOLVENT EXTRACTION

A Series of Advances

Volume 5

EDITED BY

JACOB A. MARINSKY

DEPARTMENT OF CHEMISTRY
STATE UNIVERSITY OF NEW YORK AT BUFFALO
BUFFALO, NEW YORK

YIZHAK MARCUS

DEPARTMENT OF INORGANIC CHEMISTRY
THE HEBREW UNIVERSITY
JERUSALEM, ISRAEL

1973
MARCEL DEKKER, INC., New York

MARCEL DEKKER, INC.
95 Madison Avenue, New York, New York 10016

LIBRARY OF CONGRESS CATALOG CARD NUMBER: 66-29027
ISBN: 0-8247-6061-1

PRINTED IN THE UNITED STATES OF AMERICA

PREFACE

It was pointed out in the previous volume of this series that the combination of "Ion Exchange" and "Solvent Extraction Reviews" into one series with the title "Ion Exchange and Solvent Extraction - A Series of Advances" will not affect the philosophy and objectives of presentation of material devoted to these topics which will continue to be dealt with in separate volumes. This fifth volume, devoted to ion exchange, provides the reader with a timely consideration of several important applications of the ion-exchange phenomenon. Volume 5, together with Volume 4, provides an appropriate extension of the consideration of the ion-exchange phenomenon that was provided in the first two volumes.

In these volumes an in-depth examination and expansion of a particularly important topic is ensured by the presentation of material which complements its introduction in earlier volumes of the series. New and exciting directions of research in various aspects of ion exchange are introduced to the reader (1) in the course of such development of a topic and (2) by the introduction of new topics. In addition important applications of the ion-exchange phenomenon are discussed.

Emphasis on extension of the boundaries of the problem under discussion continues to be sought from each author. Provocative speculation by the author is encouraged for this purpose. By this modus operandi, each chapter is provided with a broader base than a technical paper, which makes it more informative than a review paper and of considerable interest to practitioners in a spectrum of disciplines.

The scholarly examination of ion exchange in nonaqueous and mixed solvents that was presented in Volume 4 provides an appropriate extension of the earlier consideration of ion exchange in aqueous and molten systems that was presented in previous volumes. Similarly, the chapter on ligand exchange chromatography that appears in this volume is a suitable sequel to the earlier treatise in Volume 2 on ion-exchange behavior of sugars, sugar

alcohols, and sugar derivatives. The discussion of liquid ion-exchange technology, also presented in Volume 4, complements the chapter on the fundamentals of liquid ion exchange that was presented in Volume 1 of this series.
A stimulating and provocative consideration of organic semiconductors and
redox exchangers is affected by a probing analysis of their electronic and ion-
exchange properties as well as their conductivity and permselectivity in
another chapter of Volume 4. Finally, a chapter that outlines methods for the
quantitative estimate of ion binding in ion-exchange resins and their linear
polyelectrolyte analogs is presented in this volume to provide the nucleus
for further consideration of this aspect in future volumes of this series.

In Volume 5 analytical applications of the ion-exchange process are
emphasized. There is a detailed analysis of the ion-exchange properties of
new inorganic exchangers to provide an appropriate extension of the discussion of materials other than the commercial synthetic organic ion-exchange
resins that was initiated with consideration of glasses and zeolites in Volume
2 and organic semiconductors and redox exchangers in Volume 4.

J. A. Marinsky

CONTRIBUTORS TO THIS VOLUME

R. H. BLESSING, Department of Chemistry, State University of New York at Buffalo, Buffalo, New York

A. CLEARFIELD, Department of Chemistry, Ohio University, Athens, Ohio

CSABA HORVATH, Department of Engineering and Applied Science, Yale University, New Haven, Connecticut

G. H. NANCOLLAS, Department of Chemistry, State University of New York at Buffalo, Buffalo, New York

F. W. E. STRELOW, National Chemical Research Laboratory, Pretoria, South Africa

CONTENTS

CONTENTS OF OTHER VOLUMES

VOLUME 1

---

*Present address: Division of Biophysics and Neurobiology, Meharry Medical College, Nashville, Tennessee

*Present address: Department of Chemistry, University of the Negev,
Beersheba, Israel

VOLUME 6

ION EXCHANGE AND SOLVENT EXTRACTION

Volume 5

Chapter 1

NEW INORGANIC ION EXCHANGERS*

A. Clearfield, G. H. Nancollas, and R. H. Blessing

*The authors acknowledge the award of grants by the Office of Saline
Waters (G. H. N.) and the National Science Foundation (A. C.) during the
tenure of which much of their research in inorganic ion exchangers was
accomplished.

I. INTRODUCTION

The early ion exchangers were largely inorganic in origin, but subsequently, the ion exchange scene was dominated by the synthetic organic resins because of the ease with which reproducible preparations could be made, and their excellent mechanical and chemical stability. In addition, the organic resins possessed physical characteristics and exhibited ion exchange behavior which could be reproduced from sample to sample. In recent years interest in the inorganic exchangers has been revived with the need for the high temperature separation of ionic components in radioactive wastes. In order to make such separations, highly selective exchangers are required which are not only stable at high temperatures but which also have exchange properties unaffected by acidity and high levels of radiation. Organic ion exchange resins are unsuitable for such applications, as changes in selectivity and capacity occur on exposure to radiation, and degradation takes place at the high temperatures of interest. As a result of this renewed interest in the inorganic materials, two types of ion exchangers were developed: (1) the insoluble salts of polybasic acids with polyvalent metals; and (2) the hydrous oxides of polyvalent metals. Much of the pioneering work in this area was done by research groups at the Oak Ridge National Laboratory led by K. A. Kraus [1,2], and in the United Kingdom under C. B. Amphlett [3,4]. In this chapter we consider first zirconium phosphates, which as a group are probably the ion exchangers most extensively studied. The remaining polybasic acid salts, including salts of heteropoly anions, are then described, particularly in respect to the unique differences between them and zirconium phosphate. Finally, the hydrous oxide exchangers are discussed.

II. ZIRCONIUM PHOSPHATE ION EXCHANGERS

Zirconium phosphate has been known for over a hundred years [5] but its use as an ion exchanger is of rather recent origin [6]. The development of zirconium phosphate as an ion exchanger stemmed largely from an interest in the separation of metal ions, particularly those of the alkali metals, under high temperature aqueous conditions such as those obtaining in homogeneous aqueous reactor applications. Although early cation sorption work was concerned largely with the alkali metals encountered in nuclear fuel processing, such as cesium, it was shown that good separations were also possible with cations of different oxidation states such as Y^{3+} and UO_2^{2+} [4,7,8]. The extraordinarily high selectivity of zirconium phosphate for cesium, as compared with the other alkali metal ions, is one of the most interesting and useful characteristics of the exchangers, and is discussed later. More recently, zirconium phosphate has found potential application in many other areas. In electrodialysis applications, membranes of zirconium phosphate withstand conditions of temperature and pressure which cause deterioration of their organic counterparts, making them attractive for desalination applications [9, 10], and for use in hydrogen-oxygen fuel cells [11, 12, 13]. Paper impregnated with zirconium phosphate has been successfully used for the rapid chromatographic separations of two and four valent metal ions, and of amino acids and alkaloids [14]. The high selectivity of zirconium phosphate for ammonium ions in the presence of sodium ions, has prompted the investigation of its use in artificial kidneys [15]. Used in conjunction with urease, zirconium phosphate has the capability of rapidly removing all the ammonium ion from the hydrolysis or urea dialyzed from blood, while enabling the control of other salts in the bloodstream.

The solid precipitates which are commonly called zirconium phosphate range from amorphous gels to several well defined crystalline compounds. Amorphous gels or gels of low crystallinity were used in the initial ion exchange studies. These were prepared by reaction of a soluble phosphate or phosphoric acid with solutions of Zr (IV) salts under a variety of conditions [4]. The composition and behavior of the gels depend upon the conditions of preparation and other factors as described in Sections II. G and II. H.

Heating slurries of zirconium phosphate gels in strong phosphoric acid results in the formation of a crystalline phosphate, zirconium bis(monohydrogen orthophosphate) monohydrate, $Zr(HPO_4)_2 \cdot H_2O$ [16,17]. Since this discovery, a variety of crystalline phases has been prepared. These are listed in Table 1 together with their method of preparation. The various phases have been differentiated by assignment of Greek letters as prefixes. This is not strictly proper usage since the phases may differ in composition. However, some of the phases having identical compositions are not related to each other by polymorphic transitions. Thus, the assignment of Greek letter prefixes only to polymorphs would lead to confusion. Instead, the prefixes have been assigned to the crystalline phases in the approximate chronological order of their discovery.

It will be shown below that α-ZrP has a layered structure with an interlayer distance of 7.56 Å. The first reflection in the x-ray powder pattern of the crystals represents this interlayer distance. During exchange the layers expand or contract, so that observation of the behavior of the first reflection during exchange provides a diagnostic tool by which to follow the reaction. Similar phenomena are observed with some of the other crystalline phases. Therefore, by analogy, the first reflection for each of these phases is taken to represent their interlayer separation, and serves to distinguish one form from another. These interplanar spacings are included in Table 1.

It is also possible to prepare zirconium phosphates with crystallinities intermediate between those of the gels and the fully crystalline material.

These forms have been termed semicrystalline zirconium phosphates. The
structure and behavior of each of the forms of zirconium phosphate starting
with the crystalline ones are discussed in turn.

A. Zirconium bis (monohydrogen orthophosphate) monohydrate α-ZrP

This is the best known crystalline form of zirconium phosphate and the one
on which the most work has been done.

1. Preparation of the Crystals

Truly crystalline α-ZrP, as distinguished from semicrystalline
materials described in later sections, is prepared by refluxing slurries of
the gels in 10-15 M phosphoric acid [16,17]. The gel may be prepared
separately or in situ. A large excess of phosphoric acid insures complete
crystallization in a reasonable time, and also facilities stirring of the
mixture. The mechanism of crystallization is undoubtedly one involving dissolution of the gel and nucleation and growth of crystals. An electron micro-
graph of the product prepared by rapid precipitation in the cold is shown in
Fig. 1a and is typical of an amorphous structure [18]. On refluxing, dark
centers develop, indicative of nuclei formation while the surface of the gel
particles become smoother (Fig. 1b). Finally hexagonal platelets are
obtained as shown in Fig. 1c. Larger crystals can be grown by refluxing for
longer times in strong phosphoric acid. Qualitative data [19] show that the
rate of crystallization and the rate of growth of the crystals increases
exponentially with increasing temperature and phosphoric acid concentration.
These rates are roughly proportional to the solubility of the crystals in the
same acid media [20].

Crystallization of the gels may also be effected by boiling aqueous
slurries to which a small amount of hydrofluoric acid has been added [18].
The crystals obtained in this way and also by the phosphoric acid method are
less than a micron in size. Crystals large enough for column operation have
been prepared by Alberti and Torracca [21]. A zirconium salt is dissolved
in dilute hydrofluoric acid, and phosphoric acid is added to approach, but not
exceed, saturation. The solution is then concentrated by evaporation to
obtain the crystals.

TABLE 1

Crystalline Zirconium Phosphate Phases which Exhibit Ion Exchange Properties

Formula	Proposed designation	Interlayer spacing (Å)	Method of preparation	Ref.
$Zr(HPO_4)_2 \cdot H_2O$	α-ZrP	7.56	Reflux ZrP gel in 10-15M phosphoric acid	[16, 17]
$Zr(HPO_4)_2$	β-ZrP	9.4	Dry γ-ZrP	[17, 45]
$Zr(HPO_2)_2 \cdot 2H_2O$	γ-ZrP	12.2	Reflux ZrP gel in acid solution of sodium phosphate	[17, 45]
$Zr(HPO_4)_2 \cdot 1/2H_2O$	δ-ZrP[a]	7.13	Reflux ZrP gel in enriched phosphoric acid	[26, 32, 43]
$Zr(HPO_4)_2$	ϵ-ZrP[a]	5.59	Reflux ZrP gel in enriched phosphoric acid	[26, 32, 43]
$Zr(HPO_4)_2$	ζ-ZrP	7.41	Heat α-ZrP 100-200°C	[31, 43]
$Zr(HPO_4)_2$	η-ZrP	7.37	Heat α-ZrP 250°-300°C	[31, 43]
$Zr(HPO_4)_2 \cdot 8H_2O$	θ-ZrP	10.4	Wash $Zr(NaPO_4)(HPO_4) \cdot 5H_2O$ with acid	[29, 35]
Not established	i-ZrP	7.73	Wash $Zr(NaPO_4)_2$, Phase H, with acid	[46]
Not established	k-ZrP	6.11	Dissolve α-ZrP in HF, boil and add SiO_2	[49]
Not established	PO_4/Zr=2.2[a]		$ZrOCl_2 \cdot 8H_2O$ + fused H_3PO_4 at 100-120°C	[35]

$Zr(HPO_4)(H_2PO_4)_2$	α–ZrTP	$ZrOCl_2$(Anhyd) + fused H_3PO_4 at 85°C	[35]
$Zr(HPO_4)(H_2PO_4)_2$	β–ZrTP	$ZrOCl_2 \cdot 8H_2O$ + fused H_3PO_4 at 70°C	[35]

[a] Ion exchange behavior has not yet been firmly established.

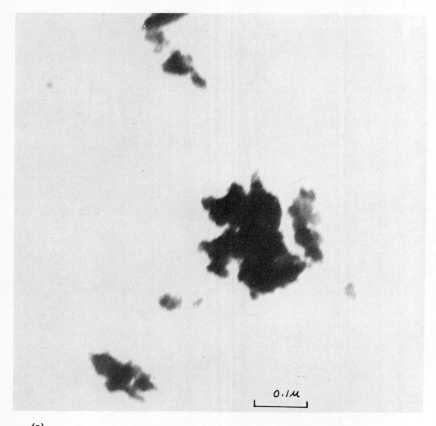

(a)

FIG. 1.   Electron micrographs of zirconium phosphates:

    a.   Gel prepared in 0.35 M H_3PO_4 (sample No. XII, Ref. 16)

    b.   Semi-Crystalline α-ZrP prepared by reflux of Gel in
        2.65 M H_3PO_4 (Sample No. XV, Ref. 16)

    c.   Crystalline α-ZrP prepared by reflux of Gel in
        12 M H_3PO_4.

Crystals suitable for the x-ray studies described in Section II.A.3 were obtained by heating the microcrystals with 12-14 M phosphoric acid in sealed quartz tubes at 150-180°C for several weeks.

(b)

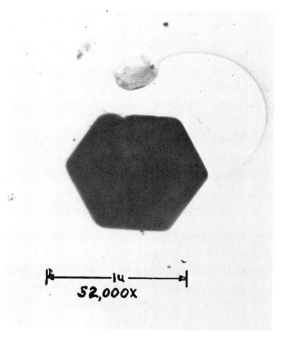

(c)

9

2. Characterization of α-ZrP

The composition of the crystals prepared under different conditions was found to be $ZrO_2 \cdot P_2O_5 \cdot 2H_2O$ provided the crystals were dried to constant weight over P_2O_5 or $CaCl_2$. The crystals lose one mole of water reversibly at 100° C without drastic change in the x-ray pattern (however, see Section II. B) or loss of ion exchange capacity. Above 400° C a second mole of water is lost with accompanying loss of crystallinity and ion exchange behavior. And finally, heating to 750° C or higher results in the formation of ZrP_2O_7. Potentiometric titrations of the original crystals showed that they contain two moles of replaceable hydrogen ion per formula weight. On the basis of these results, the formula $Zr(HPO_4)_2 \cdot H_2O$ was assigned to the crystals [16,17].

Additional evidence supporting the above formula has been presented by other investigators. Albertsson obtained dehydration results very similar to those described above (Fig. 2) [22] whereas, Alberti and co-workers [23] observed the onset of pyrophosphate formation at 300 to 350°C. However, infrared studies indicate that the phosphate groups begin to condense at 450° C [24]. An almost amorphous intermediate phase was observed to form during the water removal, and this phase crystallized as ZrP_2O_7 at 750° C. The lower temperature observed by Alberti and Torracca may have been due to the presence of excess phosphate ion, which has been shown to induce pyrophosphate formation at lower temperatures [16].

Albertsson also confirmed the presence of two moles of replaceable hydrogen ion per formula weight of α-ZrP. The evidence cited above together with the crystal structure study described in the next section firmly establish the formula of a α-ZrP crystals as $Zr(HPO_4)_2 \cdot H_2O$.

3. Crystal Structure of α-ZrP

In addition to α-ZrP, the corresponding titanium phosphate, $Ti(HPO_4)_2 \cdot H_2O$, designated α-TiP and zirconium arsenate, $Zr(HAsO_4)_2 \cdot H_2O$ designated α-ZrAs have the same structure [25-27]. These compounds are monoclinic with the unit cell dimensions given in Table 2.

The structure is a layered one [25], a portion of which is shown in Fig. 3. The zirconium atoms lie very nearly in a plane and are bridged by phosphate groups situated alternately above and below the plane of the metal atoms. Any three adjacent metal atoms in the same layer form a slightly

TABLE 2

Unit Cell Dimensions of α-ZrP Type Crystals

Compound	Cell dimensions				Ref.
	a (Å)	b (Å)	c (Å)	β (deg)	
α-ZrP	9.076±0.003	5.298±0.006	16.22±0.02	111.5±0.1	[25]
α-ZrP	9.097±0.005	5.307±0.001	16.284±0.003	111.38±0.01	[28]
α-ZrAs	9.178±0.004	5.378±0.002	16.55±0.01	111.3±0.1	[27]
α-TiP	8.631±0.001	5.002±0.001	16.176±0.002	110.20±0.01	[26]

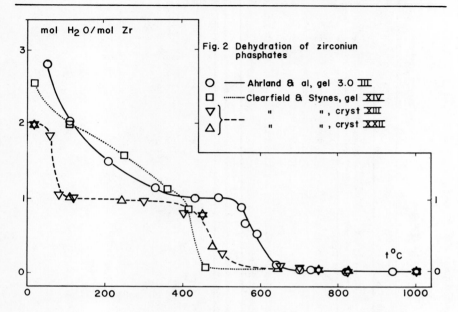

FIG. 2. Dehydration behavior of crystalline and gel zirconium phosphates (Reprinted from Ref. 8 by permission of Acta. Chem. Scand.)

distorted equilateral triangle. The phosphate groups are located such that
the phosphorus atoms are near the centers of the triangles about 1.2 Å above
or below the plane. Three oxygen atoms of each phosphate group are bonded
to the three metal atoms composing the triangle. This produces an almost
perfect octahedral coordination of oxygen atoms around the zirconium with
an average Zr-O distance of 2.07 Å. The layered arrangement creates a
hexagonal pseudocell with $a_h \cong 5.24$ Å and $c_h \cong 22.6$ Å.

The fourth oxygen atom of each phosphate group is not bonded to
zirconium and presumably bears the hydrogen atom. The two phosphate
groups (per α-ZrP formula weight) occupy slightly different positions
relative to the layers. In the one labelled P(3) (Fig. 4), the P(3) - O(10)
bond is directed almost perpendicular to the metal atom plane. The other
phosphate group has the P(2) - O(7) bond tilted away from the perpendicular.
This tilting produces a low tetrahedral bond angle of 102.6° for the O(7) -
P(2) - O(5) bond angle. Almost the same positioning of the arsenate groups
is present in α-ZrAs [27]. This difference in the two phosphate groups

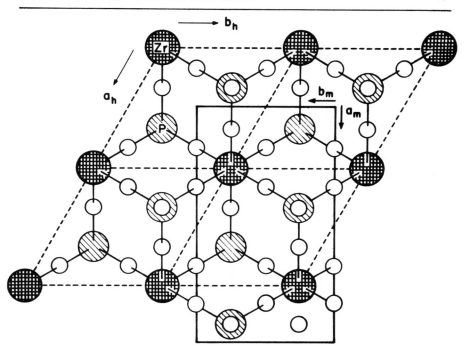

FIG. 3. Idealized layer in the α-ZrP structure showing relationship of pseudo-hexagonal cell (broken lines) to the true monoclinic cell (solid lines). (Reprinted from Ref. 25 by permission of Inorg. Chem.)

may be responsible for the differing acidities of their protons, as discussed below.

The layers in α-ZrP are situated relative to each other such that, if a line is drawn perpendicular to a layer at a metal atom, it will intersect a phosphorus atom in an adjacent layer. This arrangement produces cavities of the type shown in Fig. 4, with the water molecule, O(12), situated near the center of the cavity. There is one such cavity per α-ZrP formula in the crystal.

The cavity may be thought of as being built up of sides and faces. A typical side would be $Zr - O_7'' - P_2 - O_5 - Zr - O_7 - P_2 - O_6'$, and a typical face $Zr - O_6 - P_2 - O_4' - Zr - O_6' - P_2 - O_4$. The largest free distance in the sides occurs between zirconium and O_{10} type oxygwns and these distances are large enough to allow a spherical ion of 2.63 Å diameter to diffuse into

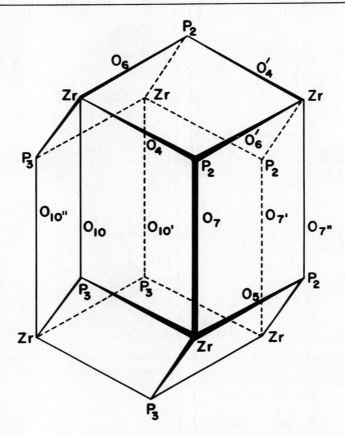

FIG. 4. Idealized picture of a cavity formed by two adjacent layers in
α-ZrP. To preserve clarity not all the oxygens have been shown. (Reprinted from Ref. 25 by permission of <u>Inorg. Chem.</u>)

the cavity without obstruction [29]. The largest free distance in the
faces is 2.4 Å.

The positions of the hydrogen atoms in the structure were not determined
from the x-ray data. Thus, the hydrogen bonding scheme is open to speculation. The possible hydrogen bond distances in α-ZrP and α-ZrAs are given
in Table 3. One possible arrangement of hydrogen bonds is that in which
the shortest hydrogen bonds originate from the two P-OH groups with water
as the acceptor atom. The bonding scheme would be O(7) - H · · · O(12) and
O(10) - H · · · O(12). The hydrogen atoms of the water molecule would form

TABLE 3

Possible Hydrogen Bond Distances in α-ZrP and α-ZAs[a]

	Phosphate	Arsenate
$O_{12} - O_7$	3.06(6)	3.18(2)
$O_{12} - O''_{10}$	2.78(3)	2.80(2)
$O_{12} - O'_7$	2.82(6)	2.78(2)
$O''_{10} - O_{10}$	3.07(6)	3.01(2)
$O''_{10} - O'_{10}$	3.07(6)	3.01(2)

[a] Estimated standard deviations in the last significant figure are given in parenthesis.

no hydrogen bonds or, at best, one long bond to O(7) in the phosphate. There are no interlayer hydrogen bonds in this scheme, so that the layers are held together by van der Waals forces. This scheme suffers from the disadvantages that it offers no explanation for the differing acidities of the two exchangeable protons.

An alternative hydrogen bond arrangement is that in which the water molecule forms the two hydrogen bonds O(12) - H$\cdots$O'(7) and O''(12) - H$\cdots$ O(10). One phosphate group then forms a very weak bond to water [P(2) - O(7) - H$\cdots$ O(12)] and the other forms very weak interlayer bonds of the type P(3) - O(10) - H$\cdots$O'(10). The first three hydrogen bonds are intralayer.

In either case the forces between layers in α-ZrP type exchangers are very weak and permit the crystals to expand and contract during exchange. This behavior is described in Section II.A.5. Additional evidence on the nature of the hydrogen bonding must await the results of a neutron diffraction study, or a more complete interpretation of infrared data. The results of preliminary infrared studies are given in Section II.A.4.

4. Infrared Studies on α-ZrP

Table 4 lists the infrared absorption bands observed for α-ZrP in the range of 200 to 4000 cm^{-1}. These data represent the results of four independent studies [18, 30-32], and are of interest mainly as a means of clarifying the hydrogen bonding scheme in α-ZrP. There are four bands in the OH stretching region, corresponding to the fact that there are four OH groups in α-ZrP. Mounier and Winand [31] ascribe the peak at 3150 cm^{-1} to water coordinated to zirconium, and the peak at 3510 cm^{-1} or 3590 cm^{-1} to a hydroxyl group attached to zirconium. They postulate the existence of two tautomeric forms in crystalline zirconium phosphates (P:Zr = 2), schematically given as:

The water molecule is dissociated by the polarizing force of the zirconium, and at the same time hydrolyzes a Zr-O-P linkage. Evidence for such tautomerism was strongest in the infrared, where two sharp peaks were found at 3570 cm^{-1} and 3610 cm^{-1}, identifiable with the vibration of OH$^-$ groups of basic character. The position of the water peak in the ir at 3150 cm^{-1} implies that this water is strongly bound. Certain anomalies were also observed in the heating curves, in that the temperature at which the zeolitic water was expelled was a function of the heating rate. This was interpreted to indicate that the rate of water loss from (1) was faster than the reverse step in the tautomerism. Metal ion exchange would then occur initially with the more acid $H_2PO_4^-$ of form (2) displacing the equilibrium in this direction until neutralization was complete. It was found that for the half-exchanged metal ion forms, the infrared peak for the zeolitic water was at 3500 cm^{-1}, and the bands attributed to a basic OH$^-$ group were no longer

TABLE 4

Infrared Spectrum of α-ZrP and Tentative Band Assignments[a]

Band (cm^{-1})	Intensity	Assignment (tentative)			
		Ref. [31]	Ref. [32]	Ref. [24,30]	Ref. [18]
3590	M, shp	ν_{OH} Basic	ν_{OH}	$\nu_{OH}(HPO_4)$	
3510	W, shp	ν_{H_2O} Zeolitic	ν_{OH}	$\nu_{OH}(HPO_4)$	
3300–3350	W, sh	ν_{OH} Acidic weak H bond	ν_{H_2O}	ν_{H_2O}	
3150	M, b	ν_{H_2O} coord. to Zr	ν_{H_2O}	ν_{H_2O} (strong H bond)	
2350	VW, b	ν_{OH} Acidic strong H bond	ν_{OH}	Not obs.	Not obs.
1620	W	δ_{H_2O}	δ_{H_2O}	δ_{H_2O}	δ_{H_2O}
1340	VW				
1250	M, shp	δ_{P-OH}	δ_{P-OH}	δ_{P-OH}	δ_{P-OH}
1120	S, sh	ν_{P-O}	ν_{P-O}	$\nu^{as}_{PO_3}$	ν^{as}_{PO}
1075	S, b		ν_{P-O}	$\nu^{as}_{PO_3}$	ν^{as}_{PO}
1045	VS, B	ν_{P-O}	ν_{P-O}	$\nu^{as}_{PO_3}$	$\nu^{as}_{PO_3}$
965	S	ν_{P-O}	ν_{P-O}	ν^{s}_{P-O}	ν^{s}_{P-O}
650	W, b			$\nu_{L}(H_2O)$	
610	VW, sh			$\nu_{L}(H_2O)$	
600	M		$\delta_s PO_2$	$\delta^{as}_{PO_2}$	
530	M	δ_{P-O} or ν_{Zr-O}	$\delta_s PO_2$	$\delta^{as}_{PO_2}$ or ν_{Zr-O}	

TABLE 4 (Cont)

Band (cm^{-1})	Intensity	Ref. [31]	Assignment (tentative)		
			Ref. [32]	Ref. [24,30]	Ref. [18]
508	W, sh		ν_1Zr-O	$\delta^{as}_{PO_2}$	
415	W		$\delta_{as}PO_2$	$\delta^{as}_{PO_2}$	
400	W – M		$\delta_{as}PO_2$		
375	W – M		$\delta_{as}PO_2$		
270	M, b		ν_2Zr-O		

[a] Symbols: S = strong; M = medium; W = weak; B = broad; shp = sharp; sh = shoulder.

present. It was concluded that the form was ZrM (HPO_4)$_2H_2O$ and tautomerism was absent; the second metal ion then exchanges with the less acid HPO_4 hydrogen at higher pH giving $ZrM_2(PO_4)_2H_2O$. This explanation requires the presence of the zeolitic water molecule and does not seem consistent with the changes in distribution coefficients for Cs$^+$ exchange with dehydration of the exchanger [48], unless the necessary water comes from the hydrated incoming ion or rehydration of the exchanger. Furthermore, the tautomerism is not consistent with the crystal structure of α-ZrP, which shows that neither a hydroxyl group nor a coordinated water molecule is present.

Deabridges [32] attributes the bands at 3150 cm^{-1} and 3320 cm^{-1} to the OH stretch of interstitial water, and the band at 1620 cm^{-1} to its bending mode. He argues that on heating α-ZrP between 100 and 160°C, where the interstitial water is lost these bands disappear. Further, on preparing $Zr(HPO_4)_2 \cdot D_2O$, these peaks shift to 2450 cm^{-1}, 2300 cm^{-1} and 1380 cm^{-1}, respectively. The peaks at 3590 and 3510 cm^{-1} are attributed to the O-H stretch of the acidic phosphate groups. The fact that the two peaks do not coincide was taken as an indication that the two monohydrogen phosphate groups differ in acidity as shown by the titration curves (Fig. 5 and Section II. A. 5).

A more detailed analysis of the infra-red spectrum was given by Vesely and his co-workers [24,30]. In essence their conclusions are similar to those of Deabridges, with some improvements. Symmetric and antisymmetric stretching vibrations for the phosphate group are to be expected in the region of 950 to 1180 cm^{-1}. The fact that there are four strong absorption bands in this region instead of the expected three led Veseley et al. to conclude that the two phosphate groups are nonequivalent. That these absorption bands, as well as the one at 1250 cm^{-1} are indeed due to P-O vibrations, was shown by examination of the infrared spectrum of α-ZrAs, $Zr(HAsO_4)_2 \cdot H_2O$ [18]. In this compound the OH and water absorption bands appear at almost exactly the same positions, as in the phosphate, but the bands at 965 to 1250 cm^{-1} are shifted to lower energies by about 200 cm^{-1}. The peak at 1250 cm^{-1} is assigned to the in plane deformation of the P-OH group. In the stretching region the following assignments were made: The bands at 3150 cm^{-1} and 3300 cm^{-1} were attributed to strong hydrogen bonds from the water OH groups to the hydrogen bearing oxygens of the phosphate groups; the bands at 3510 and 3590 cm^{-1} are then due to the long hydrogen bonds P-O - H --O-H and $P - O - H --- O\begin{smallmatrix} \diagup H \\ \diagdown H \end{smallmatrix}$. This is equivalent to the second hydrogen bonding scheme presented in Section II. A. 3. Partially deuterating α-ZrP shifted the peak at 3590 cm^{-1} to a doublet at 2667 cm^{-1} and 2637 cm^{-1}. The peak at 3510 cm^{-1} also formed a doublet at 2594 cm^{-1} and 2570 cm^{-1}, and the peak at 3150 cm^{-1} shifted to 2382 cm^{-1}. On heating to 260°C all of these peaks coalesced to a band at 2485 cm^{-1}. These results are somewhat at variance with those given by Deabridges for the deuterated product, and indicate that his assignments of the water peaks may not be as straight-forward as indicated.

Clearfield [18] found that equilibration of α-ZrP crystals with liquid D_2O gave the same results as those obtained by Vesely et al. However, when the α-ZrP was heated at 110° to remove the zeolitic water and then equilibrated with D_2O vapor or liquid, a new peak appeared in the deuterated spectrum at 2460 cm^{-1}, in agreement with Deabridges. In addition the original peak at 3150 cm^{-1} and the shoulder at ~ 3300 cm^{-1} were now resolved into two distinct peaks at 3150 cm^{-1} and 3290 cm^{-1}. The positions of the peaks

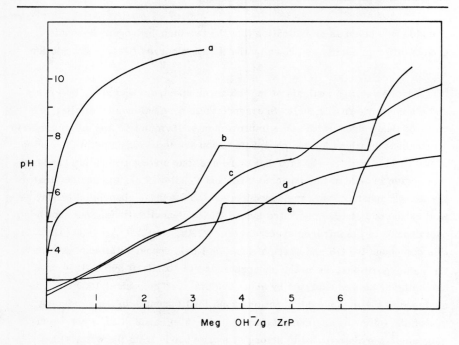

FIG. 5. Potentiometric titration curves for zirconium phosphates of different crystallinities. Curve a, crystalline ZrP titrated with 0.1 M CsOH. Curve b, crystalline ZrP titrated with 0.1 M NaOH. Curve c, gelatinous ZrP titrated with 0.1 M NaCl + 0.1 M NaOH. Curve d, semi-crystalline ZrP titrated with 0.1 M NaOH. Curve e, crystalline ZrP titrated with 0.1 M NaCl + 0.1 M NaOH. (Curves a, b, c, and e reproduced, by permission, from J. Inorg. Nucl. Chem. 26, 117 (1964)).

at 3510 and 3590 cm^{-1} remained fixed during these changes. Since the phosphate groups are held rather rigidly in the crystal, whereas the water molecule is easily lost or recovered, it is likely that the peaks at 3150 cm^{-1} and 3300 cm^{-1} do originate with the water molecule.

The infrared studies, while not completely definitive, are in qualitative agreement with certain features of the crystal structure. They tend to corroborate the observation that the two phosphate groups have different orientations. Also, the four peaks in the OH stretch region indicate the existence of four O-H···O type hydrogen bonds. The question is whether the short hydrogen bonds involve P-O-H···O type bonds, the O-H···O type, or one of each. Strong hydrogen bonding shifts the OH stretching mode to lower frequencies and greatly broadens the peak [33]. Thus, the bands at 3150 and 3300 cm^{-1} must represent those for the strong hydrogen bonds, whereas the very sharp bands at higher frequencies represent the weaker bonds. While the evidence points towards the stronger hydrogen bonds originating with the water molecule hydrogens as donors, further evidence will be required on this point.

5. Ion Exchange Properties of α-ZrP

The ion exchange behavior of α-ZrP is conditioned by two features of its structure, the size of the openings into the cavities, and the weak forces holding the layers together. The crystals do not swell in water, so that the size of the cavities determined on a dry crystal is the same as that encountered by exchanging cations. In Section II.A.3, it was shown that the largest opening into the cavity would allow a spherical cation of 2.63 Å to diffuse unobstructed into the cavity. Experimentally it is found that Li^+, Na^+ and K^+ do exchange in acid solution but Rb^+ and Cs^+ do not [16]. This behavior indicates that unhydrated or, for small cations, partially hydrated cations are exchanged.

When α-ZrP is titrated with alkali metal cations (mixtures of MCl + MOH), two types of behavior are noted. With lithium, sodium, and potassium ions, exchange begins at acidic pH values and continues until half of the hydrogen ions are displaced. Then the pH rises and the remainder of the hydrogen ion is exchanged [16, 19, 29, 31, 34-38]. With rubidium and cesium ions, no exchange takes place in acid media; but at alkaline pH values, some exchange occurs accompanied by hydrolysis of the exchanger [16, 22] (see Fig. 5).

The complete titration curve for sodium ion exchange is shown in Figure 6 [29, 46]. It is seen that the forward and backward titration curves do not coincide. This hysteresis results from the formation of different solid phases in the titrations. The exchanger greatly prefers hydrogen ion to alkali metal cations. Thus, when solutions of alkali metal halides are contacted with α-ZrP crystals, the pH rapidly drops to the equilibrium value, and uptake ceases. In the case of 0.1N sodium ion, this pH value is about 2.8 (Fig. 6). The reaction must then be driven to completion by addition of sodium hydroxide. The pH remains constant until approximately 1 mole of

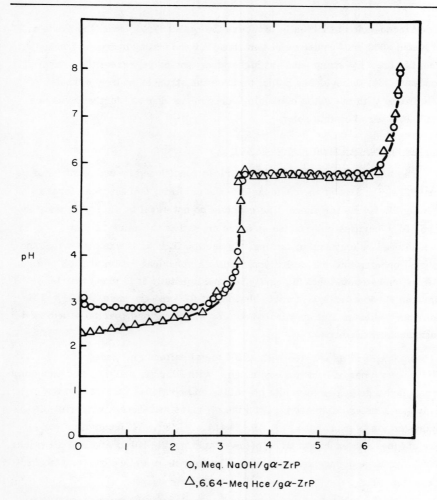

O, Meq. NaOH/gα-ZrP

△,6.64-Meq Hce /gα-ZrP

FIG. 6. Potentiometric titration curve for α-ZrP crystals. Titrant: forward direction, 0.1 N NaOH + 0.1 N NaCl, 0; backward direction, 0.1 N HCl (NaCl conc. maintained constant at 0.1N), △. (Reprinted from Ref. 46a by permission of J. Phys. Chem.)

hydrogen ion per formula weight of α-ZrP is exchanged, whereupon the pH rises sharply to the equilibrium pH of the second stage of exchange. The sodium ion concentration of the exchanging solution also remains constant along the plateau, so that the amount of sodium hydroxide added corresponds to the amount of sodium ion exchanged [16, 21, 22, 46].

Along the first plateau two solid phases are present, the unexchanged crystals and a half exchanged phase of composition $Zr(NaPO_4)(HPO_4) \cdot 5H_2O$ [29, 35]. At the half exchange point, the penta-hydrate is the only phase present. Further exchange of sodium ion results in another two phase region. The two phases are the half exchanged phase and a fully exchanged phase of composition $Zr(NaPO_4)_2 \cdot 3H_2O$. In the back titration reaction, the fully exchanged phase is converted back to the half-exchanged phase by what appears to be a reversible exchange. However, this is not the case when acid is added to the half-exchanged phase. The replacement of sodium by protons occurs at a lower pH than for the forward titration reaction. This is due to the formation of an unexchanged phase (θ-ZrP) containing 8 moles of water and having an interlayer spacing of 10.4 Å compared to 7.56 Å for α-ZrP [29, 35, 46]. Thus, the forward and reverse reactions do not follow the same path.

A tentative explanation for the above cited behavior has been given based upon structural concepts [46]. It has already been mentioned that sodium ion must exchange in the unhydrated state with α-ZrP crystals. If the proton exchanges as H_3O^+, the first step in the reaction may be represented as (1):

$$Zr(HPO_4)_2 \cdot H_2O + Na^+ \rightleftharpoons Zr(NaPO_4)(HPO_4) + H_3O^+. \qquad (1)$$

The possibility also exists that the sodium ion brings a mole of water with it, so that the initial sodium exchanged phase is a monohydrate. In either case the final product is a pentahydrate, which means that reaction (1) must be followed by diffusion of water into the cavities to rehydrate the sodium ion. In the process the interlayer spacing of α-ZrP increases from 7.56 Å to 11.8 Å in the half-exchanged phase. This latter phase, and the fully exchanged phase, have very open structures, so that further exchange is not controlled by small openings leading into the cavities. Thus, in the second stage of exchange as well as in the back titration, hydrated ions can freely diffuse into and out of the exchanger. In fact, unlike α-ZrP, the exchanged phases can exchange with cesium ion [35, 36]. Therefore, replacement of sodium ions by hydrogen ions yields a highly hydrated phase, θ-ZrP, rather than α-ZrP. Upon removal from water, θ-ZrP immediately loses water and converts back to α-ZrP. This later step is irreversible, as α-ZrP does not reform θ-ZrP in contact with water at ambient temperatures.

In determining equilibrium constants for the exchange reactions, the principle of microscopic reversibility must hold for these reactions. This is not a problem for the second stage of exchange, for which macroscopic reversibility has been demonstrated, but it must be verified for the first stage. The equilibrium constant for the overall reaction leading to the formation of the penta hydrate may be written [46]

$$K_1^{Na, H, 5H_2O} = \frac{a_H \; \bar{a}_{Na}}{\bar{a}_H \; a_{Na} \; a_{H_2O}^4} , \tag{2}$$

where the bars refer to activities in the solid state and unbarred quantities to activities in solution. Since pure solids are present during exchange, $\bar{a}_{Na} = \bar{a}_H = 1$. Thus, Eq. (2) reduces to

$$K_1^{Na, H, 5H_2O} = \frac{a_H}{a_{Na} \; a_{H_2O}^4} \tag{3}$$

and

$$pH = pK_1^{Na, H, 5H_2O} - \log a_{Na} - 4 \log a_{H_2O} \cong pK,^{Na, H, 5H_2O} + pNa. \tag{4}$$

A plot of pH vs pNa should then be a straight line with slope of one. Such a plot is shown in Fig. 7, and indeed the line has a slope of very close to 1. The value of $K^{Na, H, 5H_2O}$ determined from this plot is 2.05×10^{-2}. In a similar fashion, $K_2^{Na, H, 3H_2O}$, the equilibrium constant for the second exchange reaction, was found to be 2.13×10^{-5}.

The sodium ion exchange reactions can be represented by the following equations [46]:

$$Zr(HPO_4)_2 \cdot H_2O \; + \; Na^+ \rightleftharpoons Zr(NaPO_4) \; (HPO_4) \cdot H_2O$$

$$\uparrow -7H_2O \qquad\qquad \updownarrow \qquad 4H_2O \tag{5}$$

$$Zr(HPO_4)_2 \cdot 8H_2O \; \underset{Na^+}{\overset{H^+}{\rightleftharpoons}} \; Zr(NaPO_4)(HPO_4) \cdot 5H_2O \; \underset{H^+}{\overset{Na^+}{\rightleftharpoons}} \; Zr(NaPO_4)_2 \cdot 3H_2O. \; + 2H_2O$$

The existence of a half-exchanged monohydrate was determined separately [29, 41], and the conditions for its conversion to the pentahydrate as well as the reverse dehydration of the pentahydrate determined isopiestically [46]. Actually, a half-exchanged tetrahydrate was also shown to exist [41]. The reversibility of exchange between θ-ZrP and the half-exchanged pentahydrate was shown by titration in the forward and reverse directions. However, the

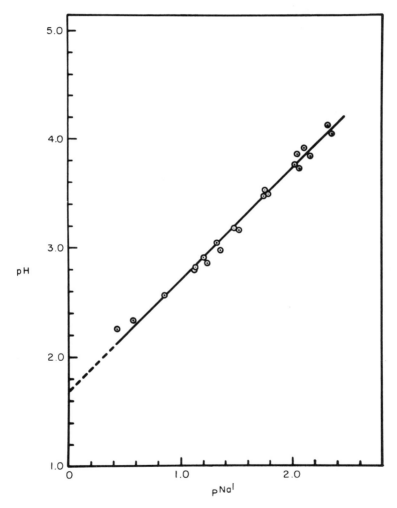

FIG. 7. Plot of pH versus pNá (eq. 4) extrapolated to pNá = 0.
(Reprinted from Ref. 46a by permission of J. Phys. Chem.)

reaction is complicated because the interplanar spacing for θ-ZrP varies from 10.8 Å to 10.4 Å as the back titration progresses [29]. This may be due to some solid solution formation or electrolyte sorption. Until this point is clarified no value for the equilibrium constant can be given.

Free energy values calculated from the two sets of equilibrium data are collected in Table 5. Equilibrium constants were obtained at 35°C and 55°C, so that approximate values of $\Delta H°$ could be obtained from the temperature variation of K. It was found that the first stage of exchange is exothermic, and the second stage endothermic. However, the entropies of exchange are negative for both reactions. The data are collected in Table 5.

In the case of exchange with potassium ions, the forward titration curve resembles that for sodium ion, except that the plateau for the second stage of exchange occurs at a considerably higher pH [31, 37]. The first exchange reaction converts α-ZrP to $Zr(KPO_4)(HPO_4) \cdot H_2O$ with an interlayer spacing of 7.95 Å, and in the second reaction this half-exchanged phase is converted to $Zr(KPO_4)_3 \cdot 3H_2O$. The interlayer spacing of the tri-hydrate is 10.8 Å. In the back titration, the hydrogen ion initially goes into solid solution and is followed by nucleation and growth of crystallites of the half-exchanged phase [37]. Solid solution formation also appears to occur when hydrogen ions are added to the half-exchanged phase. However, very little of the potassium ion is replaced unless strong acid solutions are used. Thus, the titration curves exhibit hysteresis loops.

Lithium ion exchange is unusual. A half-exchanged phase is not formed, but rather one which appears to have the composition $Zr(LiPO_4)_{1.33}(HPO_4)$ $0.67 \cdot 4H_2O$ [38]. However, this is converted to $Zr(LiPO_4)_2 \cdot 4H_2O$ on further uptake of lithium ion. As with potassium ion, back titration leads initially to some solid solution formation followed by appearance of the 66% lithium exchanged phase. Further additions of acid result in the progressive conversion of this crystalline phase to an amorphous gel.

The formation of the 66% lithium exchange phase argues against the idea that the two exchangeable hydrogens of α-ZrP have appreciably different acidities since some of both types of hydrogens must be replaced along the first plateau. Rather it is possible that both hydrogens have acidities which do not differ very much. However, upon formation of the first exchanged phase the structural changes are sufficient to cause an appreciable change

TABLE 5

Thermodynamic Data for Sodium Ion Exchange with α-ZrP

K_1 Na, H, $5H_2O$

t°C	$K \times 10^{2}$ [a]	$\Delta G°$ (kcal mole^{-1})	$\Delta H°$ (kcal mole^{-1})	$\Delta S°$ cal deg^{-1} mole^{-1}
25.0±0.1	1.96±0.19	2.33±0.06		
35.0±0.1	1.19±0.05	2.71±0.01	-5.88±0.81	-27.4±3.0
55.0±0.1	0.767±0.033	3.17±0.01		

K_2 Na, H, $3H_2O$

t°C	$K \times 10^{5}$ [a]	$\Delta G°$ (kcal mole^{-1})	$\Delta H°$ (kcal mole^{-1})	$\Delta S°$ cal deg^{-1} mole^{-1}
25.0±0.1	1.84±0.10	6.45±0.03		
35.0±0.1	2.59±0.16	6.47±0.02	+3.95±0.67	-8.1±1.7
55.0±0.1	3.46±0.17	6.70±0.03		

[a] Values obtained from titration data at $\mu = 0.1$ only.

in the pK value for the second stage of exchange. This idea is further substantiated by the exchange curve for strontium ion [39]. Only one plateau was obtained since the exchanged phase that formed immediately was the fully exchanged strontium phase.

Torracca [40] has determined the isotherms for the Na^+/K^+, Li^+/Na^+ and Li^+/K^+ exchange reactions. In each case the forward and reverse exchanges did not coincide, but exhibited appreciable differences. The curve for the sodium-potassium exchange is reproduced in Fig. 8. Along the slowly rising portion of the $K^+ \rightarrow Na^+$ curve, the solid phase consists of a solid solution of K^+ in the sodium form of the exchanger. When the solubility limit is reached, a second solid phase makes its appearance. Two solid phases coexist over the entire vertical portion of the curve and finally, the sodium-rich phase disappears, and only a solid solution of Na^+ in the potassium form of the exchanger remains. The noncorrespondence of the forward and reverse curves is attributed to limited solubility of one ion exchanged form in the other. Similar results have been obtained by Harvie and Nancollas [34].

Torracca also demonstrated that anhydrous salt phases of α-ZrP display markedly different selectivities than the hydrated forms. Since there exist a large number of partially hydrated and anhydrous phases of the salt forms [29, 31, 35, 37, 38, 40, 41], the possibility of a wide range of selectivities becomes available.

The exchange behavior of alkaline earth ions with crystalline α-ZrP exhibits some interesting features. Tracer studies by Albertsson [22] show that the exchange of strontium is not reversible, as is found in the ZrP gel having the same P:Zr ratio. Clearfield and Smith [39] studied the exchange of Ba^{2+} and Sr^{2+} on crystalline α-ZrP, and found the strontium titration curve had only one endpoint, implying all the sites were available at low pH. Barium was found to be unexchangeable in acid solution and the titration curve was similar to that obtained for Cs^+, which is sterically excluded. However, Alberti has found that barium ion does exchange, although the rate is extremely slow [42].

The x-ray pattern during strontium loadings showed changes in the interlayer distance at much lower loadings than were observed for the alkali metal ions. The changes have now been interpreted as indicating the presence of a fully exchanged strontium phase together with unexchanged α-ZrP [39].

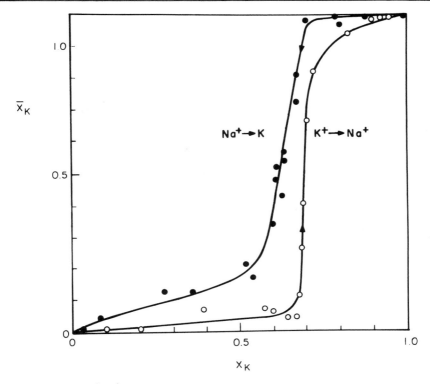

FIG. 8. Na^+/K^+ exchange on α-ZrP.

o K^+ displaces Na^+ from the sodium form dried at room temperature
(P/Po = 0.75)

• Na^+ displaces K^+ from the potassium form dried at room temperature
(P/Po = 0.75). Reprinted from Ref. 40 by permission of J. Inorg.
Nucl. Chem.)

Michael and Weiss [47] have studied the effect on interlayer distances
of the exchange of 1°, 2°, and 3° alkylammonium ions, of various alkyl chain
lengths, on crystalline α-ZrP. They found that the capacities obtained were
independent of chain length, 1° amines exhibiting the theoretical capacity value
and 2° and 3° amines 40% and 15% of this capacity, respectively. The change
in the interlayer distance was 2 to 2.2 Å/carbon atom in all cases, and these
distances were relatively independent of the solvent used. Additional carbon
atoms in alkyl chains are accommodated by the splitting of the layers, while

the observed differences in capacity are due to the increased cross-sectional area of the incoming amine going from 1° to 3°.

B. Phases Obtained by the Dehydration of α-ZrP (ζ-ZrP and η-ZrP)

If α-ZrP is dehydrated under mild conditions, the x-ray pattern indicates that only minor changes occur in the structure [16, 17]. The water loss is reversible, but rehydration occurs slowly. The loss of water must change the hydrogen bonding of the phosphate groups. This is clearly seen in the infrared patterns in which the four OH stretching bands merge into a single broad band at 3300 cm^{-1}. Such deep-seated changes might be expected to bring about an alteration in the exchange behavior of the crystals, but this estimate has not yet been tested. However, Ahrland et al. [48] have shown that a remarkable change in selectivities takes place with dehydration of gels (Section II. G. 1).

The differential thermal analysis curve of α-ZrP exhibits an endothermic peak at 110°C due to the loss of zeolitic water, another small endothermic peak at close to 200°C, and a third at about 300°C [31]. No weight loss accompanies the latter two endotherms. These peaks may be correlated with the formation of phases K and K' as reported by Mounier [31]. Clearfield et al. [43] found that heating α-ZrP below 200°C for long periods of time (2 to 7 days) converts it to phase K. This phase will now be termed ζ-ZrP in conformity with our system of naming zirconium phosphate phases. The interlayer spacing in ζ-ZrP is 7.41 Å and many of its x-ray reflections occur at about the same 2θ value as those of α-ZrP. Thus, the zeta phase is probably similar in structure to α-ZrP with a slightly reduced interlayer spacing. That the zeolitic nature of α-ZrP is retained in ζ-ZrP was shown by exchange reactions in the solid state [44]. Intimate mixtures of dry lithium or sodium chlorides with ζ-ZrP react when heated according to the following equation:

$$Zr(HPO_4)_2 + 2MCl \rightleftharpoons Zr(MPO_4)_2 + 2HCl. \tag{6}$$

This reaction does not take place with CsCl because the cesium ion is too large to migrate into the cavities. Thus, it was possible to separate lithium from cesium by the solid-solid exchange reaction.

If α-ZrP or ζ-ZrP is heated in the range of 200-300°C for a sufficiently long time, it converts to a new phase, which shall be designated η-ZrP. Mounier [31] called this phase phase K'. It has the same composition and a somewhat similar x-ray pattern to that of ζ-ZrP. At present nothing is known about its ion exchange behavior, but both ζ-ZrP and η-ZrP are able to sorb neutral polar molecules such as methanol [43].

C. β- and γ-ZrP

The β-ZrP is an anhydrous zirconium phosphate of composition $Zr(HPO_4)_2$ [45]. It differs from dried forms of α-ZrP in having a much larger interlayer spacing (see Table 1). In moist air or on contact with water β-ZrP forms a dihydrate which has been termed γ-ZrP. Thus, when the exchange behavior of β-ZrP in aqueous solution is considered, it is the γ-ZrP that is involved. These phases may be prepared by adding a 1M solution of zirconium oxychloride to a boiling solution 6M in sodium dihydrogen phosphate and 3M in HCl, and refluxing the resultant gel for 25 hours or longer. Upon drying the solid from which the sodium ion has been thoroughly washed out, β-ZrP is obtained. This anhydrous solid picks up two moles of water on standing in air to yield the γ-phase.

It has been postulated that β-ZrP has a structure which is related to that of α-ZrP in a simple way [45]. In α-ZrP the layers are staggered so that a phosphorus atom in one layer is above (or below) a zirconium atom in an adjacent layer. The β-ZrP is thought to have the same type of layer as α-ZrP, i.e., within a single layer the structure is the same, but the layers are directly over one another. This produces the larger interlayer distance of 9.4 Å and accounts for the ready exchange of Cs^+. The exchange capacity based upon the availability of two moles of replaceable hydrogen ion per formula weight of β-ZrP is 7.06 meq/g. This capacity is very nearly achieved with Ba^{2+}.

D. Phases Obtained by Refluxing ZrO_2 in Enriched Phosphoric Acid (δ-ZrP and ε-ZrP)

Deabridges [32] refluxed hydrous zirconium oxide in phosphoric acid solutions ranging from 3 to 80% in P_2O_5. With solutions of up to 70% P_2O_5

content, he obtained α-ZrP. However, when the P_2O_5 content was 70-72% and the reflux temperature 130-140°C, he obtained a phase of composition $Zr(HPO_4)_2 \cdot 1/2H_2O$ (δ-ZrP). In the narrow range from 72-73% P_2O_5 and a reflux temperature of 140-160°C, an anhydrous phase, $Zr(HPO_4)_2$, or ε-ZrP was obtained. Refluxing in yet stronger phosphoric acid produced ZrP_2O_7.

The delta and epsilon phases were also produced by refluxing dried zirconium phosphate gels in 15.7 M phosphoric acid [26, 43]. In 10 hours of refluxing, the pure delta phase was obtained. However, there was a continuous change, with reflux time, in the d-spacings exhibited by the x-ray patterns. This indicated the presence of an as yet unidentified intermediate phase which is converted by the refluxing procedure to δ-ZrP. Further refluxing of the delta phase converted it in 8 hours (at 165°C) to the ε-phase, and finally, the ε-phase converted to α-ZrP_2O_7 in 6 more hours.

Very little is known about the structure of the δ- and ε-phases. The epsilon phase loses one mole of water between 340° and 450°C. It also exhibits one broad OH stretching band and none at 1620 cm^{-1}, indicating the absence of water of crystallization. Thus, the band at 3400 cm^{-1} must be attributed to P-OH type groups in which the hydrogen bonding is much stronger than in α-ZrP. This agrees with the fact that the epsilon phase did not exchange cations in the pH range 0-9 [32].

The delta phase loses 1/2 mole of water at 100°-180°C and 1 mole at 400-500°C [31]. These water losses are consistent with its assigned formula. However, on heating to 800°C, it formed a hitherto unknown pyro-phosphate which Deabridges labeled β-ZrP_2O_7. The δ-ZrP exhibits two OH stretching bands at 3600 cm^{-1} and 3420 cm^{-1}, and possibly a third at 2300 cm^{-1}. This latter band is very weak. The presence of a strong band at 1620 cm^{-1} (δ_{H_2O}) confirms the existence of zeolitic water, or water of crystallization. Deabridges also found that δ-ZrP does not exchange cations in the pH range 0-9. However, Clearfield et al. [43] found that sodium ion does exchange at pH values less than 9. Obviously, further investigations, both of a structural and ion-exchange nature, are in order to clarify our knowledge of these two phases.

E. Miscellaneous Zirconium Phosphate Phases with P/Zr = 2

1. θ-ZrP

When the half-exchanged sodium phase of α-ZrP, $Zr(NaPO_4)(HPO_4)\cdot 5H_2O)$ is treated with dilute acid, the exchange reaction yields an octahydrate, $Zr(HPO_4)_2\cdot 8H_2O$ [29, 35]. This large amount of water of crystallization is accommodated by a spreading apart of the α-ZrP layers to an interlayer distance of 10.4 Å. In air θ-ZrP readily loses its water to reform α-ZrP. Because of its large interlayer spacing, θ-ZrP does not exclude large ions [35] (such as Cs^+), and the ions probably exchange in the hydrated condition. Exchange of θ-ZrP with sodium ion leads to the formation of the same half-exchanged phase as is obtained from α-ZrP [46].

2. i-ZrP

This phase was prepared by heating the fully exchanged sodium phase of α-ZrP to above 800°C for a short period of time to produce the anhydrous phase classified as phase $H(2Na^+)$ [41]. The sodium ion was then exchanged by hydrogen ion to produce a new exchanger phase with an interlayer spacing of 7.73 Å [46].

3. $\varkappa$-ZrP

When a mixture of α-ZrP and SiO_2 was dissolved in concentrated hydrofluoric acid and the solution boiled, crystals of a new zirconium phosphate phase formed [49]. The interlayer spacing of this phase is 6.11 Å, which on exchange with sodium ion, increases to 12.54 Å. The composition of $\varkappa$-ZrP has not yet been established [43].

F. Zirconium Phosphate Phases Having P/Zr > 2

1. P/Zr = 2.2

This phase was reported by Torracca et al. [35] to form upon reacting anhydrous zirconium oxychloride with fused phosphoric acid at 100-200°C. It is thought to be a polyphosphate. As yet it is not certain whether this phase exhibits ion exchange behavior.

2. P/Zr = 3. (α-ZrTP and β-ZrTP)

If anhydrous zirconium oxychloride is dissolved in molten phosphoric acid and the solution allowed to stand at 85°C, a crystalline product precipitates [35]. It has a phosphate-zirconium ratio of 3 and weight loss data indicates the composition is $Zr(HPO_4)$ $(H_2PO_4)_2$. It will be designated as α-ZrTP for triphosphate. The α-ZrTP is unstable in water, but one hydrogen may be replaced by Na^+ in anhydrous methanol and this substituted product is stable in water. Further exchange may now be effected until a total of three hydrogens are replaced. Potassium ion is completely excluded by α-ZrTP and its Li^+ and Na^+ salt forms.

A second triphosphate phase can be obtained from solutions of zirconyl chloride in molten phosphoric acid when the temperature of reaction is somewhat lower than for α-ZrTP [35]. It has the same composition as α-ZrTP, but with five replaceable hydrogens. Therefore, it is termed β-ZrTP. Little else has been reported about this interesting compound.

G. Amorphous Zirconium Phosphates

Rapid precipitation of zirconium phosphate in the cold yields an amorphous gel. The solids are usually not completely amorphous, but show 3 or 4 very broad x-ray reflections of low intensity. The degree of broadening depends upon such variables as temperature, rate of mixing, molar ratio of reactants, etc. Furthermore, under different conditions the ratio of phosphate to zirconium in the products can be varied from less than 1 to 2. These differences in structure and composition are responsible for the varied exchange behaviors exhibited by different preparations. Thus, it is of the utmost importance to specify preparative conditions, stoichiometry and x-ray patterns when describing the exchange behavior of a particular gel. Obviously, what is required is a better knowledge of gel structures and how changes in structure affect exchange properties. The difficulty lies in the limited information obtainable from x-ray and spectroscopic studies on gels. However, an approach which partially circumvents this difficulty will be presented in Section II. H on semicrystalline zirconium phosphates. In the meantime what little is known about the structure of zirconium phosphate gels is discussed here.

1. Structure of Zirconium Phosphate Gels

Gels result from the rapid mixing of a soluble Zr(IV) salt with a soluble phosphate. The ratio of phosphate to zirconium is variable but approaches two with increasing acidity, digestion time, and phosphate to zirconium ratio of the reactants [4, 7, 16, 17]. The gel with P-Zr ratio equal to 2 was represented by De Boer [50] as a monohydrogen phosphate, $Zr(HPO_4)_2$, but other workers [51, 52] argued that under such conditions, the formation of a zirconium rather than a zirconyl salt, such as $ZrO(H_2PO_4)_2$, was unlikely. Blumenthal [5, 52] proposed the following structural formula for the precipitated product

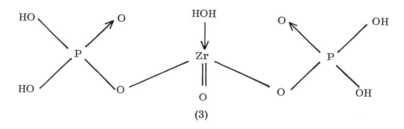

(3)

in order to account for its acidic properties, and for the observation made by Kraus et al. [2], that pyrophosphate is formed on heating the product. Amphlett and his co-workers [53] suggested a structure for the amorphous material consisting of a network of zirconium atoms linked together by bridging oxygen atoms.

By a series of weight loss, analytical and ion exchange studies similar to those described for the crystals (section II.A.2), it was established that the formula for the gels having a phosphate–zirconium ratio of 2 is $Zr(HPO_4)_2 \cdot H_2O$ [7, 8, 16]. Thus, the gels and crystals have essentially the same chemical composition (gels tend to retain some excess water) even though they exhibit wide differences in their ion exchange properties. Even when the P-Zr ratio in the gels is less than 2, the phosphate groups were shown to be present as monohydrogen phosphate [23]. Thus, the general formula can be written $Zr(OH)_x (HPO_4)_{2-2/x} \cdot yH_2O$, where x varies from 0 to above 2. The exact water content y depends upon the methods of drying.

According to the above general formula for the gels, the exchange capacity should be that corresponding to the replacement of the hydrogen from the monohydrogen phosphate groups. This assumes that exchange of protons from the hydroxyl groups is negligible. The expected exchange capacity is usually not attained in aqueous solution, as extensive hydrolysis sets in before the full exchange capacity is realized [7, 16]. However, in a molten salt bath it is possible to achieve the theoretical exchange capacity with Li^+ and Na^+ [54, 55]. Percolation of molten potassium nitrate over the exchanger in the mixed lithium-potassium form did not result in complete replacement of lithium ion. Only about 40% of the total available exchange sites were occupied by K^+. Cesium ion was completely excluded. Studies of the electrical conductance of Li^+, Na^+, K^+, and Cs^+ forms of amorphous ZrP over a range of conversion between 2 and 20%, showed a decrease in specific conductance with percentage loading for the Li^+ and Cs^+ forms [56]. In the case of the Na^+ and K^+ forms however, the specific conductance increased to a maximum at 8 to 10% conversion. These results, as well as the sieving effects in molten salts, were interpreted in terms of the existence of a variety of cavity sizes in amorphous ZrP, only the largest of which could accommodate hydrated ions. The more acidic sites are then located within these cavities. Initially, conversion to a metal ion increases the conductance. As conversion proceeds, steric effects become important and the conductivity decreases. The maximum in the conductance curve occurs at a percentage conversion which is lower the larger the ingoing metal ion. In the case of Li^+, no maximum occurs since its conductivity is less than that of the hydrogen form. Such a steric effect would be expected to show up in the exchange isotherms at high loadings as a reversal of preference. Such reversals have been observed in the Cs^+/H^+, K^+/H^+ and Rb^+/H^+ systems, even though the maximum capacity has not been utilized because of hydrolysis. The importance of steric effects with increasing loadings of ZrP is also illustrated by the results of Ahrland et al. [57]. For pH's below 6.5 they found the affinity series $Cs^+ > Rb^+ > Na^+$, while above 6.5, the order was reversed.

The evidence presented above, together with fragmentary structural data presented below, rules out earlier formulations such as those of Blumenthal and Amphlett, since they cannot account for the observed properties of the gels. Rather, it is to be expected that a theory which considers the gels as disordered forms of the crystals is more likely [16] (see also Section II. H). Figure 1 shows that the gel particles formed by rapid precipitation are very small, and the surface area is therefore quite large. The structure within the gel particles must somewhat resemble that of the crystals, since the 3 or 4 weak x-ray reflections exhibited by the gel occur at roughly the same angles as the strongest reflections in the crystal [16, 17]. However, the (002) reflection which represents the interlayer spacing is very broad, of low intensity, and usually occurs at lower 2θ angle in the gels than in the crystals [17, 22]. This lower angle shows that the average interlayer distance is larger in the gel than in the crystals. The broadening can arise from either small crystallites, a disordering of the planes so that they are not parallel but tilted toward each other, or from a combination of these factors. The lower intensity may also arise from the disorder which tends to increase the background, due to randomly scattered radiation rather than cooperative scattering at specific angles.

Under the conditions of rapid precipitation used to prepare gels, the probability that the complex stereochemical requirements necessary to form a regular layer, and to stack these parallel to each other, is small. Thus, only small crystallites form and are interspersed within regions where many atoms must be displaced from their equilibrium positions in the crystal, forming an amorphous matrix. This would tend to produce a range of cavity sizes and large residual electrostatic forces which would bind water strongly. Crystallites as small as 20-40 Å across have been measured by x-ray methods [19, 22]. One might imagine even within the crystallites a certain amount of disorder which produces different sized cavities and different sized entranceways into the cavities, rather than the regular ones present in the crystals. Only half-cavities exist on the surface of both crystals and gels, i.e., the top half of the cavities formed by the underside of one layer would be missing. Thus, even an ion as large as Cs^+ could enter these half-cavities. Then the Cs^+ could diffuse into those cavities which have large enough entranceways to permit free passage. Such a scheme accounts for the rather small Cs^+ uptake of crystals and much larger Cs^+ capacity of the gels. Exhaustive exchange with 0.1 N alkali halide solution shows that the uptake by gels decreases in the order $Cs^+ > K^+ > Li^+$ [58]. This order is the reverse of that shown in molten salts, and indicates that exchange takes place primarily with the hydrated cations,

since in aqueous solution, the larger hydrated lithium ion would tend to be
excluded from more cavities than other less highly hydrated cations.

Evidence for the presence of different sized entranceways into the
cavities was also obtained by Amphlett and McDonald [59]. These investigators examined the uptake of alkyl substituted ammonium ions. For ions of
the type NR_4^+, there was a steady decrease in uptake and saturation capacity
with increasing size of the alkyl group. This suggests that the gel possesses
a heterogenous structure in which more pores or cavities are available to
the smaller cations. With mono- and di-substituted alkyl derivatives the
uptake also decreased with increasing size of the alkyl chain. This was
attributed to the blocking of active sites by the alkyl chains which, when fully
extended, enter adjacent cavities and thus prevent full utilization of the
available capacity.

The disordered structure of the gels would give rise to hydrogen bonds
with a range of bond energies [16]. This is reflected in the infrared patterns
where only one broad band occurs in the OH stretch region compared to four
bands in the crystals [31]. Thus, the gel P-OH groups possess a broad
range of acidities, and instead of exhibiting sharp plateaux in the titration
curves, the pH rises almost continuously with successive additions of base
(see Fig. 5). The more extensive hydrolysis exhibited by the gels is also
attributable to their disordered structures. Those phosphate groups which
are in a highly strained configuration, i.e., which are displaced from their
equilibrium positions, are more readily replaced by hydroxyl groups than
phosphate groups which are held in a regular arrangement in the crystal.
Other manifestations of the disordered gel structure are the almost
continuous loss of water on heating, and the regular loss of exchange capacity
on heating above 180°C [8, 60].

2. Ion Exchange Properties of Zirconium Phosphate Gels

The product which is normally obtained by rapid precipitation of a soluble
Zr(IV) salt with a soluble phosphate is a viscous, gelatinous solid which
settles extremely slowly and is very difficult to filter. As such it is unusable
as an ion exchanger. By controlling the experimental conditions and partially
drying the precipitate, a stable granular form of the amorphous zirconium
phosphate, suitable for column operation as an ion exchanger, was obtained

[53, 61]. A typical titration curve of this amorphous form of zirconium phosphate, obtained by equilibrating samples of the solid with sodium hydroxide solution is shown in Fig. 5. It is clear that the solid contains several dissociable hydrogen atoms with a range of effective dissociation constants, and the cation exchange capacity in neutral and slightly alkaline solution is ~ 5 meq/g.

We may write, for the exchange of a metal ion M^{n+} with the hydrogen form of zirconium phosphate $ZrPH$,

$$M^{n+} + nZrPH \rightleftharpoons (ZrP)_n (M^{n+}) + nH^+, \tag{7}$$

with an equilibrium constant

$$K = \frac{[\overline{M^{n+}}] \ [H^+]^n}{[M^{n+}] \ [\overline{H^+}]^n} \quad \frac{\overline{f}_{M^+} \ f_{H^+}^n}{f_{M^+} \ \overline{f}_{H^+}^n}, \tag{8}$$

where square brackets denote concentrations, and the bars, the species within the ion exchanger phase. A number of tests for reversibility of exchange have been made using the metal ion of interest in trace amounts [1, 62, 63]. Under such conditions, $(\overline{M^{n+}}) << (\overline{H^+})$ and the extent of exchange is sufficiently small that variations in $(\overline{H^+})$ can be ignored. In addition, the activity coefficient terms may be assumed to be constant, and Eq. (8) becomes

$$\log D = npH + \log K + n \log C, \tag{9}$$

where the total capacity $C = [\overline{H^+}]$ and the distribution coefficient $D = [\overline{M^{n+}}]/[M^{n+}]$. Ignoring variations in activity coefficients, for an ideally reversible exchange reaction, a plot of log D against pH will yield a straight line of slope n. It is seen in Fig. 9 that many of the exchange reactions with inorganic exchangers are closely described by Eq. (9). Deviations from ideality were found only in the cases of Cs^+, UO_2^{2+}, and Ce^{3+}, for which the distribution coefficient increased with decreasing exchanger loading at constant pH. These deviations were attributed to the existence of small amounts (~ 0.003 meq/g) of a different functional group with a high affinity for the cations involved.

Whereas structures have been suggested consisting of a Zr-O lattice with acid phosphate groups attached to vacant Zr coordination sites [53], Baetsle

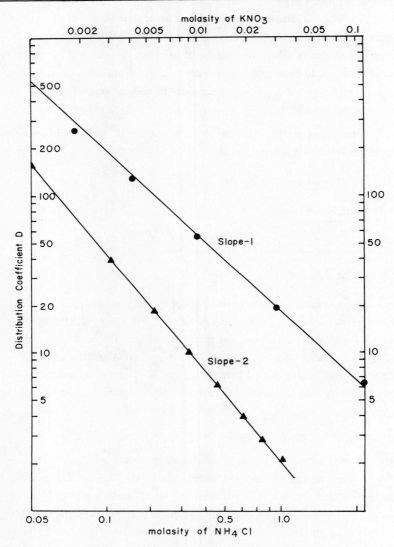

FIG. 9. Plot of log D against log (concentration of exchanging ion). ●, bromide-nitrate exchange with hydrous zirconium oxide; left-hand ordinate and upper abscissa scale. ▲, barium-ammonium exchange on zirconium tungstate; right-hand ordinate and lower abscissa scale. (Reproduced, with permission, from K. A. Kraus, H. O. Phillips, T. A. Carlson and J. S. Johnson, Proc. Second U. N. Conference on the Peaceful Uses of Atomic Energy, Geneva, 1958).

and Pelsmaekers [64] have proposed a stable limited chain structure. The molecular weight of each chain unit was 877.6, corresponding to the formula

$$
\left[
\begin{array}{c}
OPO_3H_2 \\
| \quad H_2O \\
| \quad \swarrow \\
-Zr \longrightarrow O \longrightarrow \\
| \\
OH
\end{array}
\quad
\begin{array}{c}
OPO_3H_2 \\
| \quad H_2O \\
| \quad \swarrow \\
Zr \longrightarrow O \longrightarrow \\
| \\
OPO_3H_2
\end{array}
\quad
\begin{array}{c}
OH \\
| \quad H_2O \\
| \quad \downarrow \\
Zr \longrightarrow O - P \\
| \\
OPO_3H_2
\end{array}
\quad
\begin{array}{c}
\quad O \quad OH \\
\quad \diagdown \diagup \\
\\
\diagdown \\
\quad O-
\end{array}
\right] .
$$

(4)

By comparing the observed capacities with those calculated from the maximum number of hydrogen atoms available for exchange, Baetsle and Pelsmaekers also concluded that only the phosphate groups are involved in the exchange reactions. In view of the previous discussion on the structure of the gels, this formula cannot be taken seriously. However, it is rather likely that both hydroxyl groups and dihydrogen phosphate groups reside on the surface of the gel particles. These could arise by hydrolysis, as, for example, in Eq. (10), and account for the deviations noted above.

$$
\begin{array}{c}
- Zr \\
\diagdown \\
\quad O \\
\quad \diagdown \\
-Zr-O \longrightarrow \quad P - OH \quad + \quad H_2O \longrightarrow \\
\quad \diagup \\
\quad O \\
\diagup \\
- Zr
\end{array}
\quad
\begin{array}{c}
> Zr \\
\diagdown \\
\quad OH \\
\quad | \quad O \\
-Zr \diagup \diagdown \quad \diagup OH \\
\quad \quad P \\
\quad \diagup \quad \diagdown \\
> Zr - O \quad \quad OH
\end{array}
. \qquad (10)
$$

As mentioned previously, the ion exchange properties of zirconium phosphate are dependent upon several factors associated with the method of preparation, such as water content, composition, and crystallinity [7, 8, 53, 63, 64-69]. It is possible to prepare a range of amorphous solids having P : Zr ratios ranging from 1 to 2 depending upon the nature and stoichiometric ratio of the reagents used in the precipitation, and the temperature at which they were mixed. The P : Zr ratio in the solid was lower than that in the precipitating solutions, and for values of the latter greater than 2, the resulting product was the stable glassy gel used by Amphlett and co-workers in their studies. At lower precipitating ratios, the product tended to be colloidal [53].

Hydrolysis and the resulting release of phosphate constitutes a serious disadvantage in the possible commercial use of zirconium phosphate as an ion exchanger. (However, see Section II. H). When the alkali metal substituted forms of zirconium phosphate are refluxed with water at 100°C, hydrolysis takes place and the cations are released until a new equilibrium is reached [53]. Continued treatment further reduces the distribution coefficient with progressive stripping of phosphate from the solid. This hydrolysis is enhanced in neutral to alkaline solutions [7, 63, 69], and unfortunately, these are the conditions under which a high ion exchange capacity offers the greatest promise as an ion exchanger. Baestle and Pelsmaekers [64], and Larsen and Vissers [66], after extensive water washing of the gels, found that the resulting product with a P : Zr = 1. 67 had little tendency toward further release of phosphate. Vesely and Pekarek [67] digested zirconium phosphate precipitates at 60°C in 20% phosphoric acid and showed that, once again, the product had little tendency to hydrolyze when used in subsequent exchange experiments. However, this must be the result of improved crystallinity brought about by the digestion. The phosphate-rich gels undoubtedly are very stable in acid solutions, and there is little evidence of dissolution in acids such as nitric, sulfuric, or phosphoric at concentrations as high as 8 M [7, 12]. The solubility of gels of low phosphate content in acid solutions can probably be attributed to the presence of hydrous oxides of zirconium. These impart a residual anion exchange capacity to such material at low pH [7, 53, 65] conditions where the hydrous oxides behave as anion exchangers. A careful study of the hydrolysis of the zirconium phosphate gels recently made by Horwitz [70] has confirmed the observations noted above. Samples of zirconium phosphate with PO_4 : Zr mole ratios of 1. 34 and 1. 13 showed a substantially smaller hydrolytic release of phosphate than those with higher ratios. However, upon repeated treatment with 0. 1 M nitric acid, the concentration of phosphate in the equilibrium solutions remained at an approximately constant value. At 75°C this amounted to $4. 0 \times 10^{-5}$ mmole PO_4/g of gel.

As mentioned above, the ion exchange properties of the gels are markedly dependent upon the water content of the samples. The rate of exchange of some ions, such as UO_2^{2+}, is very sensitive to changes in the water content of the gel, whereas with ions such as Sr^{2+}, the sorption rate is almost unaffected by water content [8]. The differences are readily seen in Fig. 10, which shows sorption rates obtained with zirconium phosphate gels of varying water content. The PO_4 : Zr ratio was 1.95 in each case, and for UO_2^{2+}, the sorption rate decreases considerably as the water content is decreased, and equilibrium is reached only very slowly. For Sr^{2+}, on the other hand, equilibrium is attained almost instantaneously, even with a water content as low as 20%. When the water content was above 25% (>5 mole H_2O/mole Zr), its variation had no effect upon the amount of Sr^{2+} sorbed per phosphate present in the gel. A decreased uptake of Sr^{2+} first

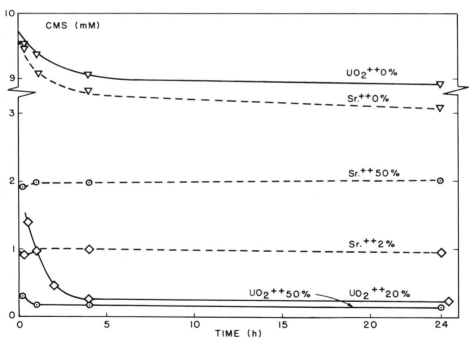

FIG. 10. Sorption rates of zirconium phosphate gels with different water contents for Sr^{++} and UO_2^{++}. The per cent water content of the gel is listed next to its sorption curve. (Reproduced from ref. 8 by permission of Acta Chem. Scand.)

became apparent as the water content fell to about 1/2 mole H_2O/mole Zr. Further removal of water by ignition led to a substantial reduction in the ion exchange properties, confirming that the last 1 to 2 moles of water are of crucial importance [8]. A thermogravimetric curve reflecting water loss upon heating the gel material is shown in Fig. 2. It can be seen that 1 mole of water per mole of zirconium or 1/2 mole per mole of phosphate is much more strongly held than the remaining water molecules. Ahrland [8] has suggested that since the final mole of water must be associated with the phosphate groups each of the latter must be monohydrogenated in agreement with the findings of others (see Section II. G. 1).

In an attempt at better characterization of the ion exchangers, recent work has been concerned with more crystalline preparations (see Section II. H). Larsen and co-workers [71] have described the preparation of a well-defined crystalline phosphate, diphosphate zirconic acid, by precipitation in sulfuric acid and subsequent digestion at 75°C for several days. Although the product is crystalline, the particle size is much too small for normal column operation as an ion exchanger. This problem can be overcome by compressing the powder into pellets and allowing them to break down in water over a period of several days [72]. The resulting material may be sieved to select a particulate size range and shows essentially no further disintegration after several days in stirred solution, or after prolonged immersion in boiling water. The material hydrolyses considerably less than the gel zirconium phosphate, and a typical titration curve is shown in Fig. 5. It should be noted that this curve still differs considerably from that of the fully crystalline product, i.e., d-ZrP.

Attention has already been drawn to the particularly high affinity of the gels for Cs^+ and Rb^+ [53, 63, 73], whereas in the crystalline form, sorption of these ions occurred only at high pH with hydrolysis and structural breakdown [16, 22]. With the exception of the most amorphous form, Albertsson [22] found this preference for Cs^+ increased with decreasing crystallinity, implying an optimum degree of disorder for the Cs^+ exchange. Affinities were also dependent on the water content, forms of the same crystallinity having very distinct selectivity changes with water loss, even at temperatures where condensation to pyrophosphate occurs [67, 74]. The distribution coefficient for the ions K^+, Rb^+, Cs^+ and Tl^+ on semicrystalline ZrP increased going from a drying temperature of 25°C to 260°C, at which about 20% of the phosphate groups were condensed [74]. Rates of attainment of equilibrium also were affected by condensation [8, 60], up to 60 days being required for Cs^+ to equilibrate with the exchanger dried at 260°C. Although the maximum attainable capacity is decreased when condensation occurs, the increased distribution coefficient leads to an increase in measured capacity at low pH [74]. Ahrland et al. [48] attribute the slow attainment of equilibrium on partially condensed forms to the slow rehydration of the pyrophosphate groups. They found that the sorption of Cs^+ reached a maximum at the point prior to condensation where all the free water molecules have been removed. Cerium and UO_2^{2+} exhibited no maximum at this point and since all the dehydrated forms regain but a fraction of their original water, such dehydration provides a means for further increasing the preference for Cs^+ over Ce^{3+} and UO_2^{2+}. The potassium-hydrogen exchange equilibrium was found to be reversible between 18°C and 160°C, with an accompanying decrease in selectivity coefficient. At temperatures above 160°C, sorption increased, reaching a maximum at 300°C. This higher sorption was maintained on cooling. This is comparable with the results of the Cs^+ exchange studies, in which an increase in preference was observed on partial dehydration. Recently Vesely et al. [75] have found that for alkali metal exchange on gel materials, the distribution coefficient increases with increasing phosphate concentration in solution. They also found that for gels dried at 260°C, the phosphate release was considerably slower than for the same materials dried at 25°C. This could explain the slow attainment of equilibrium, observed by Alberti [60], for partially condensed ZrP, the maximum value of the distribution coefficient not being attained until equilibrium between exchanger and solution phosphate was reached. Phosphate release with increasing drying temperature was found to depend on the crystallinity of the exchanger [75]. The phosphate loss for crystalline and semicrystalline forms increased with increasing drying temperature, whereas a decrease was observed for the gel materials. This is consistent with the observed effect of drying temperatures on the distribution coefficients, namely, an increase with temperature for semicrystalline ZrP [74] and a decrease for amorphous ZrP. A contributing factor to these observations is the distinct loss in crystallinity of the crystalline form dried at temperatures above 200°C [31]. The relative freedom of a portion of phosphate groups on noncrystalline ZrP was demonstrated by Barrett et al. [76], who studied the kinetics of phosphate exchange between the solid and solution phase at pH = 1.1. This exchange was found to occur in two steps, a fast surface exchange followed by a slower step within the particles, probably involving isomorphous exchange of phosphate groups in the solid phase.

As mentioned previously, early studies of ion exchange by zirconium phosphate were mainly concerned with systems in which one of the exchanging ions was present in trace amounts. Baetsle [73] has extended such studies to the exchange of Rb^+, Cs^+, Ca^{2+}, Sr^{2+}, Ce^{3+}, and Eu^{3+} with the hydrogen form of amorphous ZrP over a range of temperature from 5 to 70°C. The entropy values, calculated from the variation of distribution coefficient with temperature, were found to correlate with the unhydrated ionic radii, while the trend in the value of the ion affinities suggested that hydrated ions are exchanged. The relative affinities observed for the gels from trace studies are [53, 63, 66, 73]

$$Li^+ \; < \; Na^+ \; < \; K^+ \qquad\qquad NH_4^+ \; < \; Rb^+ \; < \; Cs^+$$

$$Mg^{2+} \; < \; Ca^{2+} \qquad\qquad\qquad Sr^{2+} \; < \; Ba^{2+}$$

$$Sr^{2+} \; > \; Na^+ \qquad\qquad\qquad UO_2^{2+} \; > \; Ce^{3+} \; > \; Sr^{2+}.$$

Alkaline earth metals were found to be more favorably absorbed in neutral rather than in acid solution, and this was attributed to the presence of the monovalent hydroxide complex at high pH [62].

Thermodynamic functions calculated from tracer studies are of doubtful value since the assumption, that the log of the selectivity coefficient is linearly related to the mole fraction of exchanging cation, is implicit in such computations. More recent studies have shown that the selectivity is a complex function of the exchanger composition with, in some cases, a reversal of preference as the exchange progresses [68, 77, 78]. A number of gel studies have been made of the exchange over the whole range of solid composition. The results are difficult to compare because of differences in behavior of the various preparations of ZrP. In addition there is now good evidence that the effective capacity of the exchanger varies with the pH of the solution, and the nature of the ingoing ion . These factors were not taken into account in many of the earlier studies. Larsen and Vissers [66] followed Li^+/H^+, Na^+/H^+, and K^+/H^+ exchange at pH = 1, using a capacity measured at pH = 5. In none of the systems did the fraction of metal ion on the exchanger exceed 35% of the capacity, and in order to obtain free energies linearity was assumed between the log of the selectivity coefficient and the fraction exchanged. Baetsle and Huys [62] obtained selectivity coefficients for the macro exchange of Na^+, K^+, Ca^{2+} and Sr^{2+} with hydrogen on a zirconium phosphate of P : Zr ratio 1.67. The results for different ions were compared at zero concentration of the ion in the exchanger, and agreed with those obtained in the tracer studies in which K^+ was preferred to Na^+, and Sr^{2+} preferred to Ca^{2+}. The capacity used for the calculation of selectivity coefficients corresponded to the maximum capacity which is only attainable at alkaline pH. Amphlett et al. [77] made a study of exchange of Cs^+/Rb^+ Cs^+/K^+ and Cs^+/H^+ Rb^+/H^+ over the whole range of exchanger composition for each exchange system studied. Column equilibrium was used for the Cs^+/Rb^+ and Cs^+/K^+ exchange; in this case no separate measurement of the capacity was necessary, as it could be obtained directly from the total metal concentration on the exchanger. In Fig. 11, it is seen that the isotherms were rectilinear in shape, in contrast to those obtained for Cs^+/H^+, Rb^+/H^+ exchange, where the sigmoid isotherms shown in Fig. 12 indicate a reversal of preference. It must be noted that the M^+/H^+ systems were batch equilibrated, and the pH was therefore different for each point on the isotherm, whereas the capacity was measured by repeated batch equilibrations with the metal ion concerned. Enthalpies were determined from the temperature coefficient of the equilibrium constant. A similar study was made by Harkin et al. [68] for the Cs^+/H^+ exchange, and a reversal of preference as the exchange progressed was also found. The overall free energy change was too small to permit the accurate calculation of other thermodynamic properties.

Nancollas and Tilak [78] have described a study of the Li^+/H^+, K^+/H^+ and Cs^+/H^+ systems, in the commercially available Bio-rad gel of P : Zr ratio 2. In this case enthalpy changes were measured directly, using a differential calorimeter, and capacities were assumed constant over the range of low pH values used. The experiments were made at a constant ionic strength of 0.1 M and a typical plot of the directly measured heat of partial exchange of K^+ with H^+ ion as a function of mole fraction of K^+ ion in the exchanger is shown in Fig. 13. Differential heats of exchange

$$\overline{\Delta H} = \delta(\Delta H)/\delta \overline{X}_M \tag{11}$$

may be obtained from such plots by applying the chord-area method [79].
Integral heats of exchange per mole of the exchanging ion are defined by the
relationship

$$\Delta H = \int_0^1 \overline{\Delta H} \, d\overline{X}_M . \tag{12}$$

Standard heats $\Delta H°$ for the hypothetical reaction RH (a = 1, equil, with
0.1 N HCl) + MCL (aq, a=1) $\rightleftharpoons$ RM(a=1, equil. with 0.1 N MCl) + HCl (aq,
a=1) + nH_2O (a=1), where n is the number of water molecules released or
absorbed by the exchanger, may be obtained after correcting for the differences in the relative apparent molal heat contents L calculated using the
relationship [78],

$$\phi_L^{RH \to RM} = \phi_L^{M^+} - \phi_L^{H^+} . \tag{13}$$

Representative thermodynamic data are given in Table 6.

The entropy change for the reaction can be written [80]

$$\Delta S° = \overline{\Delta S}_{ex} - (S_M° - S_H°), \tag{14}$$

where $\overline{\Delta S}_{ex}$ represents the entropy differences between the corresponding
ionic forms of the exchanger, and $S_M°$ and $S_H°$ the aqueous ionic entropies. Values of $\overline{\Delta S}_{ex}$ are included in Table 6 and reflect (1) changes in hydration accompanying reaction (7), and (2) the differences in lattice distortion of the two forms
of the exchanger. The corresponding enthalpy changes will be governed by
changes in the numbers and strengths of the bonds made and broken during
exchange. Electrostatic interactions will make small endothermic
contributions to $\Delta H°$, whereas formation of covalent bonds will be accompanied by an exothermic heat exchange [81]. The $\overline{\Delta S}_{ex}$ values in Table 6
show a significant increase with the size of the ingoing cation. The
observed order Li < K < Cs is consistent with a proposed increasing hydration of the alkali metal ions within the exchanger. It is seen that this trend
becomes apparent only after removing the variable $(S_M° - S_H°)$ term from
the measured $\Delta S°$. The enthalpy changes for $H^+ - K^+$ and $H^+ - Cs^+$

TABLE 6

Thermodynamic Properties for the Exchange of Metal Ions with Hydrogen on Zirconium Phosphate at 25°C

Displacing ion	$\Delta G°$ (cal mole^{-1})	ΔH (cal mole^{-1})	Φ_L (cal mole^{-1})	$\Delta H°$ (cal mole^{-1})	$\Delta S°$ (cal deg^{-1} mole^{-1})	ΔS_{ex} (cal deg^{-1} mole^{-1})
Li$^+$	1867	-1150	-25	-1125	-10.0	-12.4
K$^+$	895	-4461	-53	-4408	-17.8	-4.2
Cs$^+$	-383	-4543	-78	-4465	-13.7	3.5

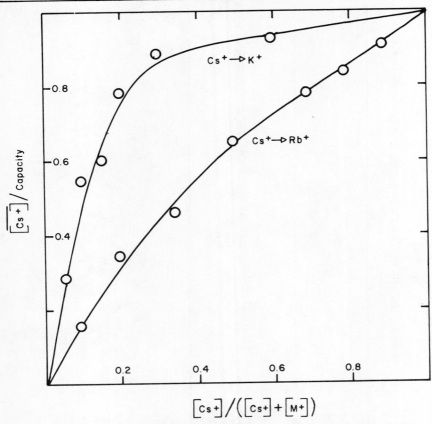

FIG. 11. Cs/Rb and Cs/K isotherms on amorphous ZrP. (Reproduced, with permission, from J. Inorg. Nucl. Chem., 26, 299 (1964)).

exchange are appreciably more exothermic than the value for H^+ - Li^+, indicating contributions by forces other than coulombic in the exchange of these ions. The more unfavorable free energy change in the case of H^+ - Li^+ exchange as compared with H^+ - Cs^+ is seen to be entirely an enthalpy effect reflecting the energy required in order to provide for the degree of lattice distortion for the entry of the hydrated or partially hydrated lithium ion.

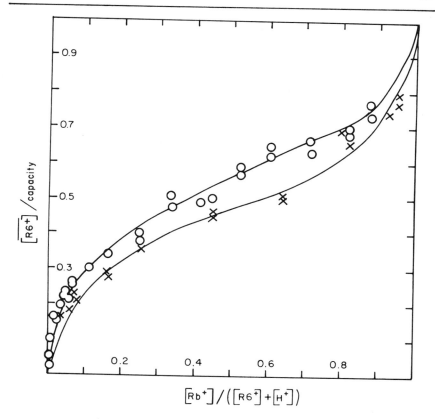

FIG. 12. Rb/H isotherms on amorphous zirconium phosphate at 25° (O) and at 40° (X). (Reproduced, with permission, from J. Inorg. Nucl. Chem., 26, 299 (1964)).

3. Kinetics of Exchange

Kinetic studies on ZrP have indicated that the rate of exchange is controlled by the rate of diffusion of ions through the exchanger particles. Nancollas and Patterson [72] followed the rate of both Na^+/H^+ and Cs^+/K^+ exchange on semicrystalline ZrP, by titrimetric and potentiometric methods as a function of ionic strength, stirring rate, and of particle size. A typical time plot of the extent of reaction F defined by

$$F = \frac{\text{The amount of exchange of time } t}{\text{The amount of exchange at infinite time}} \ , \tag{15}$$

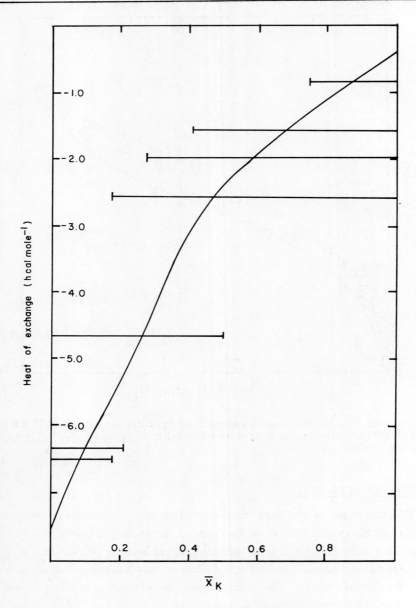

FIG. 13. Molar heats of partial H^+/K^+ exchange at 25°C on semicrystalline ZrP. (Reproduced, with permission, from J. Inorg. Nucl. Chem., 22, 3643 (1969)).

is shown in Fig. 14. It can be seen that the rate is independent of Na^+ ion concentration between 0.01 and 0.10 M, but markedly dependent upon particle size. Changes of fluid dynamics by means of rotary stirring or mechanical

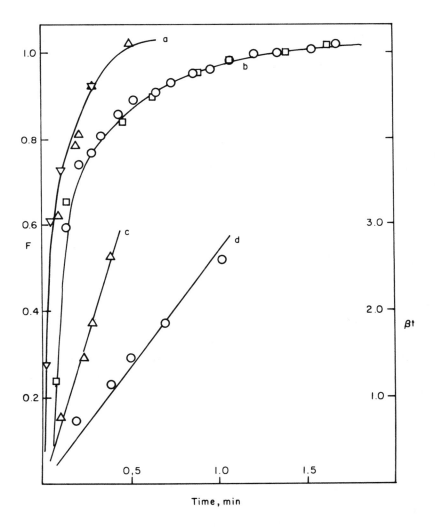

FIG. 14. Plots of F (curves a and b) and Bt (curves c and d) against time for Na/H exchange on semi-crystalline ZrP. 0.01 M NaCl, 160-200 BSS mesh size, ▲; 0.10 M NaCl, 160-200 mesh size, △; 0.10 M NaCl, 60-100 mesh size, ▫; 0.01 M NaCl, 60-100 mesh size, ⊙. (Reproduced, with permission, from J. Inorg. Nucl. Chem., 22, 259 (1961)).

shaking were without effect upon the rate of exchange. All this evidence
points to particle diffusion's being the rate controlling mechanism and, following Conway et al. [82], the theory developed by Boyd and co-workers
[83] describing diffusion into spherical particles may be applied to the
system:

$$F = 1 - \frac{6}{\pi^2} \sum_{n=1}^{\infty} \exp \frac{(-n^2 Bt)}{n^2} , \tag{16}$$

where $B = \pi^2 D_i / r^2$.

In these equations, r is the radius of the spherical particle, and D_i is the
effective diffusion coefficient of sodium and hydrogen ions within the exchanger.
F is a calculable mathematical function of Bt, and tables of values have been
published by Reichenberg [84]. Provided that D_i is independent of F, the
model under discussion, based upon particle diffusion of ions within the
exchanger, should yield linear plots of F against Bt. Two such plots are
shown in Fig. 13, and their linearity confirms that F is dependent only upon
$D_i r^2$, and is independent of the concentration of ingoing ions. A similar
study of Cs^+/H^+ exchange was made by Ollivier and Kikindai [85] on an
amorphous ZrP. They used a limited bath technique and determined the
nature of the diffusion process by an interruption technique. An increase in
the rate of fixation was found immediately after the interruption, indicating
that the rate-controlling step is diffusion within the particles. Bochinova
et al. [86] have also studied the kinetics of exchange by using ZrP gels of
different compositions in both NaCl and NaOH media. Exchange in the NaOH
solutions was followed to completion, and in NaCl to about 1% completion.
From the results obtained the authors postulate a two-step process, an initial
rapid stage on the surface with a slow diffusion from within the particle. It
seems likely that the fast process they observed was the exchange reported
by other authors [72, 85], and the slow process was due to hydrolysis,
which would occur to a significant extent for gel materials in alkaline
solutions. The difference in rate for different preparations was probably
due to hydrolysis and variations in particle size.

H. Semicrystalline Zirconium Phosphates

It has already been mentioned that a serious drawback to the use of zirconium phosphate gels is their ready hydrolysis and difficult reproducibility. The crystals do not suffer from these disadvantages but either exclude large ions or exhibit low uptake of cations in acid solutions. Ideally a combination of crystal and gel properties is desired. Efforts in this direction will now be described. To obtain a granular zirconium phosphate, Larsen et al. [71] sprayed a Zr(IV) solution into hot sulfuric acid containing phosphoric acid. They did not investigate the ion exchange properties of this product, but later investigators did [68, 69, 72]. Although zirconium phosphates made in a similar fashion exhibited rather well defined x-ray diffraction patterns [69], their dehydration curves [72] and ion exchange properties did not correspond to those of α-ZrP [4, 72]. Subsequently, it was found that, starting with an amorphous gel, it was possible to obtain an almost continuous increase in crystallinity until the true crystals (α-ZrP) were obtained [16, 19, 22, 69]. This was achieved by controlling the temperature and time of digestion and the concentration of phosphoric acid used. It is therefore necessary to define what is meant by fully crystalline α-ZrP, so that the semicrystalline products can be described in their proper perspective. By crystals we shall mean that preparation which (1) exhibits the unit cell dimensions or powder pattern of α-ZrP without line broadening, (2) exhibits the four OH stretching bands as given in Table 4, (3) gives the sharp water losses at 100° and 450°, and (4) does not exchange appreciably with Cs^+ and Rb^+ in acid solution. Semicrystalline preparations exhibit properties and behavior intermediate between those of the gels and crystals, and attempts have been made to relate their behavior to the degree of crystallinity. Some of the work described in the previous section (II.G.2) was probably done on semicrystalline ZrP rather than amorphous gels.

Albertsson [22] prepared a series of semicrystalline zirconium phosphates by refluxing portions of gel for 1 h in 3 M, 4.5 M, 6 M, and 9 M H_3PO_4. The crystallite size was shown to increase as the concentration of acid used for refluxing was increased. The affinity of the different exchangers for Cs^+ was determined from trace experiments. Denoting the different semicrystalline products as ZrP-N, where N is the concentration of phosphoric acid used, the affinity series was determined to be ZrP-3 < ZrP-4.5 > ZrP-6 > ZrP-9 > ZrP-12.

Ahrland et al. compared the dehydration, neutralization, and sorption behavior of a number of preparations varying in crystallinity [48]. The amorphous sample lost water continuously with increasing temperature. However, as the crystallinity increased, the dehydration curves began to exhibit a more pronounced break in a temperature range in which the water loss results from phosphate condensation ($\sim 450°$C), but at lower temperatures the zeolitic water was still lost in a continuous fashion. This indicated that as crystallinity increased the phosphate groups became more ordered. The more crystalline samples were more resistant to hydrolysis also. Another interesting feature of this research was the discovery that the distribution coefficient for Cs^+ sorption increased with decreasing water content of the gelatinous or semicrystalline exchangers. The maximum value of the distribution coefficient was reached when the exchangers were anhydrous, and decreased beyond this level due to condensation of phosphate groups. The more crystalline the exchanger the sharper the maximum. Uranyl ion and Ce^{3+} did not show this maximum, but gave values of the distribution coefficient which were almost independent of the water content.

A most striking illustration of the effect of both crystallinity and temperature on the exchange isotherms of uranyl ion is illustrated in Fig. 15 [87]. It is seen that the less crystalline the exchanger the greater the affinity for UO_2^{2+} relative to H^+. Furthermore, as the temperature increases, the affinity increases until at 175-250°C the gel greatly prefers uranyl ion to hydrogen ion. This effect is less marked the more crystalline the exchanger. The greater affinity with increasing temperature is attributed to the formation of uranyl phosphate [88], since some of the x-ray reflections of the exchanged solid correspond to those of uranyl phosphate. However, the evidence is not conclusive.

It is obvious from the foregoing that the structure of a particular zirconium phosphate sample greatly influences its exchange behavior. Crystallinity and water content are only two indicators of variable structure. A better control of preparative conditions, and a better understanding of the manner in which the conditions of synthesis influence changes in structure, is required to obtain well defined materials of the desired characteristics.

A start in this direction has been made by Clearfield and his co-workers [89]. Zirconium phosphate gel was prepared by rapid precipitation in dilute solutions to insure a very low degree of crystallinity in the product. Portions of this gel were then refluxed in 0.5, 0.8, 1.5, 2.5, 3.5, 4.5, 6, 9 and 12 molar phosphoric acid for 48 h. All of the products had a phosphate-zirconium ratio close to 2, and exhibited a noticeable increase in crystallinity with increasing acid concentration used for reflux. An interesting feature of the syntheses was the fact that the products refluxed in 0.5 to 2.5 M H_3PO_4 exhibited different structures when wet than when dry. The x-ray patterns of the wet samples were quite crystalline and contained a well-defined interlayer spacing at 10.6 Å. When dry, the x-ray patterns resembled those previously recorded for zirconium phosphate gels. Furthermore, once the samples were dried, they did not reform the 10.6 Å structure on wetting, except for the gel refluxed in 0.5 M acid. The ion exchange behavior reported here is for the dried samples.

The sodium ion titration curves for some of the sample prepared as described above are shown in Fig. 16. The curve for the gel prepared in 0.5 M H_3PO_4 resembled those obtained previously for the amorphous gels. As the crystallinity of the samples increased, the curves slowly transformed into those characterizing the behavior of the crystals, i.e., two plateaus at different pH values. The change in titration curves could be correlated with the different solid phases obtained in the exchange reactions. In those samples which had been refluxed in phosphoric acid solutions weaker than 3 M in strength, a single solid solution of sodium ion in the exchanger phase was obtained. The interlayer spacing varied from sample to sample, indicating different water contents. The interlayer distances decreased steadily with loading. The samples which had been refluxed with phosphoric acid stronger than 3 M exhibited two plateaus and along each of them two solid phases were present. An example is the titration curve for the sample prepared in 4.5 M H_3PO_4 shown in Fig. 16. At low loadings, where the curve rises, only 1 phase, a solid solution of Na^+ in α-ZrP structure, was obtained. At loadings near the half-exchanged point, where the curve again rises, a second solid solution, H^+ dissolved in the $Zr(NaPO_4)(HPO_4) \cdot 5H_2O$

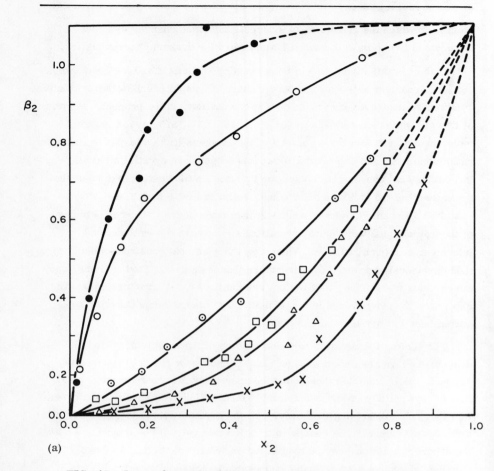

(a)

FIG. 15. Ion exchange isotherms of uranyl ion sorption on zirconium phosphates of different crystallinities. X_2 is the equivalent fraction of UO_2^{++} in solution, β_2 is the equivalent fraction of UO_2^{++} in the solid

a. Amorphous zirconium phosphate

    X - 25°   ⊙ - 100°

    △ - 50°   ○ - 175°

    □ - 80°   ● - 250°

b. Semi-crystalline zirconium phosphate. Symbols as for (a).

c. Crystalline zirconium phosphate. Symbols as for (a).
(Reproduced from ref. 87 by permission of J. Inorg. Nucl. Chem.)

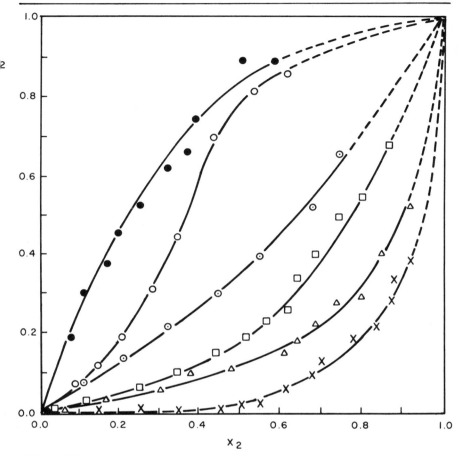

FIG. 15(b).

phase, is observed. Along the flat portion, varying amounts of the two solid solution phases are observed. The same type of behavior is observed in the second stage of exchange, but the solids are half and fully exchanged solid solutions. As the crystallinity of the exchanger increases the composition range of the solid solutions narrows until, in the true crystals, the range is very limited, or pure α-ZrP and $Zr(NaPO_4)$ $(HPO_4) \cdot 5H_2O$ are obtained. Thus, the differences observed for different α-ZrP preparations appear to stem from the differences in the solid phases obtained on exchange. Quantitative studies along these lines appear to offer a means of understating the varied behavior of α-zirconium phosphates.

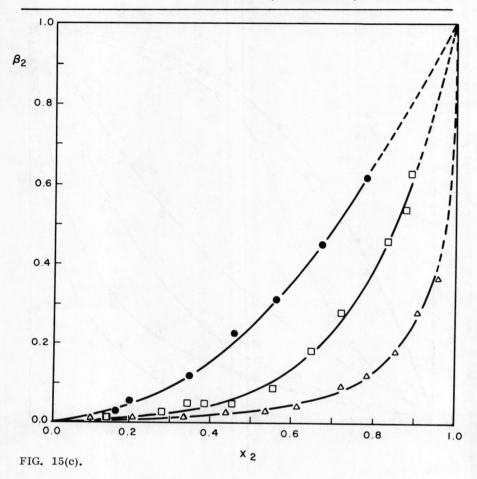

FIG. 15(c).

III. POLYBASIC ACID SALTS OTHER THAN ZIRCONIUM PHOSPHATES

In addition to the zirconium phosphates, there exists a large number of
other polybasic acid salts which exhibit ion exchange behavior. These
include the phosphates and arsenates of titanium, cerium, thorium, uranium,
silicon, germanium, tin, and lead, the molybdates and tungstates of some of
these metals, certain salts of heteropoly acids, and special preparations
including zirconium and titanium antimonate, and some tripolyphosphates.
Some of these and other interesting inorganic ion exchangers have been

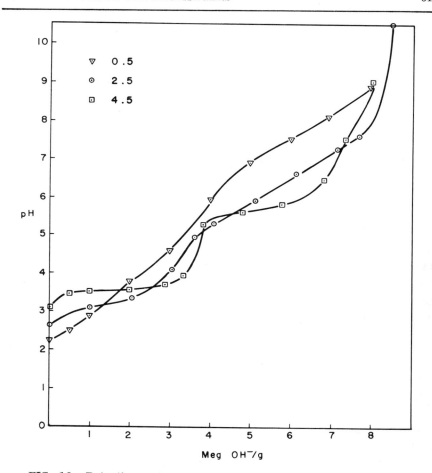

FIG. 16. Potentiometric titrations of semi-crystalline α-ZrP samples prepared by refluxing gel zirconium phosphate in H_3PO_4 of varying strength.

Titrant: 0.1 N NaOH + 0.1 N NaCl, calculated on basis of milliequivalents OH^- added per gram of anhydrous α-ZrP.

    $\triangledown$ gel refluxed 48 hrs in 0.5 M H_3PO_4.

    $\odot$ gel refluxed 48 hrs in 2.5 M H_3PO_4.

    $\boxdot$ gel refluxed 48 hrs in 4.5 M H_3PO_4.

discussed by Barrer [90]. Both amorphous and crystalline varieties of many of the salts exist. Alberti et al. [36] have made a general comparison between the crystalline salts and their amorphous counterparts. The

crystalline phases are more stable to hydrolysis and to condensation of acid
groups at elevated temperatures. In many cases the crystals exclude large
cations which the gels can sorb. In general the relationship between the
crystal and gel forms of an exchanger are similar to those described for
α-ZrP and gel zirconium phosphate. Details for the individual salts are
presented here.

A. Titanium (IV) Phosphates

Titanium phosphate can be prepared in both crystalline and amorphous
forms. The first preparations used as ion exchangers were amorphous gels
obtained by adding aqueous $TiCl_4$ solutions to an excess of phosphoric
acid [2, 61]. These gels were found to have lower exchange capacities
than zirconium phosphate gels prepared in a similar way. This was
later shown to be due to the significantly lower phosphate content of the
titanium gels, and to hydrolysis accompanying the exchange reaction [91, 92].
The hydrolysis is extensive enough, even in acid solution, to seriously limit
the use of titanium phosphate gels as exchangers.

Refluxing the gels in strong phosphoric acid converts them to a crystalline compound, $Ti(HPO_4)_2 \cdot H_2O$, which is isomorphous with α-ZrP [91, 92].
The unit cell dimensions are listed in Table 2. The α-TiP crystals exhibit
ion sieving behavior. Lithium and sodium ions are exchanged in acid
solution, but at higher pH values than when exchanged on α-ZrP. Negligible
exchange of potassium ions takes place in acid solution, but near neutral pH
uptake occurs accompanied by destructive hydrolysis of the exchanger [92]
(similar to Cs^+ on α-ZrP). Thus, the entranceways into the cavities must
be considerably narrower in α-TiP, compared to α-ZrP. The ion sieving
properties of crystalline titanium phosphate have been used to effect separations of cesium and potassium ions from sodium ion [93].

B. Zirconium and Titanium Arsenates

Zirconium arsenate gels may be prepared by precipitation methods
similar to those employed for zirconium phosphate gels [2,3]. A more
detailed study of preparative conditions revealed that the ratio of arsenate
to zirconium varied from less than 1 to almost 2 [94, 95]. As with the

zirconium and titanium phosphate gels, the arsenates are best considered as partially hydrolyzed (basic) salts of variable composition. At low pH the selectivity of a gel prepared by Torracca et al. for alkaline earth ions was $Cs^+ > K^+ > Na^+$ [96]. However, reversals of selectivity occurred at higher pH. The gels are subject to extensive hydrolysis at pH = 8 and above.

Zirconium arsenate gels are converted to crystalline α-ZrAs by refluxing in strong arsenic acid [95, 96]. The crystals are isomorphous with those of α-ZrP; structural details for the arsenate have been presented in Section II.3 and II.4. The α-ZrAs crystals exhibit sieving properties very similar to those of α-ZrP. The alkali metal ions, Rb^+ and Cs^+, are not exchanged in acid solution. With the remaining alkali metal ions, the order of selectivity for the first stage of exchange (conversion of α-ZrAs to the half exchanged phase) is $K^+ > Na^+ > Li^+$. However, for the second stage of exchange, the selectivities are $Li^+ > Na^+ > K^+$. Rubidium and cesium ions exchange only in neutral or alkaline solutions accompanied by extensive hydrolysis [92, 93]. The entranceways into the zirconium arsenate cavities are about the same size as in α-ZrP [27]. Thus, Cs^+ and Rb^+, on the basis of their size, would not be expected to exchange, unless some swelling of the crystals occurs. For this reason it was postulated that the crystals swell in neutral or alkaline solution [16]. However, other factors must be involved since Tl^+, which is about the same size as Rb^+, exchanges in acid solution [93].

Titanium arsenates, both crystalline [97] and amorphous [98], are much more susceptible to hydrolysis than the corresponding zirconium arsenates. Release of arsenate ion to the solution is marked, even in acid solution. Thus, these materials have questionable value as ion exchangers. Nevertheless, Qureshi and Nabi [98] have reported good separations of Pb^{2+} from other ions, such as Zn^{2+}, Mg^{2+}, Cu^{2+}, and Ga^{2+}, on titanium arsenate gels. In all cases some solubilization of the exchanger occurred.

C. Cerium (IV) Phosphates

Initial work on cerium phosphates centered on preparing gels and examining their ion exchange behavior [99-102]. The phosphorus-cerium ratio could be varied from about 1 to 2 by proper control of experimental conditions. The resistance of the gels toward hydrolysis in acid solution is quite good [100, 101]. Larsen and Cilley found that the capacity of a gel with $P/Ce = 1.48$ for alkali metals was in the range of $0.3 - 0.4$ meq/g. This is in contrast to the uptake of sodium ion obtained by Alberti et al. [103], for a gel with $P/Ce = 1.7$. At a pH of 6, about 1.5 meq of Na^+ per gram of cerium phosphate was exchanged, and the total capacity (pH = 10) was approximately 3 meq/g.

After the discovery of crystalline zirconium phosphates, similar methods were employed in efforts to prepare crystalline cerium phosphates. Konig and Meyn [104] obtained a crystalline product with $P/Ce = 1.5$ by dissolving a cerium phosphate gel in conc. H_3PO_4, diluting until precipitation occurred, and boiling the resultant mixture. The formula assigned to this compound is $(Ce - O - Ce)(HPO_4)_3 \cdot H_2O$. However, the exchange capacity implied by the monohydrogen phosphate groups was not realized, since only trace amounts of cations were exchanged. Alberti et al. obtained a similar crystalline product with $P/Ce = 1.5$, which also exhibited poor exchange properties [103]. In the same paper these workers describe a fibrous crystalline cerium phosphate of a probable formula $Ce(HPO_4)_2 \cdot H_2O$, and another phase with $P/Ce = 1.15$. The first compound was found to have an experimental sodium ion exchange capacity of 4.6 meq/g (5.2 meq when hydrolysis effects are considered) compared to a theoretical capacity of 5.7 meq/g. Its x-ray pattern shows that it is not isomorphous with α-ZrP. Furthermore, the powder pattern does not change significantly with uptake of sodium ion [105]. Thus, either this compound has a rigid lattice with Na^+ going into cavities, or it forms a continuous solid solution over the entire range of sodium uptake. Clearfield and Herman have prepared at least seven crystalline cerium phosphates (which include the two mentioned above) having phosphorus-cerium ratios ranging from 1 to 2. The phases of low phosphate content can be converted to those of higher phosphate content by suitable treatment with phosphoric acid. Thus, there must be simple structural relationships among the various forms. Obviously, a better understanding of this system would result if a crystal structure determination were available. Efforts in this direction are under way [103, 105].

When cerium phosphates are prepared in sulfuric acid, the resultant solids contain sulfate ion [103, 104, 106]. The general formula for these solids is $Ce_2O(HPO_4)_{3-x}(SO_4)_x \cdot 4H_2O$, with x lying between 0 and 1. The ion exchange capacity of the exchanger decreases with increasing sulfate content [106]. In acid solution these sulfate containing exchangers give the following selectivity sequence: $Na^+ > Ag^+ > Sr^{2+} > Ba^{2+} > Cs^+ > Ca^{2+}$. Furthermore, ions with a hydrated radius of 3 Å or larger, such as Co^{2+}, Fe^{3+}, Y^{3+}, and Be^{2+}, are not exchanged. In contrast to the above results, the selectivity sequence found in cerium phosphate gels [107] was reversed to $Cs^+ > Ag^+ > Na^+$.

Alberti et al. [108] were able to prepare support-free cerium phosphate sheets from the fibrous, crystalline product having a phosphate-cerium ratio of 2. The R_f values for a number of cations were determined, and several representative chromotographic separations were obtained with the cerium phosphate sheets.

Another interesting feature of cerium (IV) phosphate exchangers, and one which merits further study, is their ability to oxidize the exchanging cation [100, 101].

D. Cerium Arsenates

A number of amorphous and crystalline cerium (IV) arsenates possessing ion exchange properties have been prepared, but details on only one of them have been reported [109]. Microcrystals of a compound, $Ce(HAsO_4)_2 \cdot 2H_2O$, were obtained by refluxing (100-200 h) ceric sulfate in a solution 3 M in arsenic acid and 0.5 M in sulfuric acid. The theoretical exchange capacity for this compound is 4.38 meq/g. Experimental capacities of about 4.35 meq/g were noted with Li^+ and Na^+, and about 1.9 meq/g with K^+, while cesium ion was not exchanged. X-ray patterns taken at various stages of exchange indicate that solid solution formation occurs with the former two ions, but with K^+ a two-phase system is obtained. Resistance to hydrolysis was good up to pH = 10.

Alberti et al. [109] ascribe a layered structure of the α-ZrP type to the cerium arsenate on the basis of this behavior. However, by analogy of its x-ray powder pattern with that of α-ZrP, the interlayer spacing would be about 10.1 Å. It is hard to imagine why ions would be excluded with such a large interlayer spacing. Perhaps factors other than ion sieving are involved.

E. Thorium Phosphates and Arsenates

A fibrous thorium (IV) phosphate of composition $ThO_2 \cdot P_2O_5 \cdot 4H_2O$ has been prepared [110]. Assuming that the compound contains two replaceable hydrogen ions, its exchange capacity should be 4.18 meq/g. An experimental capacity (corrected for hydrolysis) of 3.85 meq/g was observed for Na^+. However, the observed capacity varied from ion to ion. Support-free flexible sheets could be prepared from these fibers as well.

A crystalline compound, $Th(ASO_4)_2 \cdot H_2O$ was prepared by prolonged refluxing of a solution containing Th(IV), arsenic acid, and nitric acid [111]. This compound is specific for lithium ion, exchange occurring at pH = 9.5. The titration curve and x-ray patterns indicate that the exchange reaction is

$$Th(HAsO_4)_2 \cdot H_2O + Li^+ \rightleftharpoons Th(LiAsO_4)_2 \cdot H_2O + H^+ . \qquad (17)$$

Other alkali cations are excluded, and lithium ion can be separated from them with this exchanger.

F. Uranyl Phosphates (Uranium Micas)

There exists an interesting class of minerals called autunites, with the general formula $M(UO_2)_2 (PO_4)_2 \cdot nH_2O$, where M is a divalent cation. Early attempts to synthesize these minerals led to mixed salts such as $Ca_{1/6}Na_{5/3}$ $(UO_2)_2 (PO_4)_2$ [112]. Further, it was shown that the remaining calcium ions could be replaced with Na^+ by treating the solid with strong sodium chloride solutions. Conversely, treatment with $CaCl_2$ solution yielded the pure calcium salt. Subsequently, Beintema proposed a layered structure, similar to that of mica, for these compounds [113]. In this structure divalent cations and water molecules are located between the layers. Conversion of calcium autunite to the magnesium, barium, lithium, sodium, and potassium analogs by ion exchange has been reported [114].

In the absence of foreign cations uranyl salts react with phosphoric acid under the proper conditions to form uranyl hydrogen phosphate, $H(UO_2)(PO_4) \cdot$ $4H_2O$ [115–117]. Exchange of the protons by Ca^{2+} gives $Ca(UO_2)(PO_4)_2 \cdot$ nH_2O, which is identical with the mineral autunite. Pekárek and Benešová [117] have found the selectivity of uranyl phosphate toward alkali cations to be $NH_4^+ > Cs^+$, Rb^+, $K^+ >> Na^+$. Ammonium uranyl phosphate, produced by the displacement of alkali cations from uranyl hydrogen phosphate with ammonium chloride, was found not to sorb trace amounts of K^+, Rb^+, and Cs^+, and not to convert to uranyl hydrogen phosphate on treatment with acids [117]. These results suggest that sorption involves a process of reprecipitation and therefore should be controlled by the solubility products of the uranyl phosphates produced. Indeed it was found that the solubility products did parallel selectivities [118, 119]. Thus, the question as to whether the reactions involve true ion exchange remains to be answered.

Arsenate and vanadate analogs of the uranyl hydrogen phosphates are known [114, 120]. All of these compounds have similar layered structures, and sorb alkyl ammonium ions which line up perpendicularly (or diagonally) to the layers in a regular fashion [120].

G. Tin (IV) Phosphates and Arsenates

Stannic phosphate was first prepared for use as an ion exchanger by Merz [121]. The product was gelatinous, of indefinite composition, and its ion exchange behavior was somewhat similar to that exhibited by zirconium phosphate gels. Subsequently, other workers prepared numerous gels by variation of preparative conditions [122-124]. The phosphate-tin ratio in the gels increased with increase of this ratio in the reactants. Inoue claimed that the limiting ratio was 5:4, and proposed a structure based on this result [123]. However, the 5:4 ratio appears to be an artifact of his preparative conditions.

Tin phosphate gels have been examined for possible use in the separation of fission products [125-127], and separations of ions have been carried out on paper impregnated with stannic phosphate [128, 129]. It has also been used as a support for the gas chromatographic separation of fatty acids [130].

Crystalline tin phosphate has been prepared by heating the gels in 6 to 10 M phosphoric acid [131-133]. Fuller assigns the formula $Sn(HPO_4)_2 \cdot nH_2O$ to the crystals, based on elemental analysis and on TGA and ion exchange data. If the crystals are dried over phosphorus pentoxide, $n = 1$. However, at higher humidities up to one additional mole of water is picked up without change in the x-ray pattern. Crystalline tin phosphate apparently

has a layered structure similar to that of α-ZrP. This conclusion is based
on the similarities of their x-ray powder patterns [131] and the sorption
behavior of alkyl ammonium ions [132]. However, there are several differences between the ion exchange behavior of the two compounds. Tin phosphate
crystals are strongly hydrolyzed in neutral or alkaline pH by all alkali metal
cations except Li$^+$ [133, 134]. Furthermore, the titration curves exhibit
only one endpoint, whereas two are observed with α-ZrP. Lithium ion is
anomalous in that significantly more Li$^+$ is exchanged than can be accounted
for on the basis of the proposed formula. Constantino and Gasperoni [134]
propose a tautomeric equilibrium of the type

$$
\begin{array}{ccc}
\begin{array}{c}
HPO_4 \\
\parallel \\
Sn \leftarrow H_2O \\
\parallel \\
HPO_4 \\
(5)
\end{array}
& \rightleftharpoons &
\begin{array}{c}
H_2PO_4 \\
| \\
Sn - OH \\
| \\
HPO_4 \\
(6)
\end{array}
\end{array}
\qquad , \qquad (18)
$$

to account for this result. However, this is not likely, for the same reasons
given in section II.A.4. Obviously more definitive structural data are
needed.

Tin arsenates are quite similar to the corresponding tin phosphates
[135]. Values of K_D obtained for the ion exchange of many pairs of ions on
the various forms of tin arsenate have recently been published [136, 137],
and numerous separations of cations effected.

H. Other Group IV Phosphates

Winkler and Thilo have prepared crystalline phosphates of silicon,
germanium, and lead, as well as those of titanium, zirconium, and tin,
already described [131]. The general formula for these compounds is
$H_2M(PO_4)_2 \cdot H_2O$, except for the silicon analog, which contains no water of
crystallization. X-ray powder patterns indicate that these compounds have
similar structures. However, the usefulness of the silicon, germanium,

and lead compounds as ion exchangers is severely limited by the fact that they slowly decompose in aqueous media.

I. Miscellaneous Inorganic Ion Exchangers

A large number of miscellaneous polybasic acid salts which exhibit ion exchange properties are known. These are tabulated in Table 7. The interested reader can refer to the original works for further details.

IV. HETEROPOLY SALTS: ION-EXCHANGE PROPERTIES OF THE SALTS OF HETEROPOLY ACIDS

Several good reviews dealing with the chemistry of the isopolymolybdates [164-166,170] and isopolytungstates [166-168,170], as well as the molybdo- and tungsto- heteropoly complexes [169-171] are available. In this discussion we restrict ourselves mainly to developments relevant to the ion-exchange properties of these compounds, and in this respect, enlarge upon the earlier review of Amphlett [4].

A. Preparation

The synthetic chemistry of heteropoly complexes has been extensively studied and methods for the preparation of a wide variety of these compounds are available [172, 176, 183, 192, 195]. The classic procedures of Wu [172] for the preparation of the yellow crystals of 12-molybdophosphoric acid, $H_3[PO_4(Mo_3O_9)_4] \cdot 29H_2O$, and the isomorphous, colorless crystals of 12-tungstophosphoric acid, $H_3[PO_4(W_3O_9)_4] \cdot 29H_2O$, are very reliable. We are particularly concerned with the microcrystalline, insoluble ammonium salts of these water soluble acids, which form under conditions of homogeneous precipitation as metathetic products, on mixing solutions of the heteropoly acids with solutions containing ammonium ion [172, 183, 197]; e.g., on mixing solutions of ammonium paramolybdate, $(NH_4)_6Mo_7O_{24} \cdot 4H_2O$, phosphoric acid, ammonium nitrate, and nitric acid. However, it is well known that this direct precipitation reaction is complicated by the coprecipi- tation of foreign ions, most notably, potassium. The precipitates also

TABLE 7

Miscellaneous Polybasic Acids and Salts Possessing Ion Exchange Properties

Salt	Comments	Reference
Zirconium molybdate	Amorphous gel, Mo/Zr $\cong$ 2	[2, 139–144]
Titanium molybdate	Gels with Mo/Ti $\cong$ 1 – 2	[145]
Zirconium tungstate	Gels with w/Zr $\cong$ 2	[2, 7, 8, 140, 143]
Titanium tungstate	Gels with W/Ti $\cong$ 1/2 – 2, high specificity for Pb^{2+}	[146]
Stannic molybdate	Amorphous gel with Mo/Ti $\cong$ 1, high specificity for Pb^{2+}	[147]
Stannic tungstate	Amorphous gel w/Sn $\cong$ 1/3, low capacity	[148]
Zirconium antimonate	Gel with Sb/Zr > 2, high specificity for Cs$^+$, Sr^{2+}	[149, 150]
Titanium antimonate	Gels with Sb/Zr $\cong$ 1 – 1.2, low capacities, selectivities for 21 ions determined	[151]
Zirconium selenite		[152, 153]
Zirconium tellurate	Zr(H$_2$TeO$_6$) · 4H$_2$O, only one proton exchanges	[154, 155]
Zirconium silicate	High capacity, good stability	[156, 157]

Zirconium–phosphate–silicate	SiO_2:ZrO_2:P_2O_5 = 4:1:0.8, for selective plutonium isolation	[158]
Zirconium polyphosphate	Products vary in degree of polymerization. Exchange capacity increases with increasing size of polymer	[159]
Rare earth phosphates		[160]
Chromium (III) tripolyphosphate	Glass with P/Cr $\cong$ 2.5, excludes polyvalent cations	[161]
Chromium (III) phosphates	Complex polymeric structure, complicated exchange behavior	[138, 162]
Chromium (III) arsenate	Similar to chromium (III) phosphates	[163]
Arsenophosphoric acid	$HAs(PO_4)_2$ swells in water with hydronium ion formation. Slow rates of exchange	[131]
Antimonophosphoric acid	$HSb(PO_4)_2$ isomorphous with $HAs(PO_4)_2$	[131]

occlude nitric acid and/or ammonium nitrate. The composition $(NH_4)_3[PMo_{12}O_{40}] \cdot 2HNO_3 \cdot H_2O$[†] was long accepted [176-178, 192, 195].

In view of what is known of the crystal structure and ion-exchange chemistry of the precipitates (vide infra), it is now clear that the "nitric acid" and foreign ion contamination of the precipitates arises primarily from an isomorphous partial substitution of hydroxonium ion and/or alkali metal ion for ammonium ion. Under a given set of conditions, a composition $(NH_4)_{5/2}(H_3O)_{1/2}[PMo_{12}O_{40}] \cdot xH_2O$, is typically obtained [178]. (We note in passing that the 12-molybdophosphoric acid and 12-tungstophosphoric acid of commerce, commonly called phosphomolybdic acid and phosphotungstic acid, respectively, as well as their salts, are often impure, being contaminated during their preparation as described above, and also by the admixture of other heteropoly species, e.g., $[P_2Mo_{18}O_{62}]^{6-}$ and $[SiW_{12}O_{40}]^{4-}$, and unreacted reagents, e.g., NH_4Cl and $Mo(orW)O_3$ and their hydrates).

B. Structure

The solid-state structural chemistry of the heteropoly acids and their salts is characterized by the existence of isomorphous crystals [169, 183]. There is evidence that many of the polyanions retain the integrity of their molecular structures in solution, so long as the solution pH and temperature are within the range of hydrolytic and thermolytic stability of the complexes [164-170]. Ammonium 12-molybdophosphate (AMP), and its tungsten analog (ATP), belong to one such isomorphous series of which 12-tungstophosphoric acid pentahydrate, $H_3[PO_4(W_3O_9)_4] \cdot 5H_2O$, is the prototype [184]. The yellow octahedra of 12-molybdophosphoric acid and the colorless octahedra of 12-tungstophosphoric acid, which crystallize spontaneously from solution according to Wu's procedure [172], can be represented by the formula $H_3[PO_4(M(VIB)_3O_9)_4] \cdot 29H_2O$, where M(VIB) = Mo, W [180, 182-184]. The crystals of the tungsten 29-hydrate lose 24 moles of water per formula weight at room temperature over phosphorus pentoxide in vacuo to yield a white, microcrystalline powder of the well-defined, stable

---

[†] The equivalent formulations of the heteropoly anions such as $[PO_4(Mo_3O_9)_4]^{3-}$ and $[PMo_{12}O_{40}]^{3-}$ are used interchangeably.

pentahydrate [180]. (Evidently, the molybdenum 29-hydrate does not dehydrate without decomposition [183]).

Keggin, Santos, Illingworth, and Bradley determined the essential features of the crystal structures of the acids, $H_3[PO_4(W_3O_9)_4] \cdot nH_2O$, with n = 5 and 29, and a number of their isomorphs from x-ray powder diffraction photographs [179-183]. Both acid hydrates have cubic crystal structures. The pentahydrate [179, 180] has a unit cell of dimension $\underline{a}$ = 12.141 ± 0.005 Å containing 2 formula weights in space group Pn3m; the 29-hydrate [179, 182] has $\underline{a}$ = 23.281 ± 0.002 Å and Z = 8 in space group Fd3m.

The isostoichiometric polyanions in the two acid hydrates are also isostructural [180, 182]. The anions have point symmetry $\overline{4}3m$ (Td), and are built up of a central (PO_4)-tetrahedron tetrahedrally surrounded by four groups of three condensed, edge-sharing (WO_6)-octahedra, each such group having the net composition (W_3O_9), thus giving the discrete polyanion, $[PO_4(W_3O_9)_4]^{3-}$ (see Figs. 17 and 18). Note that the polyhedral diagrams, Figs. 17A, 17C, and 18A, are only schematic: one must avoid the misconception that the polyanion structures (as opposed to the overall crystal structures) include voids or channels of atomic dimensions. The tangent-hard-sphere representation of a fragment of the whole polyanion, Fig. 17B, suggests the stereochemical density of the larger polyanion structure.

In the pentahydrate crystal structure [180], the large, roughly spherical anions pack in an interpenetrating-primitive cubic lattice (Fig. 19), which is related to the body-centered cubic lattice of the space group $I\overline{4}3m$ by an inversion of the orientation of the anions of one of the two interpenetrating lattices, relative to those of the other lattice. Thus the crystal structure is pseudo-body-centered, as is shown in Fig. 19. The anions are packed "flat-to-flat" and "reentrant-to-reentrant" (see Fig. 17D), and the inverted (stippled) anion at the body center of the (dash) outlined primitive cubic unit cell is at a corner of another primitive cell, not outlined, which interpenetrates, and is parallel to the one outlined. The water-cation structure fills the interstitial voids in the anion packing [180]. Three water molecules (or hydroxonium ions) per formula unit (six per unit cell) occupy the face centers and edge centers of the unit cell, and two

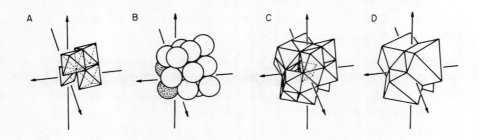

FIG. 17. Representations of the molecular structure of the 12-tungstophosphate heteropolyanion, $[PO_4(W_3O_9)_4]^{3-}$. The reference axial system in the diagrams is the one defined by the anion's three mutually perpendicular four-fold roto-inversion axes, and the (arbitrary) drawing scale is the same for A through D.

A. Polyhedral representation of a fragment of the whole polyanion show-ing the arrangement of one of the four groups of three edge-sharing (WO_6)-octahedra relative to the central (PO_4)-tetrahedron.

B. Tangent-hard-sphere representation equivalent to A. The stippled spheres represent oxygen atoms belonging to the central $(PO_4)^-$ tetrahedron.

C. Polyhedral representation of the whole polyanion.

D. A simplified concave polyhedron depicting the gross, overall geometry of C. Note the "flats" and "reentrants" described in the text.

(four) others the "reentrant-to-reentrant" voids between adjacent anions of inverse orientation.

The 29-hydrate has a face-centered cubic crystal structure in which the anion packing has a diamond-like arrangement, and the more highly hydrated water-cation structure fills the more voluminous and geometrically intricate interstitial voids [182].

In the salts isomorphous with the pentahydrate, among which are AMP and ATP [183], the cation locations are presumably the same as those found from the x-ray diffraction data for the cations in the tricesium

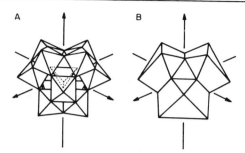

FIG. 18. A and B same as Fig. 17C and D, respectively.

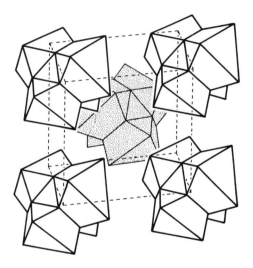

FIG. 19. Schematic illustration of the packing of the heteropolyanions in the crystal structure of the pentahydrate, $H_3[PO_4(W_3O_9)_4] \cdot 5H_2O$. The anions are represented as in Fig. 17D. Only the four anions at the corners of the frontmost face of the (dash outlined) cubic unit cell and the inverted (stippled) anion at its body center are shown.

isomorph, $Cs_3[PO_4(W_3O_9)_4] \cdot nH_2O$, n = 0 or 2 [182]. Crystallographic symmetry and their stereochemical bulk dictate that the cesium ions be located at the face- and edge-center voids in the anion packing; and thus, if the salt is not anhydrous, the water molecules must be located in the "reentrant-to-reentrant" voids [182].

C. General Properties

The usefulness of AMP and ATP as ion exchangers depends in part on their insolubility in water. In this respect they are atypical heteropoly compounds, for the latter as a rule are very soluble. The free heteropoly acids and their salts with small cations can have aqueous solubilities of up to 85% by weight of solution [179]. Solubilities are typically high in oxygenated organic solvents also. Qualitatively, these high solubilities can be rationalized in terms of a Born-Haber cycle in which the lattice energy of the crystalline solute (dependent on the efficiency of cation-anion packing) is dominant [189]. It is not surprising that salts with small cations have a high solubility, whereas those with the larger cations such as K^+, NH_4^+, Rb^+, Cs^+, Ag^+, Tl^+, Sr^{2+}, Ba^{2+}, Hg^{2+}, Pb^{2+}, alkylammonium, and quanidinium are much less soluble.

The free heteropoly acids are typically quite strong Brφnsted acids ($1 \lesssim pK_a \lesssim 3$) [179]. They are also polybasic. Hence, acid salts are commonplace [195]. However, their several protolytic functions seldom differ much in dissociation constant [179]. In strongly alkaline solution the heteropoly complexes suffer hydrolytic degradation,

$$[PO_4(Mo_3O_9)_4]^{3-} + 24OH^- \rightarrow PO_4^{3-} + 12\ MoO_4^{2-} + 12H_2O. \tag{18}$$

The crystalline free acids, and those of their salts that are also highly hydrated, melt in their own water of crystallization, generally in the temperature range 40 to 100°C [179]. Partially dehydrated or less highly hydrated compounds lose water in the 100 to 200°C range, but thermolysis of the polyanions themselves requires higher temperatures [179]. In precipitated AMP the anion begins to degrade at about 400°C [185]. Evidence regarding the dependence of the properties of heteropoly compounds on their thermal history is fragmentary.

The heteropoly compounds, especially those composed of 12-molybdo-complexes, are quite strong oxidizing agents [179]. Oxidation potentials comparable to that of chromic acid have been observed, and hence even mild reducing agents yield the complex, characteristically blue, heteropoly redox products.

Finally, exploratory measurements of the infrared (1200 to 625 cm^{-1}) spectral [186] and magnetic [187] properties of some 12-heteropoly species have been reported. Such measurements have not yet been utilized in studies of the ion exchange behavior of heteropoly compounds, but undoubtedly would provide useful information if determined at various stages of exchange.

D. Ion-Exchange Properties

The first explicit recognition that the incorporation of foreign ions into the AMP structure during precipitation occurred by a potentially useful cation-exchange process, appears to have been made by Buchwald and Thistlewaite [188]. They demonstrated the sorption by their AMP preparations of macro quantities of K^+, Rb^+, Cs^+, and Tl^+ from acidic nitrate media at room temperature. Under similar conditions, they found that Li^+, Na^+ and Ca^{2+}, Sr^{2+}, Ba^{2+} were sorbed only slightly, if at all. In a 1951 paper [189], Meir and Treadwell had analyzed their solubility and sorption data on potassium, rubidium, and cesium exchange on AMP, in terms of the thermodynamics of a Born-Haber cycle. They postulated a rapid initial surface sorption followed by a slower, diffusion-rate dependent recrystallization. Much of the subsequent investigation of the ion-exchange properties of the salts of the heteropoly acids has been carried out in the laboratories of Van R. Smit, Robb, and Jacobs and their co-workers at Pretoria [190-197], and Krtil and his co-workers at Prague [198-204].

E. Ion-Exchange Properties of AMP

Krtil and Kourim [198] studied the acidic hydrolysis and the (hydronium ion-ammonium ion)-, (hydronium ion-cesium ion)-, and (ammonium ion-cesium ion)-exchange with their analyzed preparation of AMP, $(NH_4)_{2.95}$ $(H_3O)_{0.05}$ $[PMo_{12}O_{40}] \cdot 11.6H_2O$. They employed macro concentrations in nitrate and chloride media under static , batch equilibration conditions at room temperature. The results of their material balance analysis confirmed the high sorption capacity of AMP for cesium, and demonstrated its adequate resistance to degradation in acidic solution.

Van R. Smit et al. [190-192] studied the sorption of monovalent cations at trace concentrations in ammonium nitrate media of pH = 2 at 25° C, by means of both static, batch equilibration, and dynamic, column chromatographic ion-exchange techniques. Their preparations of AMP gave the selectivity sequence: $Na^+ < K^+ < Rb^+ < Cs^+; Ag^+ < Tl^+$, paralleling the order of cation crystallographic radii. Qualitatively, this is the same as the selectivity sequence of the ammonium form of Dowex-50 ion-exchange resin under the same experimental conditions, but quantitatively, the separation factors measured for the AMP were orders of magnitude larger than those for Dowex-50.

Van R. Smit et al. also investigated the sorption and separation by ion-exchange chromatography of macro quantities of monovalent [193]: Na^+, K^+, Rb^+, Cs^+; divalent [34]: Sr^{2+}, Ba^{2+}, Cd^{2+}, VO_2^{2+}; and trivalent [34]: Y^{3+}, In^{3+} ions on columns of AMP with asbestos support. Typical results are shown in Figs. 20-22. The excellent separation of the alkali metal ions in trace quantities on an (AMP + asbestos) column is shown in Fig. 20. The similar effectiveness of the columns with macro amounts of these ions has also been demonstrated [189]. Van R. Smit et al. point out [193] that there is no other method of sodium-potassium separation as simple, rapid, or effective as AMP + asbestos ion-exchange column chromatography. They have also utilized the strongly preferential retention of cesium as the basis for a large scale, AMP ion-exchange process for the recovery of cesium-137 from fission product wastes [196, 197]. The smooth, symmetrical, sigmoid breakthrough curves, and symmetrical elution curves, indicate that the columns operated under essentially equilibrium conditions at linear column flow rates of about 1 cm/min, and suggest that, in practice, even higher flow rates might be used [193]. Presuming an ideal composition for AMP, viz., $(NH_4)_3 [PMo_{12}O_{40}] \cdot 2H_2O$, the maximum possible ion-exchange capacity corresponding to the total displacement of ammonium ion is 1.57 meq/g. In the column elution breakthrough experiments, about 70% of this capacity was realized at column saturation [193].

In a batch equilibration study of the adherence of the (trace) rubidium ion-ammonium ion-exchange to the mass action law, Van R. Smit et al. [193] obtained isotherms displaying the expected linear (slope = -1) dependence of $\log K_d^{Rb^+}$ on $\log[NH_4^+]$ for 0.02 M $< [NH_4^+] < 1$ M (see Section II.G.1)

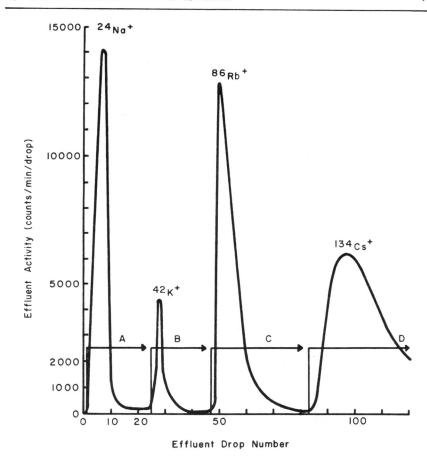

FIG. 20. Chromatographic ion exchange separation of carrier-free trace amounts of the alkali metal ion radionuclides on a column of AMP of dimensions (5 mm (diameter) X 1.6 mm (height)) at room temperature. Initial hydrodynamic column pressure head 11 cm; initial flow rate ~ 1 drop/min.

NH_4NO_3 elutriant solutions:

A. 0.01-$\underline{M}$
B. 0.2-$\underline{M}$
C. 3-$\underline{M}$
D. Saturated

(From Fig. 1, Ref. 190.)

[193]. Krtil [201] observed the same ideal behavior in isotherms relating his equilibrium data for the (trace) cesium ion-ammonium ion-exchange, on his preparations of AMP (and ATP).

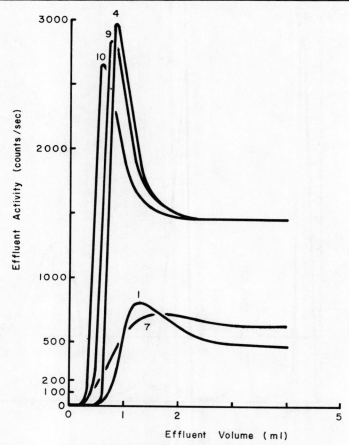

FIG. 21. The elution of $^{137}Ba^{2+}$, the daughter of $^{137}Cs^{+}$ sorbed and immobile on a 2:1 (w:w) column of (AMP + asbestos), with a succession of elutriant solutions at room temperature. Column dimensions ($0.21\ cm^2$ X 1.3 cm); linear column flow rate ~1 cm/min. Column pre-conditioned with 10 ml 1-$\underline{M}$ NH_4NO_3.

Successive elutriant solutions:

1. 1-M NH_4NO_3
4. 1-M NH_4NO_3 + 0.1-M HNO_3
7. 0.1-M NH_4NO_3 + 0.1-M HNO_3
9. 0.1-M NH_4NO_3 + 0.5-M HNO_3
10. 1-M HNO_3

(From Fig. 1, Ref. 194.)

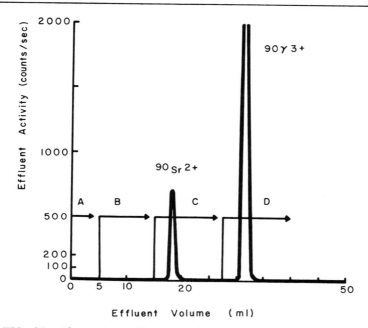

FIG. 22. Chromatographic ion exchange separation of macro amounts of Sr^{2+} and Y^{3+} on a column of (0.72 g AMP + 0.72 g asbestos) of dimensions (0.81 cm^2 X 3.6 cm) at room temperature.

Elutriant solutions:

A. Feed solution (5 ml) buffered to pH = 4.5 containing 1 mg Sr^{2+}, 1 mg Y^{3+}, and 80 mg Na(CH$_3$COO) · 3H$_2$O and tagged with ^{90}Sr-^{90}Y.

B. 0.01-M NH$_4$NO$_3$ + 0.2-M NaNO$_3$

C. 1-M NH$_4$NO$_3$

D. 1-M NH$_4$NO$_3$ + 1-M HNO$_3$

(From Fig. 3D, Ref. 194.)

The behavior of di- and trivalent ions on the (AMP + asbestos) columns is more complex than that of the monovalent ions [194]. Van R. Smit et al. observed [191, 194] that when carrier-free cesium-137, sorbed on an (AMP + asbestos) column, was allowed to decay to its barium-137 daughter, the barium could only be eluted with elutriant solutions that were either 1 N in ammonium nitrate, or strongly acidic. The results of such an experiment are illustrated in Fig. 21. None of the elutriant solutions in this experiment caused any significant column migration of the sorbed parent cesium, and the successive elutions were separated by 1/2-h intervals to allow secular equilibrium to be reestablished on the column by the decay scheme:

$$^{137}_{55}Cs^+ \ (t_{1/2} = 30 \text{ yr}) \ \xrightarrow{\ \beta^-, \ \gamma \text{ emission}\ } \ ^{137(m)}_{56}Ba^{2+} (t_{1/2} = 2.6 \text{ min})$$

γ emission
nuclear transition from
metastable ($\underline{m}$) to stable
nuclear isomer

β^-, γ emission

$$^{137}_{56}Ba^{2+} \text{ (stable)}$$

Van R. Smit et al. [194] interpreted the barium sorption in light of work by Healy et al. [195] on the cocrystallization and/or ion-exchange-recrystallization preparation of a variety of neutral, acid, and double salts of 12-tungstophosphoric acid with a selection of mono-, di-, and trivalent cations. ‡

The proposed mechanism involves a single-step cation exchange,

$$2(NH_4)_2(H_3O)[PMo_{12}O_{40}] + Ba^{2+} \ \rightleftharpoons$$

$$Ba(NH_4)_4[PMo_{12}O_{40}]_2 + 2H_3O^+, \tag{19}$$

which also accounts for the observed dependence of barium elution on ammonium ion concentration and/or acidity. It is supported by the observed slope of 2.72 (as against the expected 3) for the log K_d vs pH plot for trace Y(III) sorption in the pH range 2.0 < pH < 3.0. [By analogy, Krtil [200] observed the theoretical slope of 2 for trace Sr^{2+} sorption on ATP at pH < 3 (vide infra).]

Despite unresolved problems with the interpretation of the mechanism of an AMP cation-exchanger of somewhat uncertain composition, its

---

‡Some additional data on cocrystallization and ion-exchange-recrystallization syntheses of ammonium ion-monovalent cation double salts with molybdo phosphate are presented in Ref. [206].

effectiveness as an ion exchanger is unquestioned. Figure 22 depicts a typical divalent ion-trivalent ion separation. The important practical requirement for efficient sorption of di- and trivalent ions is that the feed solution be buffered to a less acidic pH than is used with monovalent ions. Also, more acidic elutriants must be employed for the multivalent ions [194]. Broadbank and co-workers [205] separated a mixture of traces of Cs^+, Sr^{2+}, and Y^{3+} on a shallow bed of AMP supported on filter paper. Strontium was eluted with 0.1 N and yttrium with 1 N nitric acid; cesium was retained on the bed.

The demonstrated ion-exchange capabilities of AMP have been applied in the development of analytical methods of separation and determination of sodium and potassium [207], and of several radionuclides in water samples [208], including cesium-137 in both fresh and sea waters [208-210, 196, 197]. Thin layer ion-exchange chromatography methods utilizing AMP as well as other heteropoly salts have also been developed.

F. Ion-Exchange Properties of ATP

Krtil and Kourim found [198] that their analyzed ATP preparation, $(NH_4)_{2.67}H_{0.33}[PW_{12}O_{40}] \cdot 9.8 H_2O$, had a higher capacity for cesium ion and better acid stability than their AMP preparation. In later papers Krtil reported log $K_d^{Cs^+}$ vs log $[NH_4^+]$ isotherms for the sorption of trace concentrations of cesium ion with both AMP [201] and ATP [199, 201], as a function nitric acid concentration in the solution phase. Figure 23 shows the typical parallel linear isotherms with the expected slope of -1 over the ranges 0.03 M < $C_{NH_4NO_3}$ < 3 M and 0.001 M < 10 M for both AMP $(NH_4)_{2.38}H_{0.62}[PMo_{12}O_{40}] \cdot 9.3 H_2O$, and ATP $(NH_4)_{2.2}H_{0.8}[PW_{12}O_{40}] \cdot 15 H_2O$. In these trace sorption experiments, the distribution coefficients $K_d^{Cs^+}$ for the AMP were slightly larger than those for the ATP (as was also found by van R. Smit et al. [192]. This difference disappeared with increasing acidity. As was previously observed [198] the AMP was detectably solubilized with increasing acidity, but the ATP was only negligibly so. The dependence of the trace cesium sorption on the acidity is shown in Fig. 24. The results were rationalized in terms of the following model [201]:

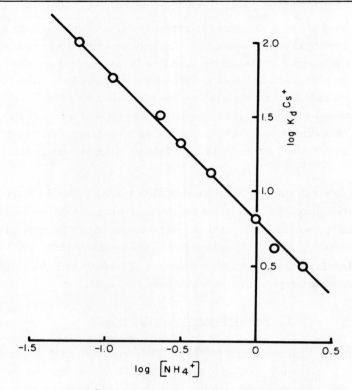

FIG. 23. Log $\underline{K}_d{}^{Cs^+}$ vs log $NH_4{}^+$ isotherm for the sorption of trace cesium from ammonium nitrate media on ATP at room temperature. (From the data in Table 1, Ref. 199.)

The AMP and ATP starting materials are in fact acid (not neutral) ammonium salts. With increasing solution-phase acidity the solid salts become more acid and approach the limiting diammonium monohydrogen salts at $C_{HNO_3} \approx 3$ M [194]. Krtil regarded the acid salt, $(NH_4)_2 H$ $[PW_{12}O_{40}]$, as a mixture of the triammonium salt and the free acid, $H_3[PW_{12}O_{40}]$. He formulated the mass action expressions assuming complete dissociation of the triammonium salt and partial dissociation of $H_3[PW_{12}O_{40}]$. This gave the result:

$$K_d{}^{Cs^+} [NH_4{}^+] = k [H^+ - X^-]/[H^+], \qquad (20)$$

where $[H^+ - X^-]$ corresponds to the acid salt fraction of the ion-exchanger

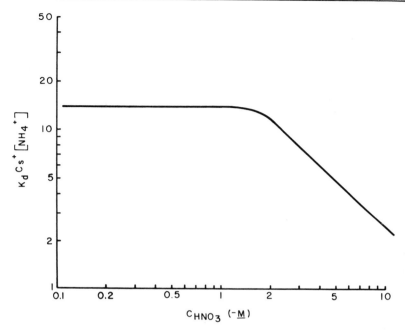

FIG. 24. Empirical relationship between log ($K_d^{Cs^+}$ [NH_4^+]) and log C_{HNO_3} for trace sorption of cesium on both AMP and ATP from ammonium nitrate-nitric acid media at room temperature. (From Fig. 2, Ref. 201.)

matrix. Assuming a Donnan equilibrium, then at low acidities, before the complete conversion to (VII), the right-hand side of Equation (20) will be constant. When conversion to (VII) is complete, according to the proposed model, [$H^+ - X^-$] is essentially constant and the product $K_d^{Cs^+}$[NH_4^+] will vary inversely as [H^+], as is shown in Fig. 24.

In another set of experiments [202], Krtil and Krivy prepared the mixed 12-heteropoly ammonium molybdo-tungsto-phosphate salts:

A M_4T_8P $(NH_4)_{2.55}H_{0.45}[PMo_4W_8O_{40}] \cdot 6.5H_2O$

A M_6T_6P $(NH_4)_{2.58}H_{0.42}[PMo_6W_6O_{40}] \cdot 7.6H_2O$

A M_8T_4P $(NH_4)_{2.48}H_{0.52}[PMo_8W_4O_{40}] \cdot 5.7H_2O.$

In each case parallel, linear isotherms, $\log K_d^{Cs^+}$ vs $\log [NH_4^+]$, were obtained, with slope -1 for trace cesium ion sorption from ammonium nitrate +0.001 M nitric acid media at room temperature. The small systematic differences in the $K_d^{Cs^+}$ values were in the order: $AM_8T_4P > AM_6T_6P > AM_4T_8P$.

Krtil also prepared ion-exchange chromatography columns of ATP precipitated on asbestos [199-200], for elution-separation experiments with rubidium and cesium, in both trace ($^{86}Rb^+$, $^{134}Cs^+$, $^{137}Cs^+$) and macro amounts, and with mixtures of trace $^{137}Cs^+$, $^{90}Sr^{2+}$, and $^{90}Y^{3+}$. A rubidium-cesium separation as efficient as that of Van R. Smit et al., on (AMP + asbestos) was achieved [195]. However, although a facile separation of trace cesium from trace strontium and yttrium in a ternary mixture was achieved, the latter two nuclides were eluted together by 1 to 6 M nitric acid [200]. Separation of trace strontium and yttrium in a binary mixture was obtained by first eluting the former with 0.3 M ammonium nitrate, and then the latter with 6 M nitric acid. This behavior is comparable to that observed by van R. Smit et al. on AMP columns (see Fig. 22).

The essentially simultaneous elution of strontium and yttrium by nitric acid elutriant solutions, is in conformity with Krtil's $\log K_d$ vs pH isotherms for the trace sorption of these two ions under batch equilibration conditions [200]. As is shown in Fig. 25, at pH < 1, the K_d values for the two ions differ by a factor of about 10. At lower pH, ATP is an acid salt, and the (hydrogen) ion-exchange reaction

$$Sr^{2+} + 2(NH_4)_2 H [PW_{12}O_{40}] \rightleftharpoons Sr(NH_4)_4 [PW_{12}O_{40}]_2 + 2H^+, \tag{21}$$

is evidenced by the linear left-branch, with slope 2, in Fig. 25, in the strontium sorption isotherm at pH < 3. At higher pH, the effects of the exchange of ammonium ion (rather than hydrogen ion) for strontium (or yttrium) begin to appear, complicated by the concomitant alkaline hydrolysis of the ATP (Krtil notes that a suspension of ATP in water has a pH of about 2 to 3) [200].

In further experiments with the sorption of polyvalent ions on ATP, Krtil and Zemenova [203] measured K_d values for the tracer sorption of ^{144}Ce, $^{106}Ru(III)$, $^{106}Ru(IV)$, and ^{95}Zr- ^{95}Nb from nitric acid-ammonium nitrate, and from nitric acid-sodium nitrate media. The salt effects were

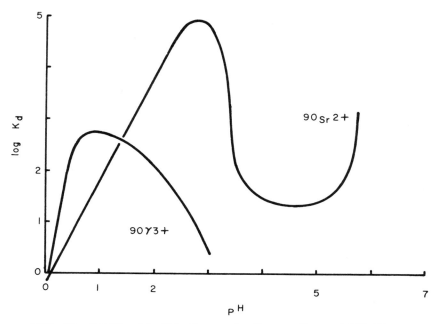

FIG. 25. Log K_d vs pH isotherms for the sorption on ATP of trace $^{90}Sr^{2+}$ and $^{90}Y^{3+}$ from dilute nitric acid through dilute aqueous ammonia solutions at room temperature. (From Fig. 1, Ref. 200.)

significant, and the results reflect the added complication of the hydrolyzed character of these polyvalent elements.

G. Ion-Exchange Properties of Miscellaneous Heteropoly Salts

The ion-exchange properties of a variety of heteropoly salts (besides AMP and ATP) have been explored. These experiments are summarized in Table 8.

In one of their early papers [192], Van R. Smit's group surveyed the preparation by several synthetic routes, and the ion-exchange properties of AMP, AMA, AMS, ATP, ATA, ATS, and 8-HQMP (Table 8). Values of $K_d^{Cs^+}$ for the sorption of trace cesium from ammonium nitrate media of pH = 2 at 25°C were measured, and although there was some variation of $K_d^{Cs^+}$ for a given salt, the general trend of the $K_d^{Cs^+}$ values was in the

TABLE 8

Ion-Exchange Experiments with Miscellaneous Salts of Heteropoly Acids (Other Than AMP and ATP)

Name and (presumed) formula	Acronym	Reference	Experiment
ammonium 12-molybdoarsenate $(NH_4)_3[AsMo_{12}O_{40}] \cdot xH_2O$	(AMA)	[192, 215]	Determination K_d^{M+} for trace sorption of $M^+ = Na^+$, K^+, Rb^+, Cs^+ from NH_4NO_3 media of pH = 2 at 25°C. Ion-exchange chromatographic sepr. of $M^+ = Na^+$, K^+, Rb^+, Cs^+ on paper impregnated with or on thin layers of heteropoly salt cast on TLC plates.
ammonium 12-molybdosilicate $(NH_4)_4[SiMo_{12}O_{40}] \cdot xH_2O$	(AMS)	[192, 215]	Same as for AMA.
ammonium 12-tungstoarsenate $(NH_4)_3[AsW_{12}O_{40}] \cdot xH_2O$	(ATA)	[192, 215]	Same as for AMA.
ammonium 12-tungstosilicate $(NH_4)_4[SiW_{12}O_{40}] \cdot xH_2O$	(ATS)	[192, 215]	Same as for AMA.

Name / Formula	Abbreviation	Ref.	Description
8-hydroxyquinolinium 12-molybdophosphate $(C_9H_8NO)_3[PMo_{12}O_{40}] \cdot xH_2O$	(8-HQMP)	[192, 215]	Same as for AMA.
potassium 12-molybdophosphate $K_3[PMo_{12}O_{40}]$	(PMP)	[205]	Sorption and separation of Cs^+, Sr^{2+}, and Y^{3+} under static, batch equilibration and dynamic, shallow-bed elution conditions.
rubidium 12-molybdophosphate $Rb_3[PMo_{12}O_{40}] \cdot xH_2O$	(RMP)	[205]	Same as for PMP.
cesium 12-molybdophosphate $Cs_3[PMo_{12}O_{40}] \cdot xH_2O$	(CMP)	[198, 205]	Same as for PMP.
methylammonium 12-molybdophosphate $(CH_3NH_3)_3[PMo_{12}O_{40}]$	(MeAMP)	[205]	Same as for PMP.
dimethylammonium 12-molybdophosphate $[(CH_3)_2NH_2]_3[PMo_{12}O_{40}]$	(Me$_2$AMP)	[205]	Same as for PMP.
trimethylammonium 12-molybdophosphate $[(CH_3)_3NH]_3[PMo_{12}O_{40}]$	(Me$_3$AMP)	[205]	Same as for PMP.

TABLE 8 (continued)

Name and (presumed) formula	Acronym	Reference	Experiment
tetramethylammonium 12-molybdophosphate $[(CH_3)_4N]_3[PMo_{12}O_{40}]$	(Me$_4$AMP)	[205]	Same as for PMP.
thallium (I) 12-tungstophosphate $Tl_3[PW_{12}O_{40}] \cdot xH_2O$	(TTP)	[211]	Ion-exchange column chromatography of $M^+ = K^+$, Rb^+, Cs^+, and Ag^+ on (TTP + paper pulp) columns. With HNO_3 and $TlNO_3$ elutriant solutions, column retention selectivity $K^+ < Rb^+ < Ag^+ << Cs^+$ gave clean separation and afforded basis for isolation Cs^+ in an NH_4^+ ion free fraction.
ammonium 12-molybdogermanate $(NH_4)_4[GeMo_{12}O_{40}] \cdot xH_2O$	(AMG)	[216]	Ion-exchange chromatography of $M^+ = Na^+$, K^+, Rb^+, and Cs^+ on paper impregnated with or on thin layers of heteropoly salt cast on TLC plates.
8-hydroxyquinolinium 12-molybdosilicate $(8\text{-}HQ^+)_4[SiMo_{12}O_{40}] \cdot xH_2O$	(8-HQMS)	[216]	Same as for AMG.

pyridinium 12-molybdosilicate	(PMS)	$(Py^+)_4[SiMo_{12}O_{40}] \cdot xH_2O$	[216]	Same as for AMG.
8-hydroxyquinolinium 12-molybdogermanate	(8-HQMG)	$(8-HQ^+)_4[GeMo_{12}O_{40}] \cdot xH_2O$	[216, 217]	Same as for AMG. Ion-exchange TLC separation of ^{137}Cs from $^{90}Sr - ^{90}Y$, $^{95}Zr - ^{95}Nb$, ^{106}Ru, and ^{144}Ce in a mixture of uranium fission products.
pyridinium 12-molybdogermanate	(PMG)	$(Py^+)_4[GeMo_{12}O_{40}] \cdot xH_2O$	[216, 217]	Same as for 8-HQMG.
6-molybdo-4-tungsto-2-vanado phosphoric acid		$H_3[Mo_6W_4V_2O_{39}] \cdot xH_2O$ and 19 other (simpler) heteropoly acids	[218]	Scavenger precipitation of traces of Cs^+ and Fr^+.

order AMP > ATP ~ AMA > 8-HQMP >> (AMS, ATS, ATA). The last
three compounds either dissolved or formed colloidal sols in the sorbate
solutions.

Broadbank and co-workers[205] prepared AMP and the corresponding
potassium, rubidium, cesium, and mono-, di-, tri-, and tetramethylammonium
salts (Table 8). All were found to be essentially insoluble in water and
dilute nitric acid. These salts performed as efficient sorbents for traces of
cesium, strontium, and yttrium ions, but none appeared to offer more
advantages than AMP.

Several groups [214-216] have developed the technique of thin-layer
ion-exchange chromatography on paper impregnated with AMP [212-216],
ATP [214], and a selection of other heteropoly salts [215-217] cast on
TLC plates (Table 8). ATP has been used for the isolation of traces of
cesium by scavenger coprecipitation [204], and 20 different heteropoly-
and-binary, and ternary mixed heteropoly acids have been similarly used
for the cesium-francium pair [218].

V. HYDROUS OXIDES

Hydrous oxides and hydroxides have been extensively studied and the
ion-exchange properties of many of them have been discussed, including
those of aluminum [219-226], iron [227-236], titanium [237-240],
zirconium [237, 241-249], niobium [2, 250, 251], tantalum [2, 250],
chromium [2], thorium [72, 237, 238, 239, 252], tungsten [237, 250],
silicon [253-263], and tin [264-267]. It has been shown that many of the
oxides exhibit amphoteric behavior, exchanging anions in acidic, and cations
in basic solutions. The strong pH dependence of the capacities was demonstrated by measuring the anion and cation exchange capacity of zirconia
and thoria as a function of pH [2]. The ion exchange properties clearly
involve the uptake and "fixation" of hydrogen ions in acidic, and of hydroxyl ions
in basic solutions, but the mechanism of the reaction is not yet fully understood.

Of the hydrous oxides, zirconia has recently received much attention as
an ion exchanger. In addition, a good deal of structural information which
sheds light on the ion exchange behavior, has become available. We
therefore largely confine our discussion in this section to hydrous zirconia.

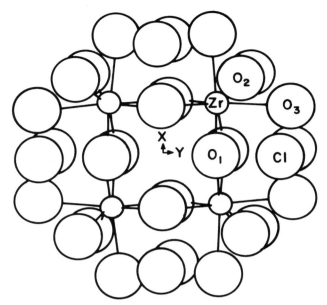

FIG. 26. Structure proposed for zirconyl ion in concentrated zirconyl halide solutions. (Reproduced from Ref. 287 by permission of J. Chem. Phys.)

From this discussion several generalizations arise which can then be applied to other hydrous oxides.

A. The Structure of Hydrous Zirconia

When sufficient base is added to a solution of a soluble Zr(IV) salt, a white, gelatinous precipitate, hydrous zirconia, is formed. Hydrous zirconia is not a single well defined substance. Its composition and properties depend upon the method of preparation and upon subsequent treatment or aging. It has variously been represented as $Zr(OH)_4 \cdot xH_2O$ [268], $ZrO(OH)_2 \cdot xH_2O$ [269], $ZrO_2 \cdot xH_2O$ [270], and $[ZrO_b(OH)_{4-2b} \cdot xH_2O]_n$ [271]. The solid is amorphous to x-rays when prepared by neutralization of soluble Zr(IV) salts, but can also be prepared in one of several crystalline forms [272]. All of these manifestations of zirconia exhibit ion exchange behavior. The ion exchange properties of hydrous zirconia are thought to stem from the presence of surface hydroxyl groups

[2,237]. At pH values below the isoelectric point, the hydroxyl groups can readily be displaced by anions, whereas at higher pH values protons are displaced by cations. The capacity of the exchanger might then be thought to depend upon the surface area and density of hydroxyl groups on the surface. However, no systematic study has been made along these lines. What is required is a better knowledge of the structure of hydrous zirconia and the ability to relate ion exchange behavior to structure. However, such a correlation is rendered difficult by the fact that hydrous oxides are generally amorphous, or poorly crystalline gels whose structures depend upon preparative conditions and subsequent treatment. Nevertheless, a beginning has been made in this direction and these concepts are developed here.

There are three crystalline polymorphs of ZrO_2: cubic, tetragonal and monoclinic. The cubic phase is stable above 2285°C [273], but can be stabilized at room temperature by additions of other oxides [274]. Cubic ZrO_2 has the fluorite structure in which each metal atom is coordinated by eight oxygens arranged in a cube [275]. The tetragonal polymorph is stable above 1200°C, but can be obtained in a metastable condition at much lower temperatures [273, 276]. Its structure is only slightly distorted from that of the cubic phase [277, 278]. The phase which is stable below 1200° is monoclinic, and here a fundamental change in structure occurs. The zirconium atom is seven coordinate [279], and Rijnten [273] has shown how the monoclinic structure can be obtained from the tetragonal by small shifts of the oxygen atoms.

Addition of sufficient base to Zr(IV) solutions leads to the formation of a gelatinous, amorphous precipitate. The exact pH at which precipitation occurs depends upon the solution concentrations and type of anion present. However, precipitation begins at a rather low pH and is complete before the endpoint of the neutralization is reached [280, 281, 282]. This is due to the retention by the precipitate of significant amounts of anions. It is almost impossible to remove the anions completely by washing with water, but this task is easily accomplished with dilute ammonia. However, some ammonium ion is retained by the precipitate. If care is not exercised to maintain carbon dioxide-free conditions, considerable CO_2 is found in the solid. Apparently this does not appreciably affect the ion exchange properties [245].

Refluxing freshly prepared aqueous slurries of amorphous hydrous zirconia produces a large decrease in the pH of the slurry [272]. This decrease in pH is caused by the anions entering the solution phase, and being replaced in the solid by hydroxyl groups. The reverse situation has also been observed. Addition of nearly neutral potassium salts to sols of hydrous zirconia causes a dramatic rise in pH. This was interpreted on the basis of the displacement by anions of hydroxyl groups from the sol particles [283]. The refluxing procedure transforms the gel into a crystalline product. However, if the anions present in the gel are first removed by washing, no decrease in pH is observed, and no crystallinity develops in the solid [272]. But addition of acid to such slurries, followed by further boiling, brings about crystallization. Thus, the crystallization must be effected by a digestion mechanism, i.e., by dissolution and reprecipitation of the gel particles.

Initially the crystallites are obtained as the cubic (or tetragonal) modification of zirconia. However, on continued refluxing they are converted to the monoclinic phase [272]. Pure cubic crystallites can be prepared by refluxing the gels in concentrated sodium hydroxide solutions. These crystalline precipitates retain the ion exchange properties exhibited by the gels. The interplanar spacings of the hydrous oxide crystallites are quite similar to those of the respective crystalline ZrO_2. Thus, within the hydrous oxide crystallite, the composition must approach that of ZrO_2. However, the crystalline hydrous zirconias still contain about 11% water and/or hydroxyl, as shown by loss on ignition. These groups must reside primarily on the surface of the particles.

The above information, together with data derived from the behavior of aqueous Zr(IV) species, has been used to develop a mechanism for the formation of hydrous zirconia [284]. The discussion below applies to Zr(IV) chloride solutions, but, with slight modification, holds true for nitrate and perchlorate solutions (and other weakly complexing anions). Crystals of zirconyl chloride (empirical formula $ZrOCl_2 \cdot 8H_2O$) contain the complex ion $[Zr(OH)_2 \cdot 4H_2O]_4^{8+}$. In this complex the zirconium atoms are situated very nearly in a square, and are linked together by hydroxo-bridges above and below the plane of the square [285]. Four water molecules are also bonded to each metal atom, making the coordination about each metal a distorted antiprism or dodecahedron [286]. The same complex ions were shown to exist in concentrated solutions of the salt [287]. However, in solution, the

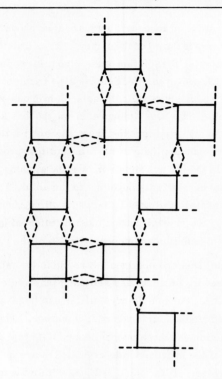

FIG. 27. Proposed two-dimensional representation of random polymeric species formed by addition of base to aqueous zirconyl ion solutions. The solid lined squares represent the original tetrameric units, $Zr_4(OH)_8$. Each dashed line represents an -OH group formed by hydrolysis. A bent dashed line connected to two squares represents a hydroxo bridge. (Reproduced from Ref. 271 by permission of Rev. Pure Appl. Chem.)

chloride ions are closely associated with the complex, as shown in Fig. 26. Solutions of zirconyl chloride are quite acidic, due to hydrolysis. The acidity in solutions of moderate concentration is such as to indicate that three hydroxyl groups are associated with each metal atom [276]. When base is added to these solutions or they are boiled, the aqueous species polymerize. It has been assumed that this polymerization occurs between tetramer units by olation [276, 284]. Since each complex ion has four metal sites at which polymerization can occur, it would be expected that rapid addition of base would lead to polymer growth in many directions simultaneously. This type of polymerization would tend to produce a random structure of tetramers, as shown in Fig. 27. In addition some of the anions associated with the tetramer groups are trapped within the polymers, due to the rapidity of the polymerization-precipitation process, and thus substitute for hydroxyl groups. The randomness of the structure accounts for the amorphous, gelatinous nature of base precipitated hydrous zirconia.

When precipitation is brought about slowly, as, for example, by refluxing zirconyl chloride solutions, the polymers are able to grow in a more orderly fashion, leading to sheets of tetramer units (Fig. 28). In the resulting sheets, each zirconium atom is surrounded by eight hydroxyl groups in the form of a distorted cubic arrangement. The cubic (or tetragonal) ZrO_2 phase can be formed from the $[Zr(OH)_4]_n$ sheets by oxolation, i.e., by condensation of water from two hydroxo groups in adjacent layers [284].

Direct evidence in support of the essential features of this hydrolytic polymerization mechanism has recently been obtained by electron microscopy [288]. Dilute solutions of zirconyl chloride were refluxed, and examined at high magnification. An initial large drop in pH occurred, accompanied by formation of sheetlike particles. Thereafter, the pH of the solution remained almost constant, while oxolation between adjacent sheets took place and the crystallites thickened. In this way the monoclinic phase of zirconia was formed with crystallites approximately 500 Å in size.

From the foregoing we may conclude that hydrous zirconia is a polymeric oxo-hydroxide of general formula $[ZrO_b(OH)_{4-2b} \cdot xH_2O]_n$. The hydroxyl groups will be of two types: bridging, and non-bridging. The non-bridging hydroxyl groups would be those which occur at the ends of the sheets, and hence would be on the surface of the crystallites. One question which is not easily resolved is the magnitude of b and the proportion of free to bridged hydroxyls. Zaitsev [289, 290] has proposed that products with a definite stoichiometry, such as $Zr(OH)_4$, $ZrO(OH)_2$, and $Zr_4O_2(OH)_{12}$, result from different preparative methods. Rijnten [276] has provided the following scheme based on a combination of density and dehydration data:

$$ZrOCl_2 \cdot 8H_2O \xrightarrow{\text{base}} Zr(OH)_4 \cdot xH_2O \xrightarrow[\text{drying}]{\text{aging or}} ZrO(OH)_2 \cdot xH_2O \quad \text{boiling.} \qquad (22)$$

$$\downarrow$$

$$ZrO_2 \cdot xH_2O$$

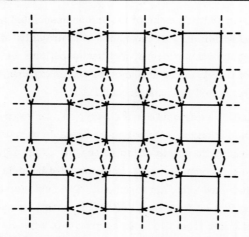

FIG. 28. Two-dimensional representation of ordered sheet polymer produced by refluxing aqueous zirconyl ion solutions. Representations are the same as for Fig. 27. (Reproduced from Ref. 271 by permission of Rev. Pure Appl. Chem.)

However, from the foregoing discussion, it would appear more likely that all forms of zirconia are best represented as oxo-hydroxides in which the value of b varies between zero and two.

The exchange capacity of hydrous zirconia is in the range of 1-2 meq/g of ZrO_2. This corresponds to 1-2 hydroxyl groups per eight zirconium atoms. Such a high density of hydroxyl groups on the surface, or just below it, requires the very high surface area of a porous structure. Precipitated zirconias treated in various ways have been shown to be porous, and undoubtedly, even the untreated hydrous oxides are highly porous. The nature of the pores may have a significant effect upon capacity, rate, and selectivity of the exchanger, but this aspect of the problem has not been explored. Rijnten found that the pore structure did vary with the method of synthesis [276], but did not correlate this with ion exchange behavior, as he was primarily interested in the catalytic activity of the zirconia prepara- tions. Certainly a fruitful line of study would involve the modification of pore structure (which might be analogous to the degree of crosslinking in organic gels), and its effect upon ion exchange behavior.

With some modifications similar hydrolytic polymerization mechanisms can be proposed for the formation of the other group IV b oxides. The end products differ in degree, not kind, from hydrous zirconia. Thus, these oxides can be represented by the general formula $[MO_b(OH)_{4-2b} \cdot xH_2O]_n$, where $M = Ti$, Zr, Hf, Th, Si. Evidence for this type of formula is extensive [291-297, 238, 284]. However, the exact nature of the polymerizing species is not known with certainty, in most cases. It would be expected that titanium and silicon would readily undergo oxolation because of their acidic character. Thus, b would be large for these elements, and decrease with increasing basicity of the central metal. It is surprising therefore that tin, with intermediate basicity, is assigned the formula $SnO_2 \cdot xH_2O$ [264].

B. Ion Exchange Properties

The ion exchange properties can be represented, in acid solution, by the equilibria:

$$R - OH + H^+ \rightleftharpoons R^+ + HOH, \tag{23}$$

or

$$R - OH + H^+ \rightleftharpoons ROH_2^+; \tag{23a}$$

and at alkaline pH by:

$$R - OH + OH \rightleftharpoons R - O^- + HOH. \tag{24}$$

The smooth dependence of capacity upon the pH of the external solution suggests extensive heterogeneity of active groups within the matrix. However, the activity of the groups would depend upon the acidity of the metal, the proximity of other active groups, and the pore structure. For example, it would be expected (other things being equal) that hydrous thorium oxide would undergo reaction (23) easier than hydrous titanium oxide. The converse would be true for reaction (24). In fact it has been found that under similar conditions, hydrous titania does exhibit higher K_d values for cations than does thoria [238].

By maintaining a constant pH of 13, studies have been made of the exchange of alkali metal ions in the exchange reaction represented by

$$RA + B^+ \rightleftharpoons RB + A^+, \tag{25}$$

in which R represents the zirconia matrix. The equilibrium selectivity coefficient is

$$S_A^{\ B} = \frac{\overline{X}_B}{X_B} \; \frac{X_A}{\overline{X}_A} \; , \tag{26}$$

where $\overline{X}_A$ and $\overline{X}_B$ refer to the mole fractions of the metal ions A^+ and B^+ in the exchanger, and X_A and X_B to the corresponding mole fractions in the solution. The thermodynamic equilibrium constant, written in terms of the activity coefficients f is then

$$K_A^{\ B} = \frac{\overline{X}_B}{X_B} \; \frac{X_A}{\overline{X}_A} \; \frac{\overline{f}_B f_A}{f_A \overline{f}_B} \; . \tag{27}$$

At constant ionic strength, f_A/f_B can be assumed to be close to unity and, $K_A^{\ B}$ is obtained from the equation

$$\ln K_A^{\ B} = \int_0^1 \ln S_A^{\ B} \; d\overline{X}_B. \tag{28}$$

The solid phase activity coefficients are given by [298]

$$\ln \overline{f}_A = (1 - \overline{X}_A) \ln S_A^{\ B} - \int_{X_A}^1 \ln S_A^{\ B} \; d\overline{X}_A, \tag{29}$$

and

$$\ln \overline{f}_B = -\overline{X}_A \ln S_A^{\ B} + \int_0^{\overline{X}_A} \ln S_A^{\ B} \; d\overline{X}_A. \tag{30}$$

In order to obtain a more precise determination of the exchange isotherm, a column equilibration technique was used in this work. Typical isotherms for Li^+/K^+ and Na^+/K^+ exchange are shown in Fig. 29, and it is seen that the order of preference is $Li^+ > Na^+ > K^+$. At high fractions of Li^+ and Na^+, however, the isotherms tend towards a selectivity reversal not unusual for exchange on zirconium compounds [245]. Analysis of the isotherms may be made by the method of Freeman [299] in order to calculate the selectivity coefficients, and to perform the integrations for the evaluation of the

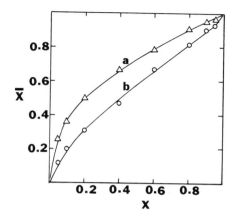

FIG. 29. Ion exchange isotherms of Li^+/K^+ (curve a) and Na^+/K^+ (curve b) exchange on zirconia. (Reproduced with permission from J. Inorg. Nucl. Chem., 31, 3864 (1969)).

activity coefficients in the solid phase. Typical data, presented in Table 9, correspond to $\Delta G° = -820$ cal mole^{-1} for the Li^+/K^+ exchange reaction. In addition to studies of cation exchange at high pH, a number of halide and pseudo halide exchanges have been investigated at a constant hydrogen ion concentration of 0.01 M [243]. Under these conditions also, the process can be expressed by means of a typical reversible ion exchange reaction, enabling activity coefficients of the ions in the exchanger phase to be calculated [243]. Calorimetric studies similar to those described for zirconium phosphate have also been made, and typical molar heat plots of partial exchange are shown in Fig. 30 for Na^+/K^+, and in Fig. 31 for NO^-_3/Cl^- exchange [244, 245]. In the former, the data refer to the hypothetical reaction,

$$RA \ (a = 1 \text{ in equilibrium with } 0.1 \text{ M AOH}) + BOH \ (aq, a = 1) \rightleftharpoons$$
$$RB \ (a = 1 \text{ in equilibrium with } 0.1 \text{ M BOH}) + AOH \ (aq. a = 1) \qquad (31)$$
$$+ nH_2O \ (a = 1),$$

and in the latter to

$$RA \text{ (unit activity in equilibrium with } 0.09 \text{ M NaA} + 0.01 \text{ M HA)}$$
$$+ B^- \ [(NaB + HB)_{aq.} \ a = 1] \rightleftharpoons RB \text{ (unit activity in equilibrium with } 0.09 \text{ M NaB}$$
$$+ 0.01 \text{ M HB)} + A^- \ [(NaA + HA)_{aq.}, \ a = 1] \ + nH_2O \ (a = 1), \qquad (32)$$

TABLE 9

Selectivity Coefficients and Solid-Phase Activity Coefficients
for Li^+/K^+ Exchange on Zirconia at 25°C

X_{Li}	$\overline{X}_{Li}$	$S_K{}^{Li}$	$\overline{f}_{Li}$	$\overline{f}_K$
0.05	0.253	6.44	0.60	0.96
0.10	0.357	5.00	0.71	0.89
0.20	0.497	3.95	0.81	0.80
0.40	0.664	2.96	0.91	0.67
0.60	0.785	2.43	0.96	0.58
0.80	0.909	2.50	0.97	0.60
0.85	0.950	2.11	0.99	0.57
0.95	0.961	1.30	1.01	0.33

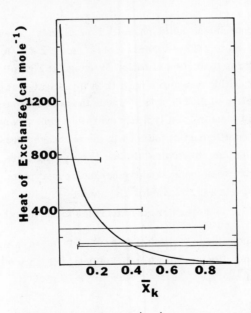

FIG. 30. Molar heats of partial Na^+/K^+ exchange on hydrous zirconia
at 25°. (Reproduced with permission from J. Inorg. Nucl. Chem., 31,
3867 (1969)).

where n is the number of moles of water released or absorbed by the exchanger. Values of the standard heats of exchange on zirconium oxide and related thermodynamic functions are given in Table 10.

The water contents of the potassium sodium, lithium, and cesium forms of zirconia are all equal at 25 ± 2%, suggesting, in terms of the osmotic theory of Gregor [300], that the ions are present in the unhydrated state. A similar conclusion has been reached about ion exchange processes on the zeolites [301], in which the dehydration is attributed to crystal lattice forces. The same forces may also be important in hydrous zirconia, which, although macroscopically "amorphous," is clearly an aggregate of small crystalline fragments [284]. The values of the thermodynamic functions lend support to

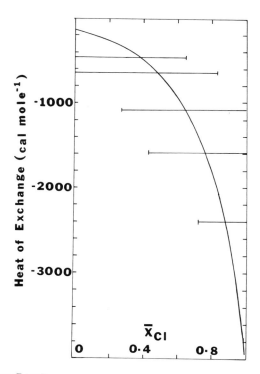

FIG. 31. NO_3^-/Cl^- ion exchange on hydrous zirconia. Heats of partial exchange at 25° plotted as a function of mole fraction of the Cl^- ion. (Reproduced with permission from J. Inorg. Nucl. Chem., 31, 216 (1969)).

TABLE 10

Thermodynamic Functions for Exchange on Zirconia

Exchange reaction	$\Delta H°$ cal. mole^{-1}	$\Delta G°$ cal. mole^{-1}	$\Delta S°$ cal. deg^{-1} mole^{-1}
$\overline{NO_3} \rightarrow \overline{Cl}$	974 ± 30	-146 ± 40	3.8 ± 0.3
$\overline{NO_3} \rightarrow \overline{SCN}$	-186 ± 24	-393 ± 30	0.7 ± 0.2
$\overline{K} \rightarrow \overline{Li}$	240 ± 60	-820 ± 20	3.5 ± 0.3
$\overline{K} \rightarrow \overline{Na}$	75 ± 20	-250 ± 20	1.1 ± 0.2

the suggestion of dehydrated alkali metal ions within the exchanger. Lindenbaum and Boyd [302], and Becker, Lindenbaum and Boyd [303], have obtained similar positive ΔS values for the exchange of cesium with lithium on weak-acid organic exchangers. They also postulated water removal from the ingoing alkali metal ion, Li^+, accompanying site-binding of this ion by the exchanger, and this conclusion was supported by the results of dilatometric measurements [304]. Zirconia may be regarded as a weak-acid exchanger at the high pH values used, and the positive entropy changes, accompanying the release of water molecules from the co-spheres of the ingoing ions, are evidently responsible for the observed sequence $Li^+ > Na^+ > K^+$, and are large enough to overcome the unfavorable enthalpy changes. The observed dependence of total capacity upon the ionic crystal radius, being larger for the smaller ions, such as Li^+, also suggests that the ions are substantially dehydrated within the zirconia.

Striking evidence of the importance of surface water in the ion exchange process is presented in a study of transition metal sorption on hydrated SnO_2 [264]. The sorbed ions give colors which are typical of their aqueous forms, and Mossbauer studies indicate that the Sn atom is not involved in the exchange process. Donaldson and Fuller propose that the distribution coefficient is related to the $M^{2+} + H_2O \rightleftharpoons M\text{-}OH^+ + H^+$ equilibrium, where the H_2O in question are those molecules on the solid surface [264]. Because the distribution coefficient is based on total capacity, and not on remaining available sites, it appears to decrease with increased ion loading (and decreased site availability). The differences in ultimate capacity of the ions investigated (Cu^{2+}, Zn^{2+}, Co^{2+}, Fe^{2+}, Mn^{2+}) can then be attributed to their effectiveness in promoting the generation of OH^- sites, and hence the relationship to the H_2O ionization. The selectivity differences have been employed to separate the ions from one another by the column chromatography technique [264].

REFERENCES

1. K. A. Kraus and H. O. Phillips, J. Am. Chem. Soc., 78, 644 (1956).

2. K. A. Kraus, H. O. Phillips, T. A. Carlson and J. S. Johnson, Proceedings of the Second International Conference on Peaceful Uses of Atomic Energy, Geneva, 1958, Paper No. 15/P/1832 United Nations (1958) Vol. 28, p. 3.

3. C. B. Amphlett, Proceedings of the Second International Conference on Peaceful Uses of Atomic Energy, Geneva, 1958, Paper No. 15/P/171 United Nations (1958).

4. C. B. Amphlett, Inorganic Ion Exchangers, Elsevier Publishing Co., Amsterdam, 1964.

5. W. B. Blumenthal, The Chemical Behavior of Zirconium, D. Van Nostrand, Co., Princeton, 1958, p. 229.

6. E. R. Russel, A. W. Adamson, J. Schubert and G. E. Boyd, U.S.A.E. Comm., Report CN-508 (1943); R. H. Beaton, V. R. Cooper, B. A. Fries, T. J. Chapelle, I. Scheft, R. A. Stoughton, and E. H. Turk, CN-633 (1943), United States Atomic Energy Commission, Washington, D. C.

7. S. Ahrland, J. Albertsson, L. Johansson, B. Nihlgard, and L. Nilsson, Acta. Chem. Scand., 18, 707 (1964).

8. S. Ahrland, J. Albertsson, L. Johansson, B. Nihlgard, and L. Nilsson, Acta. Chem. Scand., 18, 1357 (1964).

9. K. S. Rajan, D. B. Boas, A. J. Casolo, and J. I. Bregman, Desalination, 1, 231 (1966).

10. J. I. Bregman and R. S. Braman, J. Colloid Sci., 20, 913 (1965).

11. A. Brauneeks and J. I. Bregman, Chem. Eng. News., Oct. 16th 1961, P. 40.

12.   R. P. Hamlen, J. Electrochem. Soc. , 109, 746 (1962).

13.   C. Berger and M. P. Strier, J. Electrochem. Soc. , 115, 230 (1968).

14.   G. Alberti, Chromatog. Rev. , 8, 246 (1966).

15.   M. A. Greenbaum, L. A. Maranty, A. Gordon, M. Maxwell, and
       M. McArthur, Abstracts from the N. I. H. Chronic Urema Program,
       P. B. 179667.

16.   A. Clearfield and J. A. Stynes, J. Inorg. Nucl. Chem. , 26, 117
       (1964).

17.   J. A. Stynes, M. A. Thesis, Niagara Univ. , 1961.

18.   A. Clearfield, Unpublished research, Ohio University, 1964.

19.   A. Clearfield, Zirconium Phosphate, Research Report, Titanium
       Alloy Div. , National Lead Co. , Niagara Falls, N. Y. 1964.

20.   A. Clearfield and J. R. Thomas, Inorg. Nucl. Chem. Letters, 5,
       775 (1969).

21.   G. Alberti and E. Torracca, J. Inorg. Nucl. Chem. , 30, 317 (1968).

22.   J. Albertsson, Acta Chem. Scand. , 20, 1689 (1966).

23.   G. Alberti, E. Torracca, and A. Conte, J. Inorg. Nucl. Chem. ,
       28, 607 (1966).

24.   Z. Urbanec, V. Vesely, V. Pekarek, and J. Ullrich, private
       communication.

25.   A. Clearfield and G. D. Smith, Inorg. Chem. , 8, 431 (1969).

26.   A. M. Landis, M. S. Thesis, Ohio University, Athens, Ohio, June,
       1970, p. 18.

27.   A. Clearfield and W. L. Duax, Acta Cryst. , B25, 2658 (1969).

28.   S. Ahrland and J. Albertsson, Acta. Chem. Scand. , 23, 1446 (1969).

29.   A. Clearfield, W. L. Duax, A. S. Medina, G. D. Smith, and
       J. R. Thomas, J. Phys. Chem. , 73, 3424 (1969).

30.   V. Vesely, V. Pekarek, and Z. Urbanec, 5th Radiochemical
       Conference, Zvikov-Castle, Czechoslovakia, 1969.

31.   F. Mounier, D. Sc. Thesis, University of Lyon, 1969; F. Mounier
       and L. Winand, Bull. Soc. Chim. , France, 1829 (1968).

32.   J. Deabridges, Thesis, University of Strasbourg, 1969.

33. G. C. Piementel and A. L. McClellan. The Hydrogen Bond, W. H. Freeman, San Francisco, 1960, p. 74.

34. S. J. Harvie and G. H. Nancollas, J. Inorg. Nucl. Chem., 32, 3923 (1970).

35. E. Torracca, G. Alberti, R. Platania, P. Scala, and P. Galli, Soc. Chem. Ind. (London), 315 (1970).

36. G. Alberti, S. Allulli, U. Constantino, M. A. Massucci, and E. Torracca, Soc. Chem. Ind. (London), 318 (1970).

37. A. Clearfield, W. L. Duax, J. M. Garces, and A. S. Medina, J. Inorg. Nucl. Chem., 34, 329 (1972).

38. A. Clearfield and J. M. Troup, J. Phys. Chem., 74, 314 (1970).

39. A. Clearfield and G. D. Smith, J. Inorg. Nucl. Chem., 30, 3613 (1968).

40. E. Torracca, J. Inorg. Nucl. Chem., 31, 1189 (1969).

41. A. Clearfield and A. S. Medina, J. Inorg. Nucl. Chem., 32, 2275 (1970).

42. G. Alberti, private communication.

43. A. Clearfield, A. M. Landis, A. S. Medina, and J. M. Troup, J. Inorg. Nucl. Chem., 35, 1099 (1973).

44. A. Clearfield and J. M. Troup, J. Phys. Chem., 74, 2578 (1970).

45. A. Clearfield, R. H. Blessing, and J. A. Stynes, J. Inorg. Nucl. Chem., 30, 2249 (1968).

46. A. S. Medina, Ph. D. Thesis, Ohio University, Oct. 1971.

46a. J. Phys. Chem., 75, 3750 (1971).

47. E. Michel and A. Weiss, Z. Naturforsch., 20B, 1307 (1965).

48. S. Ahrland, J. Albertsson, A. Alnas, S. Hemmingsson, and L. Kullberg, Acta Chem. Scand., 21, 195 (1967).

49. J. M. Troup, private communication.

50. J. H. DeBoer, Z. Anorg. Chem., 144, 190 (1925).

51. G. Hevesey and K. Kimura, J. Am. Chem. Soc., 47, 2540 (1925).

52. W. B. Blumenthal, Ind. Eng. Chem., 46, 535 (1954).

53. C. B. Amphlett, L. A. McDonald, and M. J. Redman, J. Inorg. Nucl. Chem., 6, 220 (1958).

54. G. Alberti and S. Allulli, J. Chromatog., 32, 379 (1968).

55.   G. Alberti, A. Conte, and S. Allulli, J. Chromatog., 18, 564 (1965).

56.   G. Alberti and E. Torracca, J. Inorg. Nucl. Chem., 30, 1093 (1968).

57.   S. Ahrland and J. Albertsson, Acta Chem. Scand., 18, 1861 (1964).

58.   G. H. Nancollas and B. V. K. S. R. A. Tilak, J. Inorg. Nucl. Chem.,
       31, 3643 (1969).

59.   C. B. Amphlett and L. A. McDonald, Proc. Chem. Soc., 276 (1962).

60.   G. Alberti, A. Conte, and E. Torracca, J. Inorg. Nucl. Chem., 28,
       225 (1966).

61.   I. J. Gal and O. S. Gal, Proc. Second Intern. Conf. Peaceful Use
       Atomic Energy, United Nations, Geneva, 28, 24 (1958).

62.   L. Baetsle and D. Huys, J. Inorg. Nucl. Chem., 21, 133 (1961).

63.   G. Alberti, J. Inorg. Nucl. Chem., 28, 658 (1966).

64.   L. Baetsle and J. Pelsmakers, J. Inorg. Nucl. Chem., 21, 124
       (1961).

65.   E. Von Merz, Z. Electrochem., 63, 288 (1959).

66.   E. M. Larsen and D. R. Vissers, J. Phys. Chem., 64, 1732 (1960).

67.   V. Vesely and V. Pekarek, J. Inorg. Nucl. Chem., 25, 697 (1963).

68.   J. P. Harkin, G. H. Nancollas, and R. Paterson, J. Inorg. Nucl.
       Chem., 26, 305 (1964).

69.   G. H. Nancollas and V. Pekarek, J. Inorg. Nucl. Chem., 27, 1409
       (1965).

70.   E. P. Horwitz, J. Inorg. Nucl. Chem., 28, 1469 (1966).

71.   E. M. Larsen, W. C. Fernelius, and L. L. Quill, Ind. Eng. Chem.,
       15, 512 (1943).

72.   G. H. Nancollas and R. Paterson, J. Inorg. Nucl. Chem., 22, 259
       (1961).

73.   L. Baetsle, J. Inorg. Nucl. Chem., 25, 271 (1963).

74.   G. Alberti and A. Conte, J. Chromatog., 5, 244 (1961).

75.   V. Vesely, V. Pekarek, and A. Ruvarac, Bull. Soc. Chim., France,
       Special Issue 1832 (1968).

76.   J. Barrett, J. A. W. Dalziel, and M. K. Rahman, Bull. Soc. Chim.,
       France, Special Issue, 1853 (1968).

77. C. B. Amphlett, P. Eaton, L. A. McDonald, and A. J. Miller, J. Inorg. Nucl. Chem., 26, 297 (1964).

78. G. H. Nancollas and B. V. K. S. R. A. Tilak, J. Inorg. Nucl. Chem., 31, 3643 (1969).

79. T. F. Young and O. G. Vogel, J. Am. Chem. Soc., 54, 3030 (1932).

80. H. S. Sherry, Ion-Exchange (J. A. Marinsky, ed.), Vol. II, Marcel Dekker, New York (1968).

81. G. H. Nancollas, Interactions in Electrolyte Solutions, Elsevier, Amsterdam (1966).

82. D. E. Conway, J. H. S. Green, and D. Reichenberg, Trans. Faraday Soc., 50, 511 (1954).

83. G. E. Boyd, A. W. Adamson, and L. S. Myers, J. Am. Chem. Soc., 69, 2836 (1947).

84. D. Reichenberg, J. Am. Chem. Soc., 75, 589 (1953).

85. J. Ollivier and T. Kikindai, Compt. Rend., 262C, 175 (1966).

86. E. S. Bochinova and D. A. Sokolov, J. Appl. Chem. USSR, 38, 1695 (1965).

87. A. Ruvarac and V. Vesely, J. Inorg. Nucl. Chem., 32, 3939 (1970).

88. V. Vesely, A. Ruvarac, and L. Sedlakova, J. Inorg. Nucl. Chem., 30, 1101 (1968).

89. A. Clearfield, A. Oskarsson, and C. Oskarsson, Ion Exchange and Membranes, 1, 91 (1972).

90. R. M. Barrer, Chem. Ind., 1258 (1962).

91. A. Clearfield, Crystalline Titanium Phosphate, A Research Report, Titanium Alloy Div., National Lead Co., Niagara Falls, N. Y. 1964.

92. G. Alberti, P. Cardini - Galli, U. Constantino, and E. Torracca, J. Inorg. Nucl. Chem., 29, 571 (1967).

93. G. Alberti, G. Giammari, and G. Grassini - Strazza, J. Chromatog., 28, 118 (1967).

94. M. Jean, Anal. Chim. Acta, 3, 96 (1949).

95. A. Clearfield, G. D. Smith, and B. Hammond, J. Inorg. Nucl. Chem., 30, 277 (1968).

96. E. Torracca, U. Constantino, and M. A. Massucci, J. Chromatog., 30, 584 (1967).

97.   G. Alberti and E. Torracca, J. Inorg. Nucl. Chem., 30, 3075 (1968).

98.   M. Qureshi and S. A. Nabi, J. Inorg. Nucl. Chem., 32, 2059 (1970).

99.   D. Vissers, Ph.D. Thesis, University of Wisconsin, Madison (1959).

100.   W. A. Cilley, Ph.D. Thesis, University of Wisconsin, Madison (1963).

101.   E. M. Larsen and W. A. Cilley, J. Inorg. Nucl. Chem., 30, 287 (1968).

102.   G. G. Rocco, J. R. Wiener, and J. P. Cali, Physical Sciences Research, Paper No. 73, AFCRL 64-1018, December (1964).

103.   G. Alberti, U. Constantino, F. DiGregorio, P. Galli, and E. Torracca, J. Inorg. Nucl. Chem., 30, 295 (1968).

104.   K. H. Konig and E. Meyn, J. Inorg. Nucl. Chem., 29, 1153 (1967).

105.   A. Clearfield and R. G. Herman (unpublished results).

106.   K. H. Konig and G. Eckstein, J. Inorg. Nucl. Chem., 31, 1179 (1969).

107.   K. H. Konig and E. Meyn, J. Inorg. Nucl. Chem., 29, 1519 (1967).

108.   G. Alberti, M. A. Massucci, and E. Torracca, J. Chromatog., 30, 579 (1967).

109.   G. Alberti, U. Constantino, F. DiGregorio, and E. Torracca, J. Inorg. Nucl. Chem., 31, 3195 (1969).

110.   G. Alberti and U. Constantino, J. Chromatog., 50, 482 (1970).

111.   G. Alberti and M. A. Massucci, J. Inorg. Nucl. Chem., 32, 1719 (1970).

112.   J. G. Fairchild, Am. Mineralogist, 14, 265 (1929).

113.   J. Beintema, Rec. Trav. Chim., 57, 155 (1938).

114.   F. G. Garcia and R. R. Diaz, Ann. Real Soc. Espan. Fis. Quim. (Madrid), 55B, 399 (1959).

115.   A. Chretien and J. Kraft, Mem. Pres. Soc. Chim., 5, 1399 (1938).

116.   A. Weiss, K. Hartl and V. Hofmann, Naturforsch, 12B, 669 (1957).

117.   V. Pekarek and M. Benesova, J. Inorg. Nucl. Chem., 26, 1743 (1964).

118.   V. Pekarek and V. Vesely, J. Inorg. Nucl. Chem., 27, 1151 (1965).

119. V. Vesely, V. Pekarek, and M. Abbrent, J. Inorg. Nucl. Chem.,
      27, 1159 (1965).

120. A. Weiss, K. Hartl, and V. Hofmann, Naturforsch., 12b, 356 (1957).

121. E. Merz, Z. Electrochem., 63, 288 (1959).

122. Y. Inoue, J. Inorg. Nucl. Chem., 26, 2241 (1964).

123. Y. Inoue, Bull. Chem. Soc., Japan, 36, 1316 (1963).

124. J. Piret, J. Henry, G. Balon, and C. Beaudet, Bull. Soc. Chim.,
      France, 3590 (1965).

125. Y. Inoue, Bull. Chem. Soc., Japan, 36, 1324 (1963).

126. Y. Inoue, S. Suzuki, and H. Goto, Bull. Chem. Soc., 37, 1547 (1964).

127. A. Sato, Y. Inoue and S. Suzuki, Bull. Chem. Soc., 39, 716 (1966).

128. M. Qureshi and S. Z. Qureshi, J. Chromatog., 22, 198 (1966).

129. C. C. Chang, Hua Hsueh Hsueh Pao, 31, 57 (1965); C. A. 64,
      12140C.

130. K. Konichi and Y. Lane, Bunseki Kagaku, 13, 299 (1964); C. A.,
      62, 1237C.

131. A. Winkler and E. Thilo, Z. Anorg. Allg. Chem., 346, 92 (1966).

132. E. Michel and A. Weiss, Z. Naturforsch., 22b, 1100 (1967).

133. M. J. Fuller, J. Inorg. Nucl. Chem., 33, 559 (1971).

134. V. Constantino and A. Gasperoni, J. Chromatog., 51, 289 (1970).

135. M. Qureshi, R. Kumar, and H. S. Rathmore, J. Chem. Soc. (A),
      272 (1970).

136. M. Qureshi, H. S. Rathmore, and R. Kumar, J. Chem. Soc. (A),
      1986 (1970).

137. M. Qureshi, H. S. Rathmore, and K. Kumar, J. Chromatog., 54,
      269 (1971).

138. L. Zsinka, et al., Radiochem. Radioanal. Lett., 2, 257 (1969);
      ibid., 4, 257 (1970).

139. K. A. Kraus, T. A. Carlson, J. S. Johnson, Nature, 177, 128
      (1956).

140. A. Clearfield, Zirconium Molybdates and Tungstates Research
      Report, TAM Div., National Lead Co., Niagara Falls, N. Y. 1964.

141.   H. J. Riedel, Radiochim. Acta, 1, 32 (1962); Nucleonik., 5, 48
        (1963); Ber. Kernforsch. Juelich, 32 (1962).

142.   M. H. Campbell, Anal. Chem., 37, 252 (1965).

143.   W. J. Maeck, M. E. Kussy, and J. E. Rein, Anal. Chem., 35,
        2086 (1963).

144.   J. M. P. Cabral, J. Chromatog., 4, 86 (1960).

145.   M. Qureshi and H. S. Rathmore, J. Chem. Soc. (A), 2515 (1969).

146.   M. Qureshi and J. P. Gupta, J. Chem. Soc. (A), 1755 (1969),
        Chech, 2620 (1969).

147.   M. Qureshi and J. P. Rawat, J. Inorg. Nucl. Chem., 30, 305 (1968).

148.   M. Qureshi and K. G. Varshney, J. Inorg. Nucl. Chem., 30, 3081
        (1968).

149.   H. C. Phillips and K. A. Kraus, J. Am. Chem. Soc., 84, 2267 (1962).

150.   J. R. Feuga and T. Kikindai, Acad. Sci., Paris, Soc. C, 264, 8
        (1967).

151.   M. Qureshi and V. Kumar, J. Chem. Soc. (A), 1488 (1970).

152.   M. J. Nunes da Costa and M. A. S. Jeronimo, J. Chromatog., 5,
        546 (1961).

153.   A. E. Taylor and C. A. Jensen, J. Am. Chem. Soc., 80, 5918
        (1958).

154.   L. Zsinka and L. Zsirtes, Proc. 2nd Hungarian Conf. on Ion-
        Exchange, Balatonczcplak, Vol. II, Sept. 10-14, 1969, p. 377.

155.   M. K. Rahman and A. M. S. Huq, J. Chromatog., 53, 613 (1970).

156.   T. P. Tang, P. Sun, and K. Chen, Hua Hsuch, 33 (1965); C. A.,
        65, 1966.

157.   T. Tam, P. Sun, and K. Chen, Hua Hsuch, 9 (1967); C.A., 69,
        61785C.

158.   D. Naumann, Z. Chemie, 1, 247 (1961).

159.   E. S. Boichinova, Zh. Prikl. Khim. (Leningrad), 38, 674 (1965);
        38, 1732 (1965); ibid, 40, 1833 (1967).

160.   S. W. Pajakott, Monatsh. Chem., 1400 (1968) (Montash).

161.   D. Betteridge and G. N. Stradling, J. Inorg. Nucl. Chem., 29, 2652
        (1967); ibid., 31, 1507 (1969).

162. A. Holroyd and J. E. Salmon, J. Chem. Soc., 269 (1956); J. P. Redfern and J. E. Salmon, J. Chem. Soc., 291 (1961).

163. G. M. Lukaszewski, J. P. Redfern, and J. E. Salmon, J. Chem. Soc., 39 (1961); G. M. Lukaszewski and J. P. Redfern, J. Chem. Soc., 4802 (1962).

164. I. Lindqvist, Ph. D. Dissertation, Uppsata, Sweden, 1950.

165. J. Aveston, E. W. Anacker, and J. S. Johnson, 3, 735-46 (1964).

166. G. A. Tsiginos and C. J. Hallada, Bulletin Cdb-14, Climax Molybdenum Co., Ann Arbor, Michigan 48105, Feb. 1969.

167. D. L. Keppert, "Isopolytungstates", Progress in Inorganic Chemistry, Vol. 4 (F. A. Cotton, ed.), Wiley, New York, 1962, pp. 199-274.

168. J. Aveston, Inorg. Chem., 3, 981-6 (1964).

169. G. A. Tsiginos, Bulletin Cdb-12a, Climax Molybdenum Co., Ann Arbor, Michigan 48105, Sept. 1966.

170. D. L. Keppert, Inorg. Chem., 8, 1556-8 (1969).

171. L. C. W. Baker and J. S. Figgis, J. Am. Chem. Soc., 92, 3794-7 (1970).

172. H. Wu, J. Biol. Chem., 43, 189-220 (1920). (Especially pp. 196, 197-8).

173. Inorganic Synthesis, Vol. 1, McGraw-Hill, New York, 1939, pp. 127-33.

174. B. Gruttner and G. Jander in Handbook of Preparative Inorganic Chemistry, (G. Brauer, ed.), 2nd ed., Vol. 2, Eng. transl., Academic Press, New York, 1965, pp. 1698-1740.

175. L. C. W. Baker, G. A. Gallager, and T. P. Mc Cutcheon, J. Am. Chem. Soc., 77, 2136 (1955).

176. P. Cannon, J. Inorg. Nucl. Chem., 3, 219-231 (1960); and refs. cited therein.

177. R. B. Heslop and E. F. Pearson, Anal. Chim. Acta, 33, 522-31 (1965).

178. W. P. Thistlewaite, J. Inorg. Nucl. Chem., 28, 2143-2146 (1966); and refs. cited therein.

179. J. F. Keggin, Nature, 131, 908; ibid., 132, 351 (1933).

180. J. F. Keggin, Proc. Roy. Soc. (London), Ser. A., 144, 75-100 (1933).

181.   J. A. Santos, Proc. Roy. Soc. (London), Ser. A, 150, 309-22 (1935).

182.   A. J. Bradley and J. W. Illingworth, Proc. Roy. Soc. (London), Ser. A, 157, 113-31 (1936).

183.   J. W. Illingworth and J. F. Keggin, J. Chem. Soc., 575-80 (1935).

184.   J. W. Linnett, J. Chem. Soc., 3796-3803 (1961).

185.   W. W. Wendlandt, Anal. Chim. Acta, 20, 267-70 (1959); and refs. cited therein.

186.   N. E. Sharpless and J. S. Munday, Anal. Chem., 29, 1619-22 (1957).

187.   C. M. French and J. S. Garside, J. Chem. Soc., 2006-8 (1962).

188.   H. Buchwald and W. P. Thistlewaite, J. Inorg. Nucl. Chem., 5, 341-3 (1958).

189.   D. Meier and W. D. Treadwell, Helv. Chim. Acta, 34, 155-68 (1951).

190.   J. van R. Smit, Nature, 181, 1530-1 (1958).

191.   J. van R. Smit, W. Robb, and J. J. Jacobs, Nucleonics, 17, 116-23 (1959).

192.   J. van R. Smit, J. J. Jacobs, and W. Robb, J. Inorg. Nucl. Chem., 12, 95-103 (1959).

193.   J. van R. Smit, W. Robb, and J. J. Jacobs, J. Inorg. Nucl. Chem., 12, 104-12 (1959).

194.   J. van R. Smit and W. Robb, J. Inorg. Nucl. Chem., 26, 509-18 (1964).

195.   T. V. Healy, B. L. Davies, and G. Ingham, AERE Reports C/R: 2528 (1958); 2577 (1958); 2594 (1958); 2631 (1959); and 2969 (1959).

196.   J. van R. Smit, "The Ammonium Molybdophosphate Process for Cesium Separation," U.K.A.E.A. Reports A.E.R.E.: R4006 (1962); R4039 (1962); and R4245 (1963).

197.   J. van R. Smit and J. J. Jacobs, Ind. Eng. Chem. Process Design Develop., 5, 117-22 (1966).

198.   J. Krtil and V. Kourim, J. Inorg. Nucl. Chem., 12, 367-9 (1959).

199.   J. Krtil, J. Inorg. Nucl. Chem., 19, 298-303 (1961).

200.   J. Krtil, J. Inorg. Nucl. Chem., 22, 247-51 (1961).

201.   J. Krtil, J. Inorg. Nucl. Chem., 24, 1139-44 (1962).

202.   J. Krtil and I. Krivy, J. Inorg. Nucl. Chem., 25, 1191-9 (1963).

203. J. Krtil and J. Zemenova, J. Inorg. Nucl. Chem., 25, 1069-71 (1963).

204. J. Krtil and A. I. Kokorin, Zh Analit. Khim., 19, 438-42 (1964).

205. R. W. C. Broadbank, S. Dhabanandana, and R. D. Harding, J. Inorg. Nucl. Chem., 23, 311-6 (1961).

206. B. C. Purkayastha and S. Ser, J. Indian Chem. Soc., 42, 601-6 (1965).

207. C. J. Coetzee and E. F. C. H. Rohwer, Anal. Chim. Acta, 44, 293-9 (1969).

208. R. W. C. Broadbank, S. Dhabanandana, and R. D. Harding, Analyst, 85, 365-70 (1960).

209. C. Feldman and T. C. Rains, Anal. Chem., 36, 405-9 (1964).

210. K. Haberer and W. Weindel, Gas Wasserfach, 107, 892-8 (1966); C. A., 65, 15074 f (1966).

211. H. L. Caron and T. T. Sugihara, Anal. Chem., 34, 1082-6 (1962). See also H. Buchwald and W. P. Thistlewaite, J. Inorg. Nucl. Chem., 7, 292-5 (1958).

212. G. Alberti and G. Grassini, J. Chromatog., 4, 423-5 (1960).

213. H. Schroeder, J. Chromatog., 6, 361-3 (1961).

214. H. Schroeder, Radiochim. Acta, 1, 27-31 (1962).

215. M. Lesigang, Mikrochim. Acta., 34-43 (1964).

216. M. Lesigang and F. Hecht, Mikrochim. Acta, 508-15 (1964).

217. K. Buchtela and M. Lesigang, Mikrochim. Acta, 67-74 (1965).

218. V. Kourim, A. K. Lavrukhina, and S. S. Rodin, J. Inorg. Nucl. Chem., 21, 375-84 (1961).

219. G. M. Schwab and G. Dattler, Z. Angew Chem., 50, 691 (1937).

220. G. M. Schwab and G. Dattler, Z. Angew Chem., 52, 666 (1939).

221. R. P. Graham and A. W. Thomas, J. Am. Chem. Soc., 69, 816 (1947).

222. L. Sacconi, Discuss. Faraday Soc., 7, 173 (1949).

223. S. C. Churms, J. S. Afr. Chem. Inst., 19, 98 (1966), 19, 108 (1966).

224. K. C. Williams, J. L. Daniel, W. J. Thompson, R. I. Kaplan, and R. W. Maatman, J. Phys. Chem., 69, 250 (1965).

225. S. Tustanowski, J. Chromatog., 31, 270 (1967).

226. F. Girardi, R. Pietra, and E. Sabbioni, J. Radioanal. Chem., 5, 161 (1970).

227. A. Krause and M. Ciokowna, Z. Anorg. Chem., 204, 20 (1932).

228. M. H. Kurbatov, G. B. Wood, and J. D. Kurbatov, J. Phys. Chem., 55, 1170 (1951).

229. H. H. Stamm and H. W. Kohlschutter, J. Inorg. Nucl. Chem., 27, 2103 (1965).

230. A. Lewandowski and S. Idzikowski, Chem. Anal. (Warsaw), 11, 611 (1966).

231. A. K. Moulik, S. N. Chakravarti, and S. K. Mokheyee, J. Indian Chem. Soc., 47, 149 (1970).

232. M. Abe and T. Ito, Nippon Kagakra Zasshi, 86, 817 (1965).

233. F. Kepak, Collection Czech. Chem. Commun., 30, 1464 (1965).

234. D. Kyriacou, Surface Soil, 8, 370 (1967).

235. E. D. Reyes and J. J. Jurinak, Soil Sci. Soc. Am. Proc., 31, 637 (1967).

236. W. Schulze and M. Scheffler, Fresenius Z. Anal. Chem., 226, 395 (1967); ibid., 229, 161 (1967).

237. C. B. Amphlett, L. A. McDonald and M. J. Redman, J. Inorg. Nucl. Chem., 6, 236 (1958).

238. C. Heitner-Wirguin and A. Albu-Yaron, J. Inorg. Nucl. Chem., 28, 2379 (1966).

239. H. W. Levi and E. Schiewer, Radiochim. Acta., 5, 126 (1966); ibid., 9, 160 (1968); ibid., 14, 43 (1970).

240. C. Heitner-Wirguin and A. Albu-Yaron, J. Appl. Chem. (London), 15, 445 (1965).

241. K. A. Kraus and H. O. Phillips, J. Am. Chem. Soc., 78, 249 (1956).

242. C. B. Amphlett, L. A. McDonald, and M. J. Redman, J. Soc. Chem. Ind., 365 (1957).

243. G. H. Nancollas and R. Paterson, J. Inorg. Nucl. Chem., 29, 565 (1967).

244.   G. H. Nancollas and D. S. Reid, J. Inorg. Nucl. Chem., 31, 213
       (1969).

245.   D. Britz and G. H. Nancollas, J. Inorg. Nucl. Chem., 31, 3861
       (1969).

246.   K. M. Pant, J. Indian Chem. Soc., 46, 541 (1969).

247.   J. Belloni-Cofler and D. Pavlov, J. Chim. Phys., 62, 458 (1965).

248.   A. Ruvarac, Boris Kidric Inst. Nucl. Sci. Report. IBK-560 (1967)
       Belgrade.

249.   D. R. Vissers, J. Phys. Chem., 72, 3236 (1968).

250.   M. Abe and T. Ito, Nippon Kagaku Zasshi, 86, 1259 (1965).

251.   Yu. I. Sukharev and Yu. V. Egorev, Izv. Akad. Nauk SSSR, Neorg.
       Mater., 4, 996 (1968); ibid, 5, 2159 (1969).

252.   K. S. Rajan, D. B. Boies, A. J. Casolo, and J. I. Bregman,
       Desalinization, 1, 231 (1966).

253.   S. Ahrland, Acta. Chem. Scand., 14, 1059 (1960).

254.   A. Kozawa, J. Inorg. Nucl. Chem., 21, 315 (1961).

255.   K. Unger and F. Vydra, J. Inorg. Nucl. Chem., 30, 1075 (1968).

256.   K. Unger and K. Berg, Z. Naturforsch., B24, 454 (1969).

257.   H. Ti Tien, J. Phys. Chem., 69, 350 (1965).

258.   R. W. Maatman, J. Phys. Chem., 69, 3196 (1965).

259.   H. K. Kohlschutter, A. Risch, K. Unger, and K. Vogel, Bev.
       Bunsenges. Physik. Chem., 69, 849 (1965).

260.   F. Vydra, Anal. Chim. Acta, 38, 201 (1967).

261.   H. W. Kohlschutter and L. Schaefer, Fresenius Z. Anal. Chem.,
       245, 129 (1969).

262.   R. W. Maatman and A. Kramer, J. Phys. Chem., 72, 104 (1968).

263.   F. Vydra and V. Markova, Collection Czech. Chem. Commun., 32,
       1614 (1967).

264.   J. D. Donaldson and M. J. Fuller, J. Inorg. Nucl. Chem., 30,
       1083 (1968).

265.   J. D. Donaldson and M. J. Fuller, J. Inorg. Nucl. Chem., 32,
       1703 (1970).

266.   J. D. Donaldson, M. J. Fuller, and J. W. Price, J. Inorg. Nucl. Chem., 30, 2841 (1968).

267.   H. Nishida, Bunseki Kagaku, 14, 473 (1965).

268.   L. N. Kommissarova, Yu. P. Simanov, and Z. A. Vladimiorova, Russ. J. Inorg. Chem. (Eng. Transl.), 5, 687 (1960).

269.   L. M. Zaitsev and G. S. Bochkarev, Russ. J. Inorg. Chem. (Eng. Transl.), 7, 409 (1962).

270.   W. B. Blumenthal, The Chemical Behavior of Zirconium, Van Nostrand, Princeton, New Jersey, 1958, p. 182.

271.   A. Clearfield, Rev. Pure Appl. Chem., 14, 91 (1964).

272.   A. Clearfield, Inorg. Chem., 3, 146 (1964).

273.   H. T. Rijnten, Zirconia, Drukkerij Gebr., N. V. Nijmegen, 1971.

274.   R. S. Roth, J. Am. Ceram. Soc., 39, 196 (1956).

275.   L. Passerini, Gazz. Chim. Ital., 60, 672 (1930).

276.   H. T. Rijnten, in Physical and Chemical Aspects of Adsorbants and Catalysts (B. G. Linsen, ed.), Academic Press, London, 1970, Ch 7.

277.   O. Ruff and F. Ebert, Anorg. Allgem. Chem., 180, 19 (1929).

278.   G. Teufer, Acta. Cryst., 15, 1187 (1962).

279.   J. D. McCullough and K. N. Trueblood, Acta. Cryst., 18, 507 (1965).

280.   E. M. Larsen and A. M. Gammill, J. Am. Chem. Soc., 72, 3615 (1950).

281.   I. V. Tananaev and M. Ya. Bokmel'der, Russ. J. Inorg. Chem. (Eng. Transl.), 3, 1 (1958).

282.   R. P. Singh and N. R. Banerjee, J. Ind. Chem. Soc., 38, 865 (1961).

283.   A. W. Thomas and H. S. Owens, J. Am. Chem. Soc., 57, 1825 (1935).

284.   A. Clearfield, Rev. Pure Appl. Chem., 14, 98-102 (1964).

285.   A. Clearfield and P. A. Vaughan, Acta Cryst., 9, 555 (1956).

286.   T. C. N. Mak, Can. J. Chem., 46, 3492 (1968).

287.   J. M. Muha and P. A. Vaughan, J. Chem. Phys., 33, 194 (1960).

288. J. R. Fryer, J. L. Hutchison, and R. Paterson, J. Colloid, Interface Sci., 34, 238 (1970).

289. L. M. Zaitsev and G. S. Bochkarev, Russ. J. Inorg. Chem. (Eng. Transl.), 9, 1463 (1964).

290. L. M. Zaitsev, Russ. J. Inorg. Chem. (Eng. Transl.), 11, 900 (1966).

291. B. G. Linsen, Physical and Chemical Aspects of Adsorbents and Catalysts, Academic Press, London, 1970, Ch. 5.

292. G. Lundgren, Svensk. Kemisk Tidshrift, 71, 200 (1959); Retrav. Chim., 75, 585 (1956).

293. L. Pokras, J. Chem. Educ., 33, 152 (1956).

294. D. Vivien, J. Livage, and Ch. Mazieres, J. Chim. Phys. Physicochim. Biol., 67, 199 (1970).

295. Yu. Ya. Bobyrenko, Yu. D. Dolmatov, and M. I. Bragina, Zh. Prikl. Khim., 43, 1152 (1970).

296. Yu. D. Dolmatov and A. I. Sheinkman, Zh. Prikl. Khim., 43, 249 (1970).

297. S. Hietanen, Acta. Chem. Scand., 8, 1626 (1954); Rec. Trav. Chim., 75, 711 (1956); R. P. Singh and N. R. Banerjee, J. Indian Chem. Soc., 39, 255 (1962); A. I. Zhukov, V. N. Onoson, V. Ya Kudgakov, and B. M. Sergeev, Zh. Neorg. Khim, 8, 871 (1963).

298. E. Ekedahl, E. Hogfeldt, and L. G. Sillen, Acta. Chem. Scand., 4, 556 (1950).

299. D. H. Freeman, J. Chem. Phys., 35, 189 (1961).

300. H. P. Gregor, J. Am. Chem. Soc., 70, 1293 (1948).

301. H. P. Gregor, M. J. Hamilton, R. J. Oza, and F. Bernstein, J. Phys. Chem., 60, 263 (1956).

302. S. Lindenbaum and G. E. Boyd, J. Phys. Chem., 69, 2374 (1965).

303. K. E. Becker, S. Lindenbaum, and G. E. Boyd, J. Phys. Chem., 70, 3834 (1966).

304. U. P. Strauss and Y. P. Leung, J. Am. Chem. Soc., 87, 1476 (1965).

NOTE ADDED IN PROOF

In this chapter we have attempted to show the variety of new inorganic exchangers available to the practitioner and the state of development of the field. The properties that recommend their use are high specificity, excellent resistance to strong acids and good temperature stability. With regard to this last property it should be remembered that some of the exchangers hydrolyze and/or age at elevated temperatures. However, such shortcomings can be partly overcome by improving the crystallinity of the exchanger as has been done with zirconium phosphate. More studies along these lines are in order.

Before the new inorganic exchangers find their place in ion exchange technology it is evident that a good deal more of fundamental research must be done. Each of the exchangers is a unique compound with its own properties and behavior. For example, although α-ZrP and its titanium analogue are fairly similar, the cesium and thorium phosphates represent completely different systems. Perhaps the most similar class of compounds in their general ion exchange behavior is the hydrous oxides, but even here large differences exist.

It is a mistake to consider the inorganics as structureless gels. This has led many investigators to use exchangers which have only been poorly characterized. Since in many instances different preparations exhibit different ion exchange behavior, much of the data in the literature is only of very limited value. Thus, more definitive studies of the effect of preparative methods on composition, structure, and ion exchange properties are required. For those compounds which are crystalline the determination of the crystal structure appears to be the key to understanding their behavior. It is clear that a knowledge of the way in which the ion exchange isotherms change with variation in the structure (or preparative method) of the exchangers would help clarify the nature of the exchange processes in these systems. Related to this is the need for more definitive kinetic data.

Behold, a rich new field of ion exchange materials has been given unto you. Forsake it not!!

Chapter 2

APPLICATION OF ION EXCHANGE TO ELEMENT
SEPARATION AND ANALYSIS

F. W. E. Strelow

National Chemical Research Laboratory
Pretoria, South Africa

I. INTRODUCTION

Ion exchange chromatography is not only a method for the separation and concentration of trace elements, or for the separation of elements such as the rare earths, which are difficult to separate by any other means, but also a very powerful tool for the separation of any combination of common elements. It eliminates the adsorption and entrainment problems of precipitation reactions, and it provides quantitative separations at very much lower separation factors than those required for batch solvent extraction procedures. When completeness of separation and the accuracy of the subsequent determination are more important than time and cost considerations, ion exchange chromatography often becomes the most favorable choice for the analyst planning a procedure.

Two basic requirements have to be met to obtain favorable conditions for a good separation. First, the separation factor

$$\alpha_B^A = {}^D A / D_B \to , \tag{1}$$

expressed as the ratio of the equilibrium distribution coefficients of the elements to be separated must be favorable, keeping in mind that the distribution coefficient for the more strongly absorbed element must be high enough for quantitative retention, and that of the less strongly absorbed low enough for reasonably fast elution; and second, the kinetics of the separation, as carried out on the column, must be favorable. The importance of the second requirement is sometimes overlooked, and the merits of separations are compared on the basis of separation factors alone. Yet during actual work a separation with a separation factor of 10 sometimes may prove to be more attractive than another with a factor of 1000, because the second separation shows bad "tailing" of the less strongly retained element. Unfortunately, only very little and occasional information on "tailing" in ion exchange chromatography is available in the literature and no systematic and comparative study of this factor seems to have been made. In this chapter the author will try to include such information as is available to him, in this treatment of separations, in order to provide a better appreciation of the kinetic problem than has so far been provided by others.

The analyst looking for increased selectivities in ion exchange separations has the choice between two main approaches. He can try to tailor the exchange material for his purpose. This has been done by attaching to polystyrene and other resin matrixes, ion selective groups such as phosphonous [1], phosphonic [1-3], dipicrylamine [4], phenylfluorone [5], diphenylcarbazide [6], dimethylglyoxime [7], chromotropic acid [7], resorcinol [8], hydrochinone [8], pyrogallol [8], hydrosulfide [9], and thiolgroups [10] or chelate forming groups such as anthranilic acid [11], salicylic acid [12], 8-hydroxyquinoline [13], glyoxal-bis-2-hydroxanil [14], penylthiourea [15], orthohydroxybenzenearsonic acid [16], amino acids [11], and aminopolyacetic acids [17-21]. Furthermore, various selective inorganic ion exchange materials, such as insoluble phosphates [22-27], molybdates [28-30], tungstates [31-33], arsenates [34], antimonates [35-37], selenites [38], and silicates [39], have been used, and also the oxides of Fe(III) [40], Sn(IV) [41], Mn(IV) [42], Ti(IV) [43], Al(III) [44], Si(IV) [45], Th(IV) [46] and Zr(IV) [28, 47], and many complex cyanides [48-56] and heteropolyacids [57-61] (See Chap. 1).

Unfortunately, many of these exchange materials have exchange kinetics inferior to those of the common polystyrene based exchangers, with sulfonate (strongly acid) or quaternary amine (strongly basic) exchange groups. Many can be used only under a limited range of conditions or for the separation of a few selected elements; in addition, their properties are not reproducible, a widely different ion exchange behavior for different production batches of these materials having been obtained.

As an alternative possibility, the analyst can try to tailor the eluting agent to a particular separation, in order to retain the favorable kinetics and the chemical stability that is shown by the strongly acidic and strongly basic polystyrene resins, in all kinds of solutions. Only this second approach will be discussed in this chapter, because of the limited space available. Furthermore, instead of attempting to provide a complete literature survey, narrowly covering the whole field, the author has selected a few ion exchange systems which, in his opinion, illustrate focal points of interest in applied ion exchange separations, and proposes to discuss these and their applications to chemical analysis in more detail.

II. SEPARATIONS USING AQUEOUS COMPLEXING AGENTS

A. General Considerations

Selective complexation in aqueous solution as a means to improve ion exchange separations has been employed since the Second World War, when ion exchange first began to gain importance as a separation technique. The classic example is the separation of the rare earths and the alkaline earth elements by cation exchange chromatography in citrate buffers, as described by Tompkins et al. [62].

Generally the selectivity of a separation is expressed by the ratio of the distribution coefficients, $\alpha_B^A = \dfrac{D_A}{D_B}$, of the elements to be separated, where the mass distribution coefficient is defined for element A as

$$D_A = \frac{\text{amount of A on resin}}{\text{amount of A in solution}} \quad x \quad \frac{\text{ml solution}}{\text{g dry resin}} \quad \rightarrow \quad . \tag{2}$$

Similarly, a volume distribution coefficient can be defined by replacing "gram dry resin" by "volume wet resin." The position of the elution peak of element A in a chromatographic elution process is given by the simple expression

$$\overline{v}_A = D_A \times M + \text{dead space of column}, \tag{3}$$

where $\overline{v}_A$ is the elution volume of A in ml, D_A is the mass distribution coefficient as defined in Equation (2), and M is the mass of dry resin in the column, in grams [63, 64]. This equation is the first guide for the analytical chemist intending to employ ion exchange chromatography for quantitative analytical separations. Detailed equations predicting not only the position but also the shape of the elution peaks and the amount of cross-contamination are also available [64, 65], but require additional information such as the numerical value of diffusion coefficients, which is not available for the resin phase in most cases. However, these equations have no predictive value in cases of very asymmetrical elution curves, and of tailing due to the in-homogeneity of resin crosslinking or other factors. To take these factors into account one has to rely on empirical information. Equation (3) is strictly applicable only for trace amounts, but for columns loaded to 1% of the total capacity, deviations from prediction are negligible. For higher loads the appearance of the first traces and the position of the peak maximum move to lower elution volumes with increasing loads, and can be approximately estimated. Important is the fact that the tail end of the peak is, with very few exceptions, almost stationary, as is shown in Figure 1 for the elution of magnesium with 0.1M HCl from AG50W-X8 cation exchange resin.

The quality of a separation depends not only on the numerical value of the separation factor $\alpha_B^A = D_A/D_B$, but also on values of D_A and D_B themselves. This often is not fully appreciated. As an extreme example: a separation factor of 10 is unlikely to provide a satisfactory separation, when the distribution coefficients are $D_A = 1$ and $D_B = 0.1$, because even the more strongly retained ion will appear practically together with the elution front. Yet an excellent separation will be obtained when $D_A = 50$ and $D_B = 5$. That considerably smaller variations in D-values have an appreciable effect on the quality of a separation, keeping the separation factor constant, can be seen from the elution curves for potassium and rubidium, using 0.7 and 1.5M HCl, as published by Strelow et al. [66].

B. The Influence of Complex Formation on D-Values

In the case of cation exchange resins, the distribution coefficient of an element in the presence of a monovalent complexing ligand which is the anion of a strong acid HA is given approximately by [67]

$$D = \frac{D_o + \Delta}{1 + K_1 [A^-] + K_1 K_2 [A^-]^2 + K_1 K_2 K_3 [A^-]^3 \cdots} \rightarrow , \qquad (4)$$

where D_o is the coefficient in absence of a complexing agent, e.g., in perchloric acid solution of similar concentration, $[A^-]$ is the complexing ligand concentration, and K_1, K_2, and K_3 are the stepwise stability constants. Delta is a term due to the absorption of cationic complexes in the case of multivalent elements. Often, but not always, this term is small in comparison with D_o, and can be omitted.

When HA is a weak monobasic acid, Equation (4) can be written as

$$D = \frac{D_o + \Delta}{1 + K_1 k_1 \dfrac{[HA]}{[H^+]} + K_1 K_2 k^2 \dfrac{[HA]^2}{[H^+]^2} + K_1 K_2 K_3 k^3 \dfrac{[HA]^2}{[H^+]^2} \cdots} \rightarrow , \qquad (5)$$

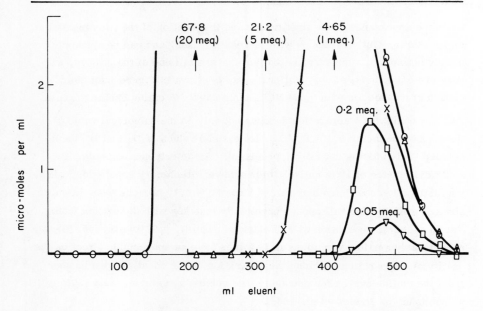

FIG. 1.   Elution curves for Mg with 1.0M HCl. Column of 60 ml (2.0 x 19 cm) AG50W-X8, 200-400 mesh. Flow rate 3.0 ± 0.5 ml/min. Various amounts of Mg.

where k_1 is the dissociation constant of the acid HA. Equations (4) and (5) can be expanded to multivalent ligands. Sometimes simplifying assumptions can be made, and approximate values for D can be calculated, provided the required complex stability and acid dissociation constants are known. Unfortunately this very seldom is the case, and often the known values are not sufficiently accurate for this purpose. Experimentally determined coefficients, therefore, are still the most valuable guides for the projected ion exchange separation.

For anion exchange the situation is even worse because various complexes often are absorbed simultaneously. Since there is very little information available about their fundamental absorbalities, their contribution to the value of D_o in Equation (5) is not known. As a consequence, the use of this approach for such systems must be empirical.

C. Anion Exchange Separations in Oxalic-Mineral Acid Mixtures

Oxalic acid is a very promising complexing agent for anion exchange chromatography, first because it is a moderately strong acid, and second because it forms relatively strong metal complexes. The effective concentration of oxalate and bioxalate anions, and therefore the metal complex and ion exchange equilibria which determine the value of the distribution coefficient can be easily modified by mixing the oxalic acid with a strong mineral acid, such as hydrochloric or nitric acid, thereby controlling its dissociation. No addition of buffer solutions which introduce unwanted cations is necessary.

Separations of elements such as Sc, Ti(IV) and V(V) [68], Ta and Nb [69, 70], and Ti(IV), Zr, Nb, Ta, W(VI) and Mo(VI) [71], have been carried out in oxalic-hydrochloric acid solutions. Occasionally oxalic acid or oxalates have been used for elution of Te(IV), Sb(V), Sn(IV) [72], Ga(III) [73], U(VI) [74], and Cu(II), Ni(II) and Al [75]. The only systematic anion exchange study in oxalate media seems to have been undertaken by De Corte et al. [76], who determined distribution coefficients for 12 elements in pure oxalic acid solutions with Dowex 1-X8 resin, using radioactive tracer amounts of the elements. A systematic cation exchange study including 19 elements has been carried out by Nozaki et al. [77]. In Table 1 some distribution coefficients are shown. They were obtained by extrapolation of a plot of the results of De Corte et al. to the desired oxalic acid concentrations. Only separations of radio tracer amounts of elements were reported by De Corte et al. but from the coefficients shown in Table 1 it appears that separations of larger amounts of Mn(II)-Co(II) at 0.05M, Co(II)-Zn at 0.10M, Zn-Cu(II) and Zn-Hg(II) at 0.25M, and Ce(III)-Lu and Ce(III)-Sc at 0.50M oxalic acid should be possible, provided excessive "tailing" is not encountered and the amounts of the elements are below the solubility limits of the insoluble oxalate precipitates.

Some common ter- and tetra-valent elements such as Al, Fe(III) and Ti(IV) do form oxalate complexes with stability constants, which are several orders of magnitude higher than those of Cu(II), Ni(II), Mn(II), etc. Oxalic acid in appropriate mixture with a strong mineral acid should therefore offer

TABLE 1

Anion Exchange Distribution Coefficients in Oxalic Acid

Element	Molarity oxalic acid							
	0.001	0.0025	0.01	0.025	0.10	0.25	0.50	0.90
Mo(VI)	$>10^5$	$>10^5$	$>10^5$	$>10^5$	$>10^5$	$>10^5$	$>10^5$	$>10^5$
In(III)	$>10^4$	$>10^4$	75000	60000	20000	3900	880	360
Sc(III)	$>10^4$	$>10^4$	48000	21500	2400	450	139	50
Lu(III)	$>10^4$	$>10^4$	$>10^4$	38000	2200	331	92	46
Cu(II)	31000	20000	7700	2850	470	112	29	25
Hg(II)	4800	3700	1900	925	236	51	28	18
Ce(III)	20000	16000	5000	1200	149	28	12	9
Zn(II)	13500	9100	3400	760	52	7.6	4.6	2.0
Co(II)	1510	1170	405	118	15	3.9	1.7	1.3
Mn(II)	98	72	18.0	4.8	0.4	0.4	0.4	0.4
As(III)	1.7	1.6	1.7	1.5	1.3	1.2	1.0	0.9

excellent prospects for a group separation between divalent and ter- and tetravalent elements. Hydrochloric acid is an attractive choice for the mineral acid because it is volatile; in addition, the chloride anion is not very strongly absorbed and therefore does not compete too strongly for resin sites. Unfortunately elements such as Zn, Cd and Hg(II) form fairly stable chloride complexes which are absorbed when oxalate complex formation is suppressed. Nitric acid is also volatile. It has only a very slight tendency toward complex formation in dilute aqueous solution, and can therefore be used for separation of the chloride complex forming elements. The nitrate anion is considerably more strongly absorbed than chloride, and should be very useful as well for separating the more strongly absorbed elements. Perchloric acid has the least tendency to form complexes but it is somewhat less volatile and very strongly absorbed, causing considerable resin contraction, which leads to restricted particle diffusion rates and, in extreme cases, even to blockage of pores and sealing off of more densely crosslinked parts of the resin. For this reason it is not considered to be an attractive eluting agent for accurate analytical work.

Anion exchange distribution coefficients in hydrochloric-oxalic acid and in nitric-oxalic acid mixtures using AGl-X8 resin are shown in Tables 2 and 3, and 4 and 5, respectively [78]. The coefficients were determined using 1 mmole of the element in 250 ml of solution equilibrated with 2.5 g resin (dry weight of chloride form at 105°C). Oxalic acid concentrations of 0.05M and 0.25M were used, and the mineral acid concentration was varied from 0.01 to 4.0M. In a number of instances, 0.05% hydrogen peroxide was included in the equilibrium mixture.

The coefficients in Table 3 indicate that Ti(IV) and Zr can be separated from Nb by elution with 1.5M HCl containing 0.25M oxalic acid and 0.05% hydrogen peroxide, and that Nb can then be eluted with 2.0M HCl containing 0.25M oxalic acid and 0.05% hydrogen peroxide, while Ta is still retained, a method described by Bandi et al. [71]. The elements Sn(IV), W(VI), Mo(VI), U(VI), and In should accompany Ta quantitatively.

Separation of Fe(III) together with Zr and Ti(IV) from Nb should be possible by replacing 1.5M HCl with 0.75M HNO_3 containing 0.25M oxalic acid and 0.05% hydrogen peroxide. The elements Ga, In(III), Al and V(V) or V(IV) should accompany Fe(III) quantitatively, together with the di- and monovalent elements. The separation between Nb and Ta probably can be improved by using between 1.0 and 1.5M HNO_3 containing 0.25M or even 0.5M oxalic acid and 0.05% hydrogen peroxide as eluting agent for Nb. Mo(VI) and W(VI) should be retained together with Ta.

The ter- and tetravalent elements, as expected, are much more strongly absorbed than the di- and monovalent ones. Al and V(V) or V(IV) are the least strongly absorbed elements of the multivalent group. Cu(II) and Ni(II), the most strongly absorbed elements of the di-monovalent group when eluted with 0.20M HCl containing 0.05M oxalic acid are separated quantitatively from Al and almost quantitatively from each other, as is shown in Figure 2. The elution of Ni is quite satisfactory, but the Cu peak is very asymmetrical, uneven, and "tails" seriously, probably because of the presence of more than one complex with slow complex conversion rates. No Al is found in the first 1000 ml of eluate. The separation factor for Cu(II) is $\alpha\frac{Al}{Cu} \approx 25$, while for Ni(II), Co(II), Mn(II), Mg and the alkaline earth metals it is larger than

TABLE 2

Anion Exchange Distribution Coefficients in 0.05M Oxalic Acid at Various Concentrations of HCl

Element	0.01M	0.1M	0.2M	0.5M	1.0M	2.0M	3.0M	4.0M
Sn(IV)	$>10^4$	$>10^4$	$>10^4$	$>10^4$	$>10^4$	$>10^4$	9700	3800
W(VI)[a]	3450	$>10^4$	9170	7610	6720	699	163	prec.
Mo(VI)[a]	$>10^4$	$>10^4$	$>10^4$	$>10^4$	2310	920	660	935
Pt(II)	1500	1480	1500	1470	1370	1230	837	525
Cd(II)[c]	51	48.9	269	472	171	195	289	427
In(III)	$>10^4$	2900	828	173	80	44.4	28.8	24.1
U(VI)	$>10^4$	6800	1630	250	66	24.2	38.1	71
Nb(V)[a]	$>10^4$	$>10^4$	5460	405	60	13.8	9.3	6.4
Zn(II)[c]	28.7	3.3	2.9	5.3	30.6	35.3	55	88
Fe(III)[a]	$>10^4$	2790	1580	105	14.5	6.0	9.5	39.0
Zr(IV)	$>10^4$	$>10^4$	4040	138	11.4	1.4	1.0	0.4
Hf(IV)	4030	3560	1700	85	8.1	1.7	0.9	0.5
Ga(III)	$>10^4$	$>10^4$	485	43.5	7.9	1.2	6.6	30.7
Al(III)	$>10^4$	1840	211	5.4	0.5	< 0.5	< 0.5	< 0.5
V(V)[a,b]	5370	570	160	17.7	2.3	0.6	< 0.5	< 0.5
Cu(II)[c]	620	39.7	8.4	1.4	0.7	0.4	1.1	2.2
Ni(II)[c]	84	0.8	< 0.5	< 0.5	< 0.5	< 0.5	< 0.5	< 0.5
Be(II)	68	8.1	1.5	< 0.5	< 0.5	< 0.5	< 0.5	< 0.5

Co(II)[c]	9.2	< 0.5	< 0.5	< 0.5	< 0.5	< 0.5	< 0.5	< 0.5
Mn(II)	< 0.5	< 0.5	< 0.5	< 0.5	< 0.5	< 0.5	< 0.5	< 0.5
Li, Na, K, Rb, S, Mg, Ca, Sr, Ba	< 0.5	< 0.5	< 0.5	< 0.5	< 0.5	< 0.5	< 0.5	< 0.5

[a] 0.1% H_2O_2 present;

[b] Partial reduction to $V(IV)$;

[c] 0.1 mmole cation.

TABLE 3

Anion Exchange Distribution Coefficients in 0.25M Oxalic Acid at Various Concentrations of HCl

Element	0.01M	0.1M	0.2M	0.5M	1.0M	2.0M	3.0M	4.0M
Sn(IV)	$> 10^4$	$> 10^4$	$> 10^4$	$> 10^4$	$> 10^4$	9100	6800	5300
W(VI) [a]	5790	3260	1920	582	219	84	46.3	33.0
Ti(IV)	$> 10^4$	7800	5200	1450	213	6.2	2.1	< 0.5
U(VI)	$> 10^4$	6650	2590	492	145	51	51	104
In(III)	5320	2340	1230	321	145	76	50	31.9
Cd(II) [c]	30.3	12.2	72	170	120	242	237	226
Nb(V) [a]	$> 10^4$	$> 10^4$	6570	680	108	16.9	8.8	6.0
Zn(II) [c]	7.0	2.5	3.3	8.3	46.0	59	58	56
Fe(III) [a]	$> 10^4$	3920	1450	236	35.2	6.6	8.1	27.6
Hf(IV)	$> 10^4$	$> 10^4$	7320	261	22.0	2.8	0.9	0.5
Zr(IV)	$> 10^4$	$> 10^4$	6800	348	18.4	3.1	1.7	0.9
Ga(III)	$> 10^4$	9300	1044	120	18.0	2.2	5.9	36.7
Ti(IV) [a]	2340	1280	457	80	15.0	2.8	1.1	0.6
V(V) [a,b]	3370	483	201	41.3	8.3	1.6	0.5	< 0.5
Cr(III)	76	66	34.6	10.6	2.4	< 0.5	< 0.5	< 0.5
Al(III)	4250	1840	571	36.6	1.8	< 0.5	< 0.5	< 0.5
Cu(II) [c]	110	62	17.3	2.7	1.3	0.8	1.4	1.7
Be(II)	16.3	6.4	1.2	< 0.5	< 0.5	< 0.5	< 0.5	< 0.5

Ni(II)[c]	13.1	1.7	1.1	0.5	< 0.5	< 0.5	< 0.5	< 0.5
Co(II)[c]	2.5	< 0.5	< 0.5	< 0.5	< 0.5	< 0.5	< 0.5	< 0.5
Mn(II)	< 0.5	< 0.5	< 0.5	< 0.5	< 0.5	< 0.5	< 0.5	< 0.5
Li, Na, K, Rb, Cs, Mg, Ca, Sr, Ba	< 0.5	< 0.5	< 0.5	< 0.5	< 0.5	< 0.5	< 0.5	< 0.5

[a] 0.1% H_2O_2 present;

[b] Partial reduction to V(IV);

[c] 0.1 mmole cation.

TABLE 4

Anion Exchange Distribution Coefficients in 0.05M Oxalic Acid, at Various Concentrations of HNO_3

Element	0.01M	0.10M	0.20M	0.50M	1.00M	2.00M	3.00M	4.00M
W(VI) [a]	$> 10^4$	$> 10^4$	$> 10^4$	2570	535	86	30.1	13.0
Mo(VI) [a]	$> 10^4$	$> 10^4$	$> 10^4$	1570	380	81	27.1	11.9
Sn(IV)	60	53	34.8	21.6	prec.	prec.	prec.	prec.
Zr(IV)	$> 10^4$	2280	240	11.1	2.7	0.7	< 0.5	< 0.5
Fe(III) [a]	6670	543	85	8.2	2.4	0.8	< 0.5	< 0.5
U(VI)	9630	413	92	11.4	5.7	3.7	5.2	6.7
Ga(III)	7230	342	74	6.0	1.0	0.6	< 0.5	< 0.5
Ti(IV) [a]	4520	258	67	8.1	2.5	< 0.5	< 0.5	< 0.5
V(V) [a,b]	2520	164	53	6.7	2.0	0.7	< 0.5	< 0.5
Al(III)	8470	106	16.5	< 0.5	< 0.5	< 0.5	< 0.5	< 0.5
In(III)	1130	22.5	3.6	< 0.5	< 0.5	< 0.5	< 0.5	< 0.5
Cu(II) [c]	202	6.4	1.8	0.9	< 0.5	< 0.5	< 0.5	< 0.5
Be(II)	12.1	1.1	< 0.5	< 0.5	< 0.5	< 0.5	< 0.5	< 0.5
Ni(II) [c]	9.5	0.6	< 0.5	< 0.5	< 0.5	< 0.5	< 0.5	< 0.5
Zn(II) [c]	3.2	< 0.5	< 0.5	< 0.5	< 0.5	< 0.5	< 0.5	< 0.5
Co(II) [c]	2.7	< 0.5	< 0.5	< 0.5	< 0.5	< 0.5	< 0.5	< 0.5
Cd(II) [c]	0.6	< 0.5	< 0.5	< 0.5	< 0.5	< 0.5	< 0.5	< 0.5

Mn(II)	< 0.5	< 0.5	< 0.5	< 0.5	< 0.5	< 0.5	< 0.5
Li, Na, K, Rb, Cs, Mg, Ca, Sr, Ba	< 0.5	< 0.5	< 0.5	< 0.5	< 0.5	< 0.5	< 0.5

[a] H_2O_2 present (0.5 ml 30%);

[b] partial reduction to V(IV);

[c] 0.1 mmole cation.

TABLE 5

Anion Exchange Distribution Coefficients in 0.25M Oxalic Acid, at Various Concentrations of HNO_3

Element	0.01M	0.10M	0.20M	0.50M	1.00M	2.00M	3.00M	4.00M
W(VI)[a]	$> 10^4$	$> 10^4$	$> 10^4$	4130	889	201	71	29.2
Mo(VI)[a]	$> 10^4$	$> 10^4$	$> 10^4$	2890	782	196	68	28.3
Ta(V)[a]	-	2510	1750	222	47.3	14.6	9.8	6.9
Nb(V)[a]	$> 10^4$	1680	535	99	12.0	5.2	3.6	2.7
Sn(IV)	60	55	47.6	25.2	11.1	5.9	3.4	2.8
Zr(IV)	$> 10^4$	3360	420	22.1	2.9	0.8	< 0.5	< 0.5
U(VI)	7500	749	193	25.6	7.5	5.1	6.6	8.3
Fe(III)[a]	6670	729	181	21.4	2.9	1.0	0.6	< 0.5
Ga(III)	4990	511	149	16.9	3.6	1.3	0.7	< 0.5
Ti(IV)[a]	1630	256	86	14.7	3.4	1.2	0.6	< 0.5
Al(III)	2110	201	48.7	2.5	< 0.5	< 0.5	< 0.5	< 0.5
V(V)[a,b]	702	148	64	13.7	4.0	1.4	0.6	< 0.5
In(III)	404	46.0	10.1	1.3	0.6	< 0.5	< 0.5	< 0.5
Cu(II)[c]	77	12.1	3.9	1.2	< 0.5	< 0.5	< 0.5	< 0.5
Be(II)	6.9	11.0	< 0.5	< 0.5	< 0.5	< 0.5	< 0.5	< 0.5
Ni(II)[c]	3.8	6.8		< 0.5	< 0.5	< 0.5	< 0.5	< 0.5
Zn(II)[c]	1.9	< 0.5		< 0.5	< 0.5	< 0.5	< 0.5	< 0.5

Co(II) [c]	1.8	< 0.5	< 0.5	< 0.5	< 0.5	< 0.5	< 0.5	< 0.5
Cd(II) [c]	< 0.5	< 0.5	< 0.5	< 0.5	< 0.5	< 0.5	< 0.5	< 0.5
Mn(II)	< 0.5	< 0.5	< 0.5	< 0.5	< 0.5	< 0.5	< 0.5	< 0.5
Li, Ma, K, Rb, Cs, Mg, Ca, Sr, Ba	< 0.5	< 0.5	< 0.5	< 0.5	< 0.5	< 0.5	< 0.5	< 0.5

[a] 0.5 ml 30% H_2O_2 present;

[b] partial reduction to V(IV);

[c] 0.1 mmole cation.

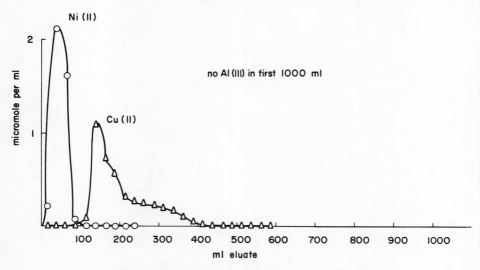

FIG. 2.   Elution curves for Cu(II), Ni(II), and Al with 0.2M HCl + 0.05M oxalic acid.   Column of 46 ml (2.0 x 15 cm) AG1-X8 resin, 200–400 mesh. Flow rate 3.0 ± 0.5 ml/min.

200.   All these elements, including the alkali metals, and excepting only Cu(II), can also be eluted with 0.10M HCl containing 0.05M oxalic acid and 0.05% hydrogen peroxide, leaving Ti(IV), Fe(III), Zr, V(V), Hf, Mo(VI), W(VI), Ta, Nb, U(VI), Sn(IV), In(III), Ga, and Cd on the column together with aluminium.   A method for accurate rock analysis has been developed on the basis of these observations.   It is described in detail later in this chapter.

According to their distribution coefficients, In(III) and Ga should be easily separable in oxalic acid systems.   Indium should be absorbed from solutions 2M in HCl and containing 0.05 or 0.25M oxalic acid, while Ga is eluted, the separation factor being about 20 in 0.05M and 35 in 0.25M oxalic acid.   Curiously enough the situation is reversed in nitric–oxalic acid mixtures, with Ga being predicted to be preferentially absorbed from 0.2M nitric acid containing 0.05M oxalic acid, while In is eluted with a separation factor of about 20.   Because Ga approximately retains its position in the selectivity sequence relative to other elements, while In is much more strongly absorbed from HCl than from HNO_3 solutions relative to other elements, it is believed that the formation of mixed anionic complexes of In containing both chloride and oxalate ligands may be responsible for its behavior.

In 3M nitric acid containing 0.25M oxalic acid and 0.05% hydrogen peroxide, W(VI) and Mo(VI) apparently can be separated from all other elements including Sn(IV), In(III), U(VI), Cd and Zn; these are separations which are either difficult or impossible in the corresponding HCl-oxalic acid system.

Other separations that are indicated to be feasible by a study of Tables 2-5, include the following: Al-Be with 0.2M HCl-0.25M oxalic acid or 0.1M HNO_3-0.25M oxalic acid; U(IV)-V(V) with 2.0M HCl-0.25M oxalic acid-0.05% hydrogen peroxide; and Sn(IV) from In(III), Cd and Zn in 0.2M HNO_3-0.05M oxalic acid. None of these separations has actually been attempted; the quality of the separations will depend largely on the column kinetics encountered.

D. Comparative Cation Exchange Behavior of Group IIA Elements

1. Introduction

Separation factors for cation exchange chromatography of the alkaline earth elements in aqueous hydrochloric or other acids not forming complexes with these elements, are rather small [79-82]. Many complexing agents such as acetate [83-84], formate [85], citrate [86-87], lactate [88], malonate [80], α-hydroxy isobutyrate [89-90], EDTA [91], DCyTA [92-93], EGTA [94], 2,6-pyridinedicarboxylate [95], and acetylacetonate [96], have therefore been used in attempts to enhance separation of these elements. In almost all cases their mode of employment seems to have been developed empirically by testing a few eluting agent concentrations and settling for the best one. A comparative study of distribution coefficients from which the most favorable eluent concentrations can be estimated directly, and which makes an evaluation and comparison of the various eluting agents possible, has been published recently by the author and his coworkers [97]. Included are the following complexing agents and other eluting agents: acetate, formate, lactate, citrate, tartrate, α-hydroxy isobutyrate, malonate, malate, acetylacetonate, EDTA, DCyTA, EGTA, HCl, NH_4Cl, HNO_3, and $HClO_4$. The resin used was the AG50W-X8 cation exchanger.

2. Separation of Adjacent Element Pairs

In evaluating the merits of the various eluting agents, a distribution coefficient of 10 was arbitrarily assigned to the less strongly adsorbed

element of adjacent element pairs in the expression of separation factors.
The corresponding coefficient for the more strongly absorbed element was
obtained from plots of the experimentally determined coefficients against
eluent concentration, or against pH value (for EDTA, DCyTA and EGTA).
Table 6 presents a summary of these separation factors and the corresponding eluent concentrations or pH values.

It has already been stressed that satisfactory column kinetics are required,
in addition to a favourable separation factor, when a good chromatographic
separation is to be obtained. The quality of some separations of adjacent
alkaline earth elements, at near optimum working conditions, has been
demonstrated by experimental elution curves [97]. The most important
observations that have been compiled for this chemical group are summarized
here:

a. Mg-Be. The largest separation factor $\alpha \frac{Mg}{Be} \approx 90$ and the best
separations are obtained with 0.05M ammonium malate of pH 7.0 as eluting
agent. The excellence of the separation of millimole amounts of each element
on a 5-g (15 ml) resin column (16% resin loading) is demonstrated in Figure
3. The separation factor is somewhat smaller, $\alpha \frac{Mg}{Be} \approx 45$, but the beryllium
peak even narrower, with 0.10M malate. Citrate, malonate and tartrate also
provide reasonably large separation factors and very good separations with
negligible tailing [80, 97]. With ammonium acetylacetonate, separations
are less satisfactory because Mg appears in the eluate sooner than predicted
by the distribution coefficient. An attractive method which separates Be not
only from Mg but also from almost all other elements, except the alkali
metals and ammonium ion, employs 0.6M HCl in 90% isopropanol, effective
separation being effected by selective exchange of anionic species on AG1-X8
or Dowex 1-X8 resin [98]. The other elements, including Mg, are retained,
while Be and the alkalies are eluted. The separation factor for the Mg-Be
pair is 3.7. Unfortunately, information about column kinetics and elution
curves does not appear to be available. Other systems which should yield
high separation factors for the Mg-Be pair exploit differences in cation and
anion exchange behavior in sulfosalicylate or fluoride media. Though
separations of Be from other elements in these systems have been described
[99-101], no information about separation factors for the Mg-Be pair and
about their column behavior has been uncovered by the author.

TABLE 6

Separation Factors[a]

Eluting agent	Mg/Be		Ca/Mg		Sr/Ca		Ba/Sr	
	Conc., M	Factor	Conc., M	Factor	Conc., M	Factor	Conc., M	Factor
Acetylacetonate	0.08	⩾10	0.18	~320	~2.0[b]	~15[b]	–	–
Citrate	0.02	~50	0.06	1.3	0.07	4.3	0.15	2.9
α-hydroxy-isobutyrate	0.30	4.0	0.55	1.9	0.74	3.8	1.40	3.2
Lactate	0.33	3.1	0.53	2.0	0.72	3.0	1.17	2.8
Malate	0.035	~100	0.27	1.3	0.30	2.9	0.49	2.8
Malonate	0.04	~30	0.23	4.3	0.44	2.4	0.64	2.7
Formate	0.48	3.4	0.87	2.4	1.33	1.9	1.82	2.3
Acetate	0.67	1.9	0.92	2.2	1.34	2.0	1.92	2.5
Tartrate	0.075	28	0.21	0.40	0.21	3.7	0.38	2.7
NH$_4$Cl	1.85	0.6	1.32	2.4	2.32	1.4	3.00	2.0
HCl	1.25	1.4	1.50	2.1	2.55	1.4	3.00	1.9
HClO$_4$	1.32	1.6	1.75	2.1	3.10	1.3	4.20	1.9
HNO$_3$	1.33	1.5	1.85	1.1	2.03	1.1	2.10	1.2

TABLE 6 (Cont'd)

Eluting agent	Ca/Mg		Sr/Ca		Ba/Sr	
	pH	Factor	pH	Factor	pH	Factor
0.02M EDTA + B	4.77	1/7.4	4.77	34	6.21	5.5
0.02M EDTA	5.43	1/11	5.43	28	6.68	7.1
0.10M EDTA	4.48	1/12	4.48	27	5.65	6.8
0.02M DCTA	5.33	1/3.6	5.33	148	6.92	38
0.02M DCTA + B	4.65	1/2.8	4.65	34	6.72	9.1
0.02M EGTA	6.36	1/54	6.36	66	7.59	1.2
0.02M EGTA + B	5.40	1/8.2	5.40	15	6.85	4.3

[a] Reprinted from Ref. [97], p. 5, by courtesy of Pergamon Press Ltd.

[b] From elution curves.   B = buffer of 0.30M NH_4 acetate.

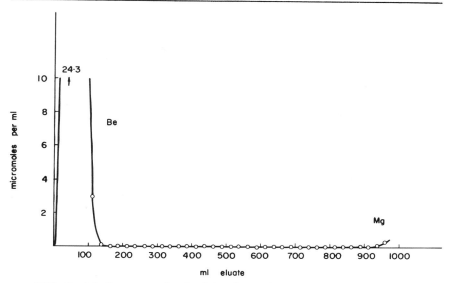

FIG. 3. Elution curve for Be/Mg, 1 mmole each, with 0.05M NH$_4$-malate of pH 7.0. Column of 5 g (15 ml) AG50W-X8, 200 to 400 mesh, resin. Column diameter 15 mm. Flow rate 2.0 ± 0.3 ml/min; reprinted from Ref. [97], p. 6, by courtesy of Pergamon Press.

b. Ca-Mg. The most effective separation for the Ca-Mg pair is obtained with 0.20M ammonium acetylacetonate of pH 9 at the very large separation factor $\alpha_{Mg}^{Ca} \approx 200$ [96, 97]. The eluting agents, 0.10M EGTA [94, 97] at pH 6.0 (Ca eluted first), 0.10M EDTA at pH 4.5 [91, 97] (Ca eluted first), containing 0.3M and 0.2M of sodium acetate, respectively, and acidified with acetic acid to the desired pH value, and 0.20 or 0.225M ammonium malonate at pH 7 [80], are also very effective. Malonate, though providing a smaller separation factor, is attractive because it is more easily destroyed than the other reagents. The most attractive eluting agent for this separation seems to be 3.0M HCl containing 60% ethanol, acetone, dioxane or tetrahydrofuran [81]. This method is discussed later.

c. Sr-Ca. The eluting agent, 0.10M DCyTA at pH 4.7 to 5.0, and containing 0.30M ammonium acetate [92-93, 97], provides the best separation for this pair, with 0.10M EDTA [91, 97], under the same conditions, nearly as effective. A typical elution curve is shown in Figure 4. Separations of the same quality can be obtained by increasing the concentration of the

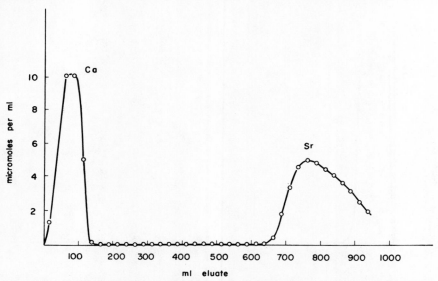

FIG. 4.   Elution curve for Ca/Sr with 0.10M EDTA of pH 5.0, containing
0.30M ammonium acetate.   Column of 60 ml (2.2 x 19 cm) AG50W-X8, 200
to 400 mesh resin.   Flow rate 3.0 ± 0.3 ml/min; reprinted from Ref. [97],
p. 8, by courtesy of Pergamon Press.

complexing agent and lowering the pH value, or vice versa, provided the
concentration of the species H_2EDTA^{2-} or H_2DCyTA^{2-}, responsible for the
complex formation, is kept the same.   An even more effective separation can
be obtained with 2.0M ammonium acetylacetonate of pH 9.0 [97], but the
removal of the reagent is quite troublesome.   A 0.10M EGTA solution at
pH 5.8, and containing 0.3M ammonium acetate, also provides an excellent
separation [94, 97].   With 0.067M ammonium citrate ranging in pH from
7 to 9, or 0.70M ammonium α-hydroxy isobutyrate, somewhat lower separation factors are obtained, but still quite good separations are provided [97].
The sharper elution peaks obtained with α-hydroxy isobutyrate under similar
conditions of column operation [97], seem to indicate superior column
kinetics.   Nevertheless, the use of citrate is quite attractive because good
separation can be obtained at low eluting agent concentrations.   This
facilitates its removal from the final product.   After acidification the eluate
can be passed directly onto a small cation exchange column in the H^+-form,
to absorb the Ca while the citrate passes through.   Ammonium lactate [88,
97] and malate [97] are less effective than α-hydroxy isobutyrate [89, 90,

97], but still quite satisfactory. Malonate is superior to acetate [83, 84] and formate [85], which, in turn, give higher separation factors than aqueous HCl, $HClO_4$, or HNO_3.

Tsubota [102] has recommended 1M ammonium formate containing 50% acetone and 1M ammonium acetate containing 50% methanol, as eluting agents for the improved separation of Ca from Sr. Even though the separation factor $\alpha \frac{Sr}{Ca} \sim 6$ is considerably larger than in aqueous formate or acetate, the elution curves do not show very much improvement [102], apparently because the larger separation factors are accompanied by less favorable column kinetics. The separations appear to be less effective than those with α-hydroxybutyrate or citrate.

d. Ba-Sr. A 1.20M solution of ammonium α-hydroxy isobutyrate at pH 7.0 [89, 90, 97] seems to be the best complexing eluting agent for the separation of large amounts of Sr from small amounts of Ba, while 0.02M DCyTA at pH 7.0, and containing 0.3M ammonium acetate [93, 97] provides definite advantages for the separation of small amounts of Sr from large amounts of Ba. With DCyTA the separation factor is largest for this pair. Unfortunately the factor decreases with increasing concentrations of DCyTA and with decreasing pH values. Reasonable separations can also be obtained with 1.0M ammonium lactate [88, 97], 0.43M ammonium malate [97], and 0.55M ammonium malonate [80, 97], all at pH 7.0, or with 0.10M EDTA at pH 6.0, and in the presence of 0.3M ammonium acetate [97]. Much more attractive for practical reasons is 3.0M HCl containing 20% ethanol [82], as is shown later (Section III C).

III. SEPARATIONS USING AQUEOUS-ORGANIC SOLVENT MIXTURES

A. General Considerations

One of the most fertile approaches to the enhancement of ion exchange selectivity has been provided by the addition of water mixable organic solvents to influence complex formation in the external phase (see Vol. 4, Chap. 1 of this series). The first deliberate attempts to take advantage of this approach for analytical application are probably due to Kember et al. [103], who tried to improve the separation of some transition metals by adding an

organic solvent to the hydrochloric acid eluting agent, and to Samuelson et al.,
who tried to improve the separation of alkali metals from transition metals,
by adding ethanol to obtain a better absorption of the EDTA complexes of the
transition metals on anion exchange resins [104]. While Kember et al.
were able, on this basis, to suggest a good method for the separation of copper
and nickel, they were unable to define conditions for separating these elements
from iron, manganese, and cobalt, simply because systematic information
about distribution coefficients in mixed media was not available at the time.
Carleson [105] investigated the cation exchange behavior of several elements
in mixtures of HCl and methyl-n-propyl ketone. Because of its limited
solubility in water this reagent can only be used in mixtures containing small
percentages of concentrated HCl. Furthermore, some elements, such as
ferric iron, tail strongly. Other "early" work includes that of Berg et al.
[106], who took advantage of selective exchange of anion species formed in
HCl-methanol for the separation of Zn, Cd and Hg(II). Y. Yoshino et al.
[107], mixed HCl with acetone and various alcohols to enhance the anion
exchange separation of Cu(II) and Zn. Kojima [108, 109] and Van Erkelens
[110] also investigated the anion exchange behavior of several transition
metals in mixtures of HCl with acetone and alcohols. Van Erkelens [110]
concluded that certain separations such as Co(II)-Mn(II), and Fe(III)-Cu(II)-
Zn(II) could not be effected by this approach. As was clearly shown by the
work of Fritz and Pietrzyk [111, 112], the favorable conditions for these
separations were not detected because of the lack of systematic information.

The first systematic study of cation exchange distribution coefficients in
partly organic solvent media, conducted with the aim of improving analytical
separation procedures, were apparently carried out by Fritz et al. [113] in
their investigation of the exchange behavior of 14 elements in HCl-acetone
mixtures. A more comprehensive survey has been published recently by
Korkisch et al. [114], who presented coefficients for 20 elements in HCl
combined with the solvents methanol, ethanol, n-propanol, isopropanol,
methyl glycol, acetone, tetrahydrofuran and acetic acid, respectively. The
first systematic study of anion exchange distribution coefficients for a large
number of elements in HCl mixed with different organic solvent is due to
Fritz and Pietrzyk [111, 112]. Further systematic work includes the study
of cation exchange in nitric [115], and in hydrobromic acid [116] contained
in various organic solvents, cation exchange in HCl-dimethylsulfoxide [117],

and in ammonium thiocyanate-acetone [118], anion exchange in sulfuric acid mixed with various organic solvents [119], and anion exchange in HCl combined with various organic solvents [120].

Numerous less comprehensive studies, often including only a few elements, are available for systems that involve cation exchange in a nitric acid-tetrahydrofuran mixture containing dithizone [121], cation and anion exchange in HCl and HNO_3 containing methanol or acetone and an organic complexing agent such as EDTA or citric acid [122], anion exchange in nitric acid-tetrahydrofuran mixtures [123], anion exchange in hydrobromic acid mixtures with methanol and other solvents [124], anion exchange in hydrochloric acid-methanol-dimethyl sulfoxide media [125], which, interestingly, dissolve macro-amounts of lead and silver, anion exchange in nitric acid-alcohol mixtures [126], cation exchange in nitric acid-methanol-trioctylphosphine oxide media [127, 128], cation exchange in hydrochloric acid-methanol-pyridine-thenoyl trifluoroacetone media [129], and cation exchange in hydrofluoric acid mixed with eight organic solvents [130].

In cation exchange attention has been focused mainly on elements which exhibit reasonably large differences in their tendencies to chloride complex formation, because of the promise of most spectacular increases in selectivities. Fritz et al. [113], and also Korkisch et al. [114] limited the upper values of the hydrochloric acid concentrations in their investigations to 1.0 and 1.2M, respectively, probably because chloride complex formation can be promoted as well by increasing the organic solvent as by increasing the hydrochloric acid concentration. In addition, the first method often has the advantage of yielding better column kinetics. But it has been shown by Strelow et al. [81, 82, 131] that some very interesting separation possibilities for elements with negligible tendencies to chloride complex formation can be found at high acid concentrations.

B. Theoretical Aspects

Some insight with respect to the factors governing ion exchange selectivity, as expressed by distribution coefficients in aqueous-organic solvent media, has been sought by assuming, as a first approximation, that (1) the approach of Eisenman [132, 133] applies to ion exchange in such media; and (2) the total change in free energy of a system in which ion 1 is absorbed from solution and exchanged for ion 2 at the fixed exchange group, being given by

$$\Delta G^o{}_2^1 = \left[\frac{e_A e_2}{r_A + r_2} - \frac{e_A e_1}{r_A + r_1} \right] - \left(\Delta G_2 - \Delta G_1 \right) \rightarrow, \qquad (6)$$

where e_A, e_1, and e_2 are the electrical charges of the fixed exchange group, and the ions 1 and 2, respectively: r_A, r_1, and r_2 are the respective radii; and G_1 and G_2 are the differences in the free energy of solvation of the exchanged ions between the state in solution and the adsorbed state. That this model can be only qualitatively applicable, at best, may be seen from the very detailed analysis of ion exchange in nonaqueous and mixed media presented by Marcus. The complexity of these systems is much too formidable to permit accurate analysis of the terms in Equation (6). Such treatment can provide, at best, only reasonable rationalizations of the observed results.

The first term in Equation (6) is a static energy term. For the sulfonic acid group, the value of r_A is relatively large, and for monovalent elements, the static energy term will be relatively small by comparison with the solvation energy term. Furthermore, for a specific mono- or multivalent cation species, the values of r_A, r_1, and r_2 will vary only very slightly over a wide range of organic solvent concentrations in the external solution, e. g., in the case of bulkier, nonpolar organic materials such as acetone, because a predominantly aqueous solution will be present within the resin particle up to fairly high organic solvent concentrations outside. In these instances, the static energy term will therefore remain not only small, but approximately constant. Thus one can write

$$\Delta G^o{}_2^1 \approx \text{const} - (\Delta G_2 - \Delta G_1) \rightarrow, \qquad (7)$$

since

$$\Delta G^o{}_2^1 = -RT \ln K_2^1 \rightarrow, \qquad (8)$$

we have

$$\ln K_2^1 \approx \frac{1}{RT} [\Delta G_2 - \Delta G_1 - \text{const}] \rightarrow. \qquad (9)$$

For the sake of simplicity, competitive solvation by the organic component is neglected, and K_2^1 in this case is the thermodynamic equilibrium constant with respect only to the fully hydrated cation species of elements 1 and 2. In the case of fully hydrated species of cations of elements with similar outer electron shells, the value of the thermodynamic equilibrium constant is therefore mainly dependent on the differences of free energy of hydration between the adsorbed and nonadsorbed state for the two cations. It should be pointed out here that "free energy of hydration" is used in the classical sense, but includes the free energy changes originating from changes in the longer range interaction of the cations with the structure of their surroundings, as pointed out by Diamond [134].

Since the water inside the exchanger is believed to be already much less structured, this effect is essentially buffered in the resin phase; thus changes in $[\Delta G_2 - \Delta G_1]$ are expected to be predominantly a consequence of what is happening in the external phase. Considering then only the external solution, the presence of increasing amounts of an organic solvent, such as acetone, in water will tend to loosen the fixed hydration shell. Furthermore the structure differences between the region of "structure breaking" [135] and "structurally normal" solution will be lowered. In a series of cations of similar electronic structure, the region of "structure breaking" is believed to be larger for the larger cation [135]. At low concentrations the organic solvent therefore will decrease the free energy of hydration in the solution phase more strongly for the larger cation than for the smaller one and thus increase the numerical value of the difference $\Delta G_2 - \Delta G_1$. Increased values of $\ln K_2^1$ and increased separation factors therefore could be expected for such a case.

Generally, it is found that cation exchange distribution coefficients in HCl measured against the hydrated hydrogen cation, increase with increasing organic solvent concentration for all those elements which have negligible tendencies to chloride complex formation. This is shown by the distribution coefficient curves for the alkaline earths in 3M HCl containing various amounts of ethanol, in Figure 5. Table 7 lists the separation factors calculated from the curves. The separation factors of neighboring pairs of elements increase with increasing ethanol concentrations, the Ca/Mg and Ba/Sr pairs showing quite remarkable increases. More favorable conditions for separating such elements therefore can be expected to be found in partly

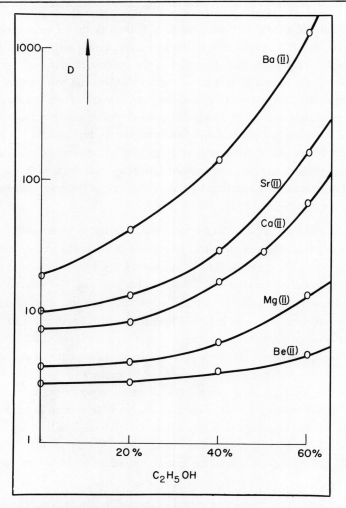

FIG. 5. Distribution coefficients of alkaline earth elements in 3M HCl
containing various amounts of ethanol with AG50W-X8 cation exchange resin.
2. 5 g resin in 250 ml solution containing 5 mEq cation.

nonaqueous solutions of mineral acids than in purely aqueous solutions.
Very useful separations have been developed for these elements [81, 82] on
this basis (Figure 6).

For an element with some tendency to chloride complex formation, the
curves obtained by plotting the distribution coefficients against organic

TABLE 7

Separation Factors for Adjacent Alkaline Earth Element Pairs in
3.0M HCl and Various Amount of Ethanol

Element pair	Percentage Ethanol			
	0	20	40	60
Mg–Be	1.36	1.38	1.69	2.51
Ca–Mg	1.92	2.10	3.67	5.61
Sr–Ca	1.37	1.56	1.73	2.35
Ba–Sr	1.85	3.52	4.88	8.27

solvent concentrations show a shape quite different from those in Figure 5.
When the fixed hydration shell has been loosened sufficiently, the water
dipoles in the coordination sphere will be replaced by chloride anions, and
anionic chloride complexes which are not absorbed will eventually form.
The distribution coefficient curve for an element which is predominantly
present as aquo-ion in aqueous hydrochloric acid may therefore show an
initial increase, due to the "hydration effect," followed by a sharp decline,
often considerably below the values in pure aqueous solutions. The curves
for Cu(II) and Co(II) in Figure 7 demonstrate this. The curve for Ni(II) is
typical for an element with only a very slight amount of chloride complex
formation, probably as $NiCl^+$, at the highest acetone concentration, while
Zn and Cd already show chloride complex formation in aqueous 0.2M HCl,
as is indicated by their anion exchange behavior in aqueous solution [136].

Furthermore, the extent of chloride complex formation, and therefore
the numerical value of the distribution coefficient of a particular element,
does not depend on the concentration of chloride (or its activity) and the
concentration of the solvent alone, but also on the structure breaking
properties of the solvent. Acetone, with its lower dielectric constant,
promotes chloride complex formation at comparatively lower solvent and
chloride concentrations than ethanol.

Another interesting aspect of ion exchange chromatography in partly
organic media is that, for some organic solvents, it sometimes contains

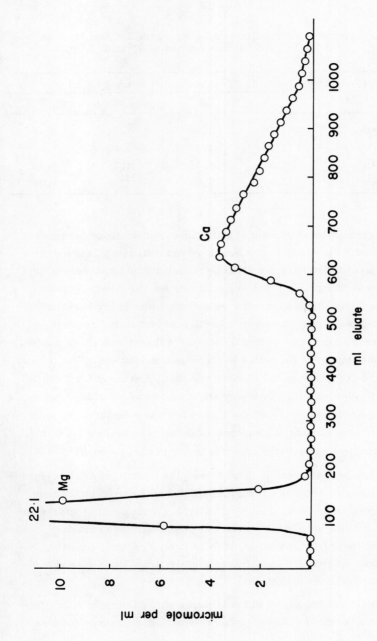

FIG. 6. Elution curve for Ca/Mg with 3.0M HCl in 60% ethanol. Column of 30 ml (2.0 x 10 cm) AG50W-X8, 200 to 400 mesh resin. Flow rate 1.8 ± 0.3 ml/min; reprinted from Ref. [81], p. 532, by courtesy of Elsevier Publishing Company.

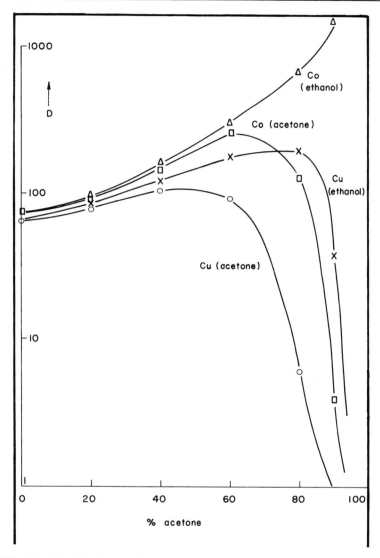

FIG. 7. Distribution coefficients of Cu(II) and Co(II) in 0.5M HCl with various amounts of ethanol and acetone. 2.5 g AG50W-X8 cation exchange resin in 250 ml solution containing 5 mEq cation.

features resembling those encountered in partition chromatography or
solvent extraction. Davis and Owen [137] recognized this when they
determined the distribution of acetone between a cation exchanger and an
external solution, and compared the exchange process with partition
chromatography. Unequal distribution of water-organic solvent mixtures
between resin particles and the external phase has also been described by
Gregor et al. [138], but the analytical implications of this were not stressed.
Korkisch [139, 140] has suggested that in some such cases, a "liquid ion
exchanger" is formed in the aqueous phase which may compete with the solid
ion exchanger, and has called this the "CIESE" effect. For example, uranium
is not absorbed as the nitrate complex by an anion exchange resin from nitric
acid solutions containing tetrahydrofuran. The THF acts as Lewis base and
forms a "liquid ion exchanger,"

$$THF + HNO_3 \rightleftharpoons [THF \rightarrow H]^+ \; NO_3^- \longrightarrow , \tag{10}$$

which further reacts

$$2[THFH] \; NO_3 + [UO_2(NO_3)_4]^{2-} \rightleftharpoons [THFH]_2[UO_2(NO_3)_4] + 2NO_3^- \rightarrow , \tag{11}$$

The "liquid ion exchanger" thus competes with the resin for the uranium.
Even when such a reaction is not encountered, a situation analogous to
solvent extraction can persist. The sulfonic acid and, to a somewhat lesser
extent, the quaternary amine group retain water very tenaciously, so strongly
in fact that a dry Dowex 50-X8 resin removes water from a silica gel drying
agent until it has taken up 1 molecule of water per exchange group. An additional 3 molecules of water per exchange group are also held fairly strongly
[137]. Water thus tends to concentrate within the resin particles when only
limited amounts are available, and nuclear magnetic resonance studies have
indicated [141] that in a solution containing 90% acetone and 10% water, the
concentration of water in the resin may be between 70 and 80%. This is in
fairly good agreement with the results obtained by Davis et al. [137] by
chemical methods for a different resin. Therefore, two different phases
which have a fairly large difference in polarity exist, a situation resembling
solvent extraction, except that the polarity differences are somewhat

smaller. Because of this, a true phase boundary which could impair the free passage of ions is probably not encountered. Even more important from a kinetic point of view, is the fact that within the resin particles we have a predominantly aqueous phase. Diffusion rates within resin and especially cation exchange resin particles are therefore as fast or almost as fast as in the corresponding aqueous solutions. Exchange rates for cation exchangers in partly organic solvents are therefore sometimes very favorable, and flow rates of 2 ml/cm^2 still give sharp elution peaks for many elements, provided separations can be carried out at reasonably low acid concentrations. At higher acid concentration, resin particles contract, and exchange rates are slowed down similarly to their behavior in purely aqueous solutions, but to a slightly greater degree. Strongly basic anion exchangers have a somewhat lower affinity for water, and their kinetics at higher solvent concentrations are not always as satisfactory.

C. Cation Exchange Separations in HCl-Ethanol

Tables 8-13 list cation exchange distribution coefficients for 45 elements in HCl-ethanol mixtures ranging from 0.1 to 3.0M HCl, and from 0 to 95% ethanol, where 1M HCl in 80% ethanol is defined as 25 ml of 10M HCl mixed with 25 ml of H_2O and 200 ml absolute ethanol, ignoring volume changes on mixing [142]. The coefficients were determined by equilibrating 2.5 g of dry resin with 250 ml of solution containing 5 mEq of the cation. A summary of the analytical applications of such systems follows:

1. Alkali Metals

Coefficients increase with increasing ethanol concentration. Those of sodium increase faster than those of lithium and good separations can be obtained by eluting lithium with 1.0M HCl in 70% ethanol [143], while sodium is retained, and can be eluted with 1.0M aqueous HCl. The separation factor is 3.4 as compared with 1.7 in aqueous HCl, and the separation is improved considerably. Nevoral [144] has used 0.6M HCl in 60% ethanol, which provides a separation factor of 2.8, and also quite satisfactory separations; Šulcek et al. [145] used 0.5M HCl in 80% methanol, and Ratner et al. [146]

TABLE 8

Cation Exchange Distribution Coefficients in 0.10M HCl[a]

Element	Percentage Ethanol						
	0	20	40	60	80	90	95
Ga(III)	$\sim 10^4$	$> 10^4$	$> 10^4$	$> 10^4$	$> 10^4$	6730	153
Sn(IV)	$\sim 10^4$	ppt.	ppt.	ppt.	43.1	3.5	1.1
Fe(III)	9000	$> 10^4$	$> 10^4$	$> 10^4$	$> 10^4$	3340	176
U(VI)	758	1300	3200	$> 10^4$	$> 10^4$	4960	3330
Mn(II)	1360	1580	3020	$> 10^4$	$> 10^4$	$> 10^4$	$> 10^4$
Co(II)	1270	1450	2840	6500	$> 10^4$	$> 10^4$	$> 10^4$
Ni(II)	1230	1470	2950	10^4	$> 10^4$	$> 10^4$	$> 10^4$
Fe(II)	1220	1410	2830	6400	$> 10^4$	9800	1010
Zn(II)	1030	1200	2150	2250	876	47.5	5.7
Cu(II)	1010	1200	2190	4410	4280	1250	430
Mg(II)	860	990	$> 10^3$	$> 10^3$	$> 10^3$	$> 10^4$	$> 10^4$
In(III)	806	210	193	153	83	29.2	6.3
Cd(II)	410	367	332	317	123	81	20.8
Mo(VI)	10.9	35.0	43.0	39.8	36.1	38.8	40.9
Rh(III)	4.2	3.1	2.2	1.5	0.9	0.6	< 0.5
Tl(III)	2.1	2.4	2.7	1.9	2.2	2.6	2.4
Hg(II)	1.6	1.1	0.8	0.6	< 0.5	< 0.5	< 0.5
Pd(II)	1.6	0.8	1.0	0.8	0.9	0.7	0.5
Pt(IV)	1.4	1.5	1.6	2.1	2.7	3.1	3.4
As(V)	1.4	~ 2	~ 5	~ 3	< 1	< 1	< 1
Ir(IV)	1.4	1.5	1.4	1.3	1.0	1.1	0.9
W(VI)[b]	1.1	1.3	1.7	1.8	8.1	3.0	-
Se(IV)	1.1	1.3	1.0	1.5	1.7	1.0	0.8
Au(III)	0.8	1.1	0.9	1.2	1.3	0.8	1.0
Ge(III)	0.5	0.6	0.4	0.5	1.7	1.8	1.7
Mo(VI)[b]	< 0.5	< 0.5	< 0.5	< 0.5	< 0.5	< 0.5	< 0.5

[a] Reprinted from Ref. [142], p. 82, by courtesy of Elsevier Publishing Company.

[b] H_2O_2 present.

TABLE 9

Cation Exchange Distribution Coefficients in 0.20M HCl[a]

Element	Percentage Ethanol						
	0	20	40	60	80	90	95
Fe(III)	3400	3600	5100	6000	1410	31.7	15.7
Ga(III)	3040	8680	$>10^4$	$>10^4$	3860	446	6.9
Mn(II)	510	690	1240	2280	5280	5410	4260
Co(II)	460	625	1120	2160	5010	$>10^4$	9330
Ni(II)	450	610	1110	2140	4960	8380	6320
Fe(II)	430	580	1020	2010	4370	1460	249
Cu(II)	380	424	706	1060	1040	308	69
Zn(II)	361	368	489	299	48.3	5.2	1.7
Mg(II)	350	361	369	1510	1990	6400	5100
U(VI)	252	284	469	847	1270	1430	1133
In(III)	110	53	48.8	38.1	17.9	6.0	2.9
Cd(II)	84	118	88	34.8	13.7	2.7	0.6
Sn(IV)	45	3400	1610	18.1	3.6	0.7	0.5
V(V)	7.0	19.7	39.1	84.0	202	ppt.	ppt.
V(V)[b]	6.5	6.6	9.0	57	488	529	336
Mo(VI)	4.5	17.7	25.9	25.7	23.1	12.6	7.4
Mo(VI)[b]	<0.5	<0.5	<0.5	<0.5	<0.5	<0.5	<0.5

[a] Reprinted from Ref. [142], p. 83, by courtesy of Elsevier Publishing Company.

[b] H_2O_2 present.

TABLE 10

Cation Exchange Distribution Coefficients in 0.50M HCl[a]

Element	Percentage Ethanol					
	0	20	40	60	80	90
Ga(III)	260	633	1470	4650	428	3.5
Fe(III)	225	226	304	361	153	6.6
Mn(II)	84	90	162	285	608	730
Mg(II)	74	78	126	234	601	1140
Cr(III)	73	93	118	170	279	421
Co(II)	72	93	159	305	671	1830
Ni(II)	70	96	165	315	689	880
Fe(II)	66	69	131	252	408	136
Cu(II)	65	88	119	176	195	35.9
U(VI)	58	67	111	182	264	220
Zn(II)	64	64	48.3	17.8	4.1	1.5
Cs(I)	44.2	63	108	229	852	–
V(IV)	44.1	53	84	157	286	508
Be(II)	42.3	47.3	69	114	170	–
Ti(IV)	39.1	121	265	634	1700	ppt.
Rb(I)	33.2	42.8	73	165	571	–
K(I)	29.1	47.3	89	201	838	–
Na(I)	13.5	19.1	34.1	79	254	–
Li(I)	8.1	10.8	17.1	28.8	50	–
In(III)	7.6	7.8	8.5	7.2	4.2	2.4
Cd(II)	6.5	6.0	4.6	1.4	<0.5	<0.5
Sn(IV)	6.2	5.9	3.6	2.2	1.3	0.6
V(V)	5.0	19.5	42.6	86	143	142
V(V)[b]	2.1	4.7	23.9	59	129	140
Mo(VI)	<0.5	7.6	11.0	12.8	11.0	7.3
Mo(VI)[b]	<0.5	<0.5	<0.5	<0.5	<0.5	<0.5
Bi(III)	<0.5	<0.5	<0.5	<0.5	<0.5	<0.5

[a] Reprinted from Ref. [142], p. 83, by courtesy of Elsevier Publishing Co.

[b] H_2O_2 present.

TABLE 11

Cation Exchange Distribution Coefficients in 1.00M HCl[a]

Element	Percentage Ethanol				
	0	20	40	60	80
Gd(III)	183	259	498	1460	$\sim 10^4$
Yb(III)	153	178	331	841	4340
Ba(II)	128	193	615	1920	5140
Sc(III)	120	345	925	3680	$> 10^4$
Al(III)	61	74	124	251	502
Sr(II)	60	76	162	543	3490
Ga(III)	42.6	102	204	347	5.8
Ca(II)	41.3	55	106	310	1570
Fe(II)	33.5	31.9	39.4	47.3	6.9
Cr(III)	26.7	35.9	53	83	114
Ni(II)	21.9	19.7	41.8	82	182
Co(II)	21.3	27.6	38.2	78	175
Mn(II)	20.2	28.2	42.4	78	157
Mg(II)	20.1	19.3	33.0	71	166
Fe(II)	19.8	25.8	46.9	81	184
U(VI)	19.2	22.1	34.2	58	70
Cs(I)	19.1	27.0	44.1	96	358
Cu(II)	17.5	17.8	21.9	23.2	24.7
Zn(II)	16.0	9.7	5.3	3.5	2.4
Rb(I)	15.4	21.4	36.8	81	326
K(I)	13.9	20.0	39.3	94	609
Be(II)	13.3	13.5	19.0	31.6	50.5
Ti(IV)	11.9	18.2	57	181	496
V(IV)	7.2	15.4	22.6	38.8	76
Na(I)	6.9	9.7	16.6	36.5	138
Li(I)	3.8	5.1	7.8	13.1	28.8
In(III)	1.8	1.81	1.9	1.3	0.7
Sn(IV)	1.6	1.4	0.8	< 0.5	< 0.5
Cd(II)	1.6	0.5	0.2	< 0.2	< 0.2

TABLE 11 (Continued)

Element	Percentage Ethanol				
	0	20	40	60	80
V(V)	1.1	4.7	10.3	23.1	43.0
Mo(VI)	0.8	4.2	6.9	7.3	5.8
Bi(III)	0.8	0.6	<0.5	<0.5	<0.5
Hg(II)	<0.5	<0.5	<0.5	<0.5	<0.5
Ge(IV)	<0.5	<0.5	<0.5	<0.5	<0.5

a Reprinted from Ref. [142], p. 84, by courtesy of Elsevier Publishing Company.

TABLE 12
Distribution Coefficients in 2.0M HCl[a]

Element	Percentage Ethanol					
	0	20	40	60	70	80
Zr(IV)	489	925	2720	6400	$> 10^4$	$> 10^4$
Th(IV)	239	298	672	3170	$> 10^4$	$> 10^4$
La(III)	48.1	68	143	474	1200	$> 10^4$
Gd(III)	36.2	49.8	116	313	610	1280
Ba(II)	36.0	74	197	951	3260	-
Y(III)	29.7	32.4	72	196	490	1800
Sc(III)	28.8	57	140	470	1140	-
Yb(III)	27.4	36.2	59	151	298	-
Sr(II)	17.8	22.3	49.3	192	542	-
Al(III)	12.5	12.7	16.9	44.8	69	118
Ca(II)	12.2	16.3	31.7	90	202	-
Cs(I)	10.4	10.4	17.1	32.6	60	-
Rb(I)	8.1	10.0	16.4	39.6	77	-
Cr(III)	7.9	7.5	12.3	27.2	33.3	-
Ga(III)	7.8	13.5	20.9	6.3	1.5	< 0.5
K(I)	7.4	10.0	21.0	54	118	-
Ni(II)	7.2	7.4	11.7	23.1	31.5	47.3
U(VI)	7.0	7.2	10.4	15.6	16.1	15.4
Co(II)	6.7	8.9	15.4	30.4	44.7	-
Mg(II)	6.2	7.2	12.1	23.8	36.2	55
Mn(II)	6.0	7.7	10.6	18.4	26.2	-
Be(II)	5.2	5.6	7.0	10.8	14.9	-
Fe(III)	5.2	5.0	6.2	5.0	3.1	0.6
V(IV)	5.0	5.8	7.6	13.3	16.4	17.8
Cu(II)	4.2	4.2	4.8	5.1	2.8	0.9
Fe(II)	4.1	4.3	6.9	8.5	6.3	1.8
Na(I)	3.8	5.5	8.9	24.5	57	-
Ti(IV)	3.7	3.8	9.8	41.9	88	123
V(V)	< 0.5	2.9	5.2	10.3	13.4	-

TABLE 12 (Continued)

Element	Percentage Ethanol					
	0	20	40	60	70	80
In(III), Sn(IV), Bi(III), Hg(II), Ge(IV), Mo(VI)[b]	< 0.5	< 0.5	< 0.5	< 0.5	< 0.5	< 0.5

[a] Reprinted from Ref. [142], p. 85, by courtesy of Elsevier Publishing Company.

[b] H_2O_2 present.

TABLE 13

Distribution Coefficients in 3.0M HCl[a]

Element	Percentage Ethanol				
	0	20	40	60	70
Th(IV)	114	142	363	2360	–
Zr(IV)	61	152	343	2800	ppt.
La(III)	18.8	32.6	72	239	948
Ba(II)	18.5	42.6	143	1340	–
Gd(III)	15.3	22.8	51	178	495
Sc(III)	14.9	30.9	76	281	–
Y(III)	13.6	17.7	32.6	128	288
Yb(III)	12.2	15.2	25.2	76	–
Sr(II)	10.0	13.1	29.8	162	–
Ca(II)	7.3	8.4	17.2	69	–
Cs(I)	5.9	5.7	9.3	19.9	–
Rb(I)	5.3	6.5	10.6	28.7	–
K(I)	4.9	7.1	14.3	40.4	–
Cr(III)	4.8	3.9	4.9	11.4	–
Al(III)	4.7	4.3	7.3	13.2	–
Mg(II)	4.3	3.7	5.9	12.3	–
Co(II)	4.2	3.8	6.2	11.8	–
Mn(II)	3.9	3.5	5.5	8.6	–
Fe(III)	3.6	1.8	2.4	2.2	–
V(IV)	3.5	4.3	5.6	7.4	–
U(VI)	3.5	3.5	5.5	6.3	–
Fe(II)	2.9	3.0	4.1	4.3	–
Na(I)	2.7	3.8	6.8	20.5	–
Ti(IV)	2.4	3.1	5.3	22.1 (6.8)[b]	–
Ni(II)	2.0	2.1	4.5	6.7	–

[a] Reprinted from Ref. [142], p. 86, by courtesy of Elsevier Publishing Company.

[b] H_2O_2 present.

1.1M HCl in 90% methanol. In the last case, exchange rates are slow, and slow flow rates need to be used, while in the first case a large separation factor of 5.1 is obtained, but the large distribution coefficient of Li($D_{Li} \approx 50$) will require large elution volumes. Probably the best separation of this pair is obtained with BIO-REX-40, a phenol formaldehyde resin containing $-CH_2SO_3H$ cation exchange groups. Lithium can be eluted with 1.0M HCl containing 80% ethanol while sodium is retained. The separation factor is about 5.0 and $D_{Li} \approx 12$ [66]. With 2.4M HCl containing 80% methanol or ethanol, the separation achieved, though quite satisfactory for tracer amounts [147], is somewhat less satisfactory for larger amounts, because the sodium appears quite early in the eluate.

Separations of the K/Na pair with polystyrene cation resins in partly organic solvent media are not more favorable than those in aqueous solutions of HCl or HNO_3. Relatively small increases of separation factors are accompanied by slower exchange rates which cause peak broadening. Separation factors of the Rb/K and the Cs/Rb pairs become smaller with increasing concentration of organic solvent, and selectivity reversals occur [142, 147]. Good separations of the K/Na pair are obtained with BIO-REX-40 or an equivalent phenol formaldehyde resin, by using 1.0M HCl in 65% ethanol or in 60% acetone as eluting agent [148]. The separation factor with BIO-REX-40 is about 2.8. Separations by anion exchange in dioxane mixtures with HCl or HNO_3 [149] seem to be less effective than the cation exchange separations in ethanol or acetone mixtures named above. By cation exchange in methanol-phenol-HCl mixtures, lithium can be separated from sodium [150], but the separation is less satisfactory than in HCl mixtures with ethanol or methanol. Sodium and potassium cannot be separated effectively [150], but the heavy alkalies can, with a reversed selectivity Cs < Rb < K [151]. Separation in aqueous solution with BIO-REX-40 resin is preferable [66].

2. Alkaline Earth Metals

An excellent separation of Ca from Mg, Be, Al, Fe(III), Ti(IV), Mn(II), Co(II), Ni(II), Cu(II), Zn(II), Cd(II), Hg(II), Ga(III), In(III), Tl(III), Au(III), the platinum metals, and some other elements, is possible by eluting the elements with 3.0M HCl containing 60% ethanol or acetone from a column of AG50W-X8 cation exchange resin, while calcium is retained [81]. Only Sr, Ba, Zr, Hf, Th, the rare earth metals, and the heavier alkalies (partially)

stay with the calcium. The separation is considerably better than those
obtained with anion exchange in nitric acid-methanol [152, 153], or cation
exchange in 6.4M $HClO_4$ - 2.6M HCl [154]. A typical elution curve is shown
in Figure 6.

Barium can be separated by elution with 3.0M HCl containing 20%
ethanol or acetone [82], from Sr, Ca, Al, and all other elements of the
periodic table except Th, Zr, Hf, Sc, the rare earth elements, and those
elements which form precipitates under the experimental conditions. The
separation factors for the most critical element pairs are comparable to
those obtained with organic complexing agents, but the removal of the excess
eluting agent is much simpler. The kinetics are very similar to those in
aqueous 3M HCl. Even larger separation factors can be obtained in higher
ethanol concentrations (Table 7), but the coefficients for strontium become
inconveniently large, and the exchange kinetics progressively less satisfactory.

The separation factors for the Mg/Be and Sr/Ca pairs increase much less
strongly with increasing ethanol concentration. Separation of beryllium from
magnesium, though not very satisfactory, is still somewhat better than in
aqueous solution. The separation factor of 2.3 in 2.0M HCl containing 70%
ethanol is raised from about 1.5 in aqueous 1.0M HCl. For the Sr/Ca pair,
the slight advantage gained by an increased separation factor is lost by the
slower exchange rates. For the separation of this pair, DCyTA and EDTA
seem to be the most attractive eluting agents [91-94, 97]. They are
definitely superior to anion exchange in nitric acid-methanol [153, 155], and
in nitric acid-dioxane [149]. Together with calcium, strontium can easily
be separated from most other elements in 3.0M HCl containing 60% ethanol
[81].

3. Al, Ga, In(III), Tl(III)

Tendencies toward chloride complex formation increase, in this group,
with increasing atomic weights. Excellent separations with separation
factors larger than 100 can be obtained by using the following elution
sequence: 0.10M HBr for Tl(III); 0.20M HCl in 90% ethanol for In(III);
0.75M HCl in 90% ethanol for Ga, and 3.0M HCl for Al. Furthermore, Al
can be separated from Fe(III), U(VI), Be, Cu(II), Ga, In(III), Pb(II), Sn(IV),
and Bi(III) by eluting these elements with 2.0M HCl containing 70% ethanol.

The coefficients for U(VI) and Be(II) are somewhat high and U(VI) tends to tail. Indium (III), together with Cd, Zn, and Sn(IV), can be separated by elution with 0.2M HCl in 90% ethanol from Cu(II), Co(II), Mn(II), Ni(II), Fe(III), V(IV), and other elements which are retained.

4. V(V), Mo(VI), W(VI)

The elements Mo(VI) and W(VI) can be eluted easily with 0.1M HCl containing hydrogen peroxide and ethanol between 0 and 95%, and thus are separated from most other elements, including Fe(III), Al, Ti(IV), Mg, Ca, Na, and K, though the best separation and the most selective one is obtained in the absence of the organic solvent. In the absence of hydrogen peroxide W(VI) precipitates, the elution behavior of Mo(VI) does not correspond to that predicted from batch distribution coefficient measurements. This apparently is due to the presence of several ionic species with slow complex conversion rates. In the absence or presence of peroxide [142], the elution behavior of Vanadium (V) is in complete disagreement with distribution coefficient predictions. Some vanadium appears in the eluate, not far behind the elution front, even with a coefficient of >100 [0.2M HCl in 80 percent ethanol], while the bulk remains absorbed at the top of the column, and appears in the eluate gradually. This result is apparently due to the simultaneous presence of several cationic species, such as VO^{3+}, VO_2^+, their peroxide complexes, and their polymerization products, together with a small amount of a neutral species, which is eluted and slowly reforms on the column. Only neutral or anionic species are present above pH 2, and vanadium (V) can be eluted very effectively with 0.01M or more dilute aqueous HCl or HNO_3 containing hydrogen peroxide [157], and is thus separated from most other elements, with the exception only of Mo(VI), W(VI), Tl(III) [in HCl], Hg(II), Au(III), the platinum metals, and oxyanion forming elements such as As(III), Sb(III), Se(IV) and Ge(IV). Separation of vanadium (V) from large amounts of titanium is better carried out in aqueous 0.25M sulfuric acid containing peroxide [156], because titanium is more stable to hydrolysis in this reagent.

5. Cr(III)

Chromium (III) can be separated from Th, Zr, Hf, Ca, Sr, Ba, Sc, Y, and the rare earth elements by elution with 3.0M HCl in 60% ethanol, while these elements are retained. Separation from other elements cannot be obtained because the distribution coefficient of Cr(III) is a composite of different coefficients, due to various ionic species existing in solution simultaneously. Bands due to the species $[CrCl_3(H_2O)_3]^0$ green, $[CrCl_2(H_2O)_4]^+$ green, $[CrCl(H_2O)_5]^{2+}$ dirty blue-gray, and $[Cr(H_2O)_6]^{3+}$ red-violet, can be observed during column work. The uncharged species passes through the column without adsorption, but its presence can be avoided by boiling the solution in very dilute HCl. If this is done, separation from W(VI), Mo(VI), V(V), As(V), Sb(III), and Se(IV) should then become possible by eluting these elements with 0.01M HCl containing peroxide, while the chromium (III) species are retained. Coefficients for the other three chromium species were estimated from column runs to be about 50, 400, and > 2000, respectively, in 1.0M HCl containing 80% ethanol; and 5, 60, and 400, respectively, in 2.0M HCl containing 60% ethanol. Separation of these various hydrated chromium complexes from each other is even better in ethanolic solutions than in aqueous solutions.

6. Au(III), Pt(IV), Pd(II), Rh(III) and Ir(IV)

These elements are only weakly, or not at all absorbed from all investigated concentrations and combinations of HCl and ethanol. They can be eluted with aqueous 0.1M HCl, and thus separated from most other elements of the periodic table. For Rh(III) and Pd(II) this separation is not quantitative, and residual traces are retained tenaciously by the column. Quantitative separations and much reduced tailing can be obtained with 0.1M HCl in 90 or 95% ethanol. Rhodium (III) shows one elution peak with this eluting agent, but shows two peaks on elution with 0.1M HCl in 40% ethanol. The first peak is large and appears with the elution front; the second is considerably smaller and corresponds to a distribution coefficient of 10. The two peaks are believed to be due to the presence of two different complexes, probably $[RhCl_3(H_2O)_3]^0$ not absorbed, and $[RCl_2(H_2O)_4]^+$ weakly absorbed, which have slow complex conversion rates.

7. Zn, Cd, Hg(II) and Sn(IV)

The four elements can be separated by the elution sequence: 0.1M HCl in 80% ethanol or 0.2M HCl in 40% ethanol for Hg(II); 0.1M HCl in 90% ethanol for Sn(IV); 0.5M HCl in 20% ethanol for Cd, and 0.50M HCl in 80%

ethanol for Zn. Elements such as Cu(II), Co(II), Mn(II), Ni(II), Fe(III),
U(VI), Ga(III), the alkaline earth metals, the rare earths, Ti(IV), Be, Al,
Zr, Hf, and Th are still retained by the column, and thus can be separated
from Zn. Indium accompanies Cd in the above scheme. An excellent separation of In from Cd seems to be possible by eluting Cd with 0.1M HBr in 90%
ethanol [116], In being retained.

8. Ge(IV), Se(IV), Te(IV), As(III), Sb(III), Nb(V), Ta(V)

These elements tend to form either anionic oxyacids or chloride
complexes at all hydrochloric acid concentrations. They can be separated
from all other elements by elution with 0.1M aqueous HCl. The Nb(V)
requires the presence of peroxide to prevent hydrolysis, and a higher acid
concentration, preferably 0.25M sulfuric acid for reasonably fast quantitative
elution [156]. The elements Ta(V), Sb(III) and Te(IV) tend to form insoluble
hydrolysis products in aqueous 0.1M HCl, or in ethanol and peroxide containing mixtures.

9. Fe(III), U(VI)

Iron (III) can be eluted with 1.0M HCl in 85% ethanol and separated from
U(VI), Be, Mg, Ca, Sr, Ba, Al, Mn(II), Ni(II), V(IV), Li, Na, K, Rb, Cs,
Ti(IV), Zr, Hf, Th, Sc, Y, and the rare earths which are retained by the
column. The Cu(II) is also retained, but the separation factor is rather low,
and a column of 60 ml (20 g) AG50W-X8 resin of 200 to 400 mesh particle
size is required for the separation of 1 mmole each of Fe(III) and Cu(II).
The elements Zn, Cd, Hg(II), In(III), Sn(IV), Bi(III), Ge(IV), As(III), Se(IV),
and the platinum metals can be eluted with 0.50M HCl in 80% ethanol, before
the iron is eluted. Other elements such as Mo(VI), W(VI), Nb(V), and
Au(III) can also be eluted and separated. The first three require the presence
of peroxide to avoid hydrolysis. Some elements cannot be present, because
of the interfering precipitation of oxidation-reduction reaction products. The
only element actually accompanying iron (III) is gallium.

U(VI) can be separated from Al, Ca, Sr, Ba, Zr, Hf, Th, Se, Y, and
the rare earths by elution with 2.0M HCl in 70% ethanol, Al, etc. being
retained; but the operating distribution coefficient for uranium is fairly high
[D = 16.1], and fairly strong tailing occurs. More attractive separations
of uranium can be obtained by cation or anion exchange in other systems
[158-161].

10. Zr, Hf, Th, Sc, Y and the Rare Earth Elements

These elements are strongly adsorbed from 3.0M HCl containing 50 or 60% ethanol. Most other elements, including Al, Fe(III), Mg, Mn(II) and Ti(IV) can be eluted and separated in the presence of peroxide [162]. The separation factor for the Sc/Al pair is about 21 in 3M HCl containing 60% ethanol, as compared with 3.2 in 3M aqueous HCl, while for the Y/Al pair the respective values are 10 and 2.9. The exchange rates for these strongly adsorbed elements are slower in the ethanol solutions than in aqueous HCl, and resin of small particle size, 200 to 400 mesh, and slow flow rates, about 0.5 ml/min/cm^2, considerably improve separations of the rare earths from Al, etc.

Thorium can be separated from all other elements of the periodic table including Zr, Hf, Sc and the rare earth elements, except only those which form precipitates in the eluting agent, by eluting all elements with 4M aqueous HCl from a column of AG50W-X12 resin of 200 to 400 mesh particle size, while thorium is retained [163]. This separation is not improved by working in ethanol containing mixtures.

11. Cu(II), Co(II), Ni(II), Mn(II), and V(IV)

The last four elements show a behavior approximately similar to that of magnesium, an element with negligible tendencies to chloride complex formation in the HCl-water-ethanol mixtures investigated, and the coefficients increase with increasing ethanol concentrations. Those for Cu(II) increase less strongly at low, and decrease at the highest, HCl and ethanol concentrations. Thus Cu(II) can be separated from the other elements above by elution with 1.5M HCl in 80% ethanol. The separation factor is about 6 for the V(IV)/Cu(II) pair, and about 10 for the separation of Cu(II) from Co(II), Ni(II), and Mn(II). The alkaline earth elements, Al, Ti(IV), Zr, Hf, Th, Sc, Y, the rare earths, and the alkali metals except lithium, are retained together with Co(II), etc., and are separated from Cu(II) with separation factors larger than 10. Copper (II) can also be separated from U(VI) by this method, but the separation factor is only about 5, and fairly large columns are required. Other more favorable methods are available [158-161].

D. Cation Exchange Separations in HCl-Acetone

Elements such as Co(II), Mn(II), V(IV) and Ni(II), which have only relatively slight tendencies to chloride complex formation, cannot be separated efficiently by cation exchange in HCl-ethanol mixtures. A solvent, which promotes chloride complex formation more strongly, is required for this purpose. Figure 7 shows the distribution coefficients of Co(II) and Cu(II) in 0.5M HCl containing various amounts of ethanol and acetone. The curves demonstrate that in acetone, chloride complex formation and the resulting decrease in the numerical values of the distribution coefficients, becomes effective at a considerably lower solvent concentration than in ethanol. Cobalt shows no chloride complex formation effect in ethanol, but a very distinct effect in acetone.

Furthermore, chloride complex in acetone is not only more pronounced, but, it appears also that a kind of solvent extraction effect may be super-imposed. This is shown by the results of Hazan et al. [164], who found that ferric iron is not absorbed from 0.6M HCl in 90% acetone by Dowex 1-X8 anion exchange resin, and can be separated from Co(II), Mn(II) and Ni(II), which are retained. Since Fe(III) also is not absorbed from 0.6M HCl in 90% acetone by AG50W-X8 or Dowex 50W-X8 cation exchange resin [165], it seems reasonable to assume that this behavior is due to the formation of neutral compounds, probably $HFeCl_4 \cdot 2$ acetone$\cdot nH_2O$, analogous to those found during the extraction of ferric iron with methyl isobutyl ketone, or other water immiscible ketones. Similar behavior can be expected from elements such as Au(III), Ga and Tl(III), which are also extracted as neutral tetra-chloroacids into ketones.

1. Alkali Metals and Alkaline Earths

Distribution coefficients are similar to those in HCl-ethanol mixtures. Separation factors for the Na/Li pair are slightly less favorable than in HCl-ethanol, but quite good separations are still possible by using 1.0M HCl in 60% acetone, or 2.0M HCl in 70% acetone, as eluting agent [166].

An excellent separation of the alkali metals from large amounts of Mn(II) can be obtained by eluting manganese with 0.75M HCl in 90% acetone, while the alkalies are retained [167]. The separation factor is about 20 for

the Li/Mn(II) pair and larger for the other alkali metals. The elements
Co(II), Cu(II), Zn, Cd, Hg(II), Fe(III), In, Ga, Tl(III), Pb(II), Sn(IV), Bi(III),
Au(III), the platinum metals, Se(IV), Ge(IV), As(III), Sb(III), and Te(IV) are
even less strongly absorbed, and accompany Mn(II) quantitatively. Magnesium,
Be, Al, Ti(IV), Ca, Sr, Ba, Zr, Hf, Th, Sc, Y, and the rare earths accompany
the alkali metals, but can easily be separated by other methods [191, 193].
This separation of manganese from the alkali metals is not possible in HCl-
ethanol mixtures. Even larger separation factors for the alkali/Mn(II) pairs
can be obtained in 1.0M HCl containing 92% acetone [113], but actual separations are less favorable, due to the considerable tailing that arises from
unfavorable column kinetics.

Separations of calcium from magnesium and other elements in 3.0M HCl
containing 60% acetone, and of barium from strontium, calcium and other
elements in 3.0M HCl containing 20% acetone are excellent, and comparable
to those obtained in the corresponding HCl-ethanol mixtures.

2. Al, Ga, In(III), Tl(III)

Separations of these elements in HCl-acetone mixtures are obtained at
considerably lower percentages of organic solvent than in HCl-ethanol
mixtures of the same HCl concentration. Excellent separations are provided
by the elution sequence: 0.10M HCl or 0.10M HBr for Tl(III); 0.5M HCl in
40% acetone for In(III); 0.5M HCl in 90% acetone for Ga, and 3.0M HCl for
Al.

Furthermore, Al can be separated from Fe(III), U(VI), Be(II), Cu(II),
Co(II), Mn(II), Ga, In(III), Zn, Cd, Hg(II), and some other elements by
eluting these elements with 2.0M HCl containing 70% acetone. Indium (III)
together with Cd and Sn(IV) can be separated from Cu(II), Co(II), Mn(II),
Ni(II), Fe(III), and many other elements by eluting the first three elements
with 0.5M HCl in 40% acetone. In 0.5M HCl containing 30% acetone, the
elution peaks of In(III), Cd and Sn(IV) are somewhat broader, but Zn and
Pb(II) are retained on the column, together with Cu(II), etc.

3. V(V), Mo(VI), W(VI), Cr(III)

The behavior of these elements is very similar to that in HCl-ethanol
solutions, but V(V) is reduced to V(IV) at a considerably faster rate in HCl-
acetone solutions, even after addition of hydrogen peroxide.

4. Au(III), Pt(IV), Pd(II), Rh(III), Ir(IV)

These elements are only weakly, or not at all absorbed at the HCl-acetone concentrations investigated. Au(III) can be very effectively eluted with 0.1M HCl containing 80 or 90% acetone. The tendency of trace amounts of gold to be retained by a column is completely absent in this eluent. No gold (< 0.5 microgram) could be detected when a 30 ml column of AG50W-X8 resin had been ashed, after 100 mg of Au(III) had been eluted with 300 ml of 0.1M HCl in 90% acetone. On elution with aqueous 0.1M HCl, between 5 and 20 µg of gold were found in the resin ash. The elution behavior of the other elements in HCl-acetone mixtures does not appear to have been investigated.

5. Zn, Cd, Hg(II), Sn(IV)

These elements can be separated by the following elution sequence: 0.2M HCl in 20% acetone for Hg(II), 0.1M HCl in 60% acetone for Sn(IV), 0.5M HCl in 20% acetone for Cd, and 0.5M HCl in 60% acetone for Zn. Elements such as Cu(II), Co(II), Mn(II), Ni(II), Fe(III), U(VI), Ga, Be, Mg, Ca, Sr, Ba, Al, the alkali metals, the rare earths, Ti(IV), Zr, Hf, and Th are retained by the column, and can thus be separated from zinc. Indium(III) accompanies cadmium.

6. Pb(II)

Lead is only sparingly soluble in aqueous HCl of low concentration ($\lesssim 0.5M$), but the solubility increases considerably in the presence of large concentrations of acetone. It can be separated from Cu(II), Co(II), Mn(II), Ni(II), V(IV), Ti(IV), Be, Mg, Ca, Sr, Ba, Na, K, and many other elements by elution with 0.7M HCl in 60% acetone, the other elements being retained. Indium(III), Cd and Sn(IV) can be eluted with 0.5M HCl in 30% acetone and thus separated from Pb(II), but Zn accompanies Pb(II). Satisfactory separations of Zn from Pb(II) are obtained by anion exchange in 8M HCl [136], or by anion exchange in 0.5M HNO$_3$, 90% tetrahydrofuran [168]. The elution peaks are fairly broad, indicating that the kinetic properties of this system are not as good as those encountered in cation exchange separations named above. Excellent separations of Pb(II) from Zn and many other elements can be carried out by cation or anion exchange in aqueous HBr. This separation is discussed later.

7. Ge(IV), Se(IV), Te(IV), As(III), Sb(III), Nb(V), Ta(V)

These elements tend to form either anionic oxyacids or chloride complexes at all hydrochloric acid and acetone concentrations, as they do in HCl-ethanol mixtures. By elution with 0.1M aqueous HCl Ge(IV), Se(IV), and As(III) can be eluted and separated from most other elements, excluding only Au(III), Hg(II), the platinum metals, Mo(VI), W(VI) and V(V). Tantalum (V) and Sb(III) tend to form insoluble compounds in aqueous 0.1M HCl, and in its mixtures with acetone and peroxide. The Te(IV) is fairly strongly absorbed from 0.1M aqueous HCl, but can be eluted with 0.2M HCl in 90% acetone. The elution of Nb(V) with 0.1M aqueous HCl containing hydrogen peroxide is very prolonged, and 0.5M HCl or preferably 0.25M H_2SO_4 [156] containing peroxide are required to effect a reasonably rapid elution. Niobium(V) tends to precipitate in acetone containing mixtures, the extent of precipitation increasing with the acetone concentration. Selenium(IV) also tends to precipitate in acetone containing solutions.

8. Fe(III), U(VI)

Iron (III) can be eluted with 0.2M HCl in 85% acetone, while Cu(II), U(VI), Be, Mg, Ca, Sr, Ba, Mn(II), Co(II), Ni(II), V(IV), Li, Na, K, Rb, Cs, Ti(IV), Zr, Hf, Th, Sc, Y, and the rare earths are retained by the column.

The separation factor for the Fe(III)/Cu(II) pair, the most critical one, is about 20, and separations are excellent. With 0.2M HCl in 82% acetone, a larger separation factor of about 35 can be obtained, but there is some tailing of iron. At the lower acetone concentration, Ga is retained in addition to Cu(II), but not very strongly. A larger separation factor for the Ga/Fe(III) pair is obtained in 0.1M HCl containing 85% acetone, but the separation is critically dependent on acetone concentration, and Fe(III) shows some tailing.

Zinc, Cd, Hg(II), In(III), Sn(IV), Bi(III), Ge(IV), As(III), Se(IV), Au(III), and the platinum metals can be eluted with 0.5M HCl in 60% acetone, while Fe(III) is retained. Molybdenum (VI), W (VI), and Nb(V) can be eluted prior to the others using 0.5M aqueous HCl containing peroxide.

Uranium(VI) can be separated from V(IV) by elution with 0.5M HCl in 90% acetone, or 1M HCl in 80% acetone. Uranium(VI) shows some tailing in both eluting agents, and fairly large eluting volumes are required for quantitative recoveries. Aluminum, Ti(IV), Be, Mg, Ca, Sr, Ba, Zr, Hf, Th, Sc, Y, and the rare earths, and Li and the alkali metals are retained with V(IV). The least tailing is obtained with 1M HCl in 80% acetone, the best eluting agent for separation from Mn(II).

9. Zr, Hf, Th, Sc, Y, La and the Rare Earths

These elements exhibit the same behavior in HCl-acetone as in HCl-ethanol mixtures, and equivalent separations can be obtained under comparable conditions.

10. Cu(II), Co(II), Mn(II), Ni(II), V(IV)

The first four of these elements can be separated by the elution sequences: 0.5M HCl in 80% acetone for Cu(II), 1.0M HCl in 80% acetone for Co(II), 0.75M HCl in 90% acetone for Mn(II), and 2.0M aqueous HCl for Ni(II). The separation factors of 21 and 40 for the Cu(II)/Co(II) and Mn(II)/Ni(II) pairs, respectively, are fairly large, and good separations can be obtained with relatively small columns. The separation factor of about 5 for the Co(II)/Mn(II) pair is considerably lower. Quite good separations nevertheless are possible, provided sufficiently large columns using resin of small particle size are used, as is shown in Figure 8. On a 90-ml column of the same resin, 100 μg of cobalt can be separated from 500 mg of manganese and analyzed with excellent results. For the separation of traces of manganese from up to about 1 g of cobalt, a 90-ml resin column is also sufficient.

A 1.0M HCl solution in 80% acetone is a better eluting agent for Co(II) than the 0.5M HCl, 90% acetone solvent mixture recommended by Fritz et al. [113], because there is less tailing of the cobalt (Figure 8). The separation of Co(II)/Mn(II) by cation exchange in 1.0M HCl containing 80% acetone is also better than that by anion exchange in 3M HCl containing 55% isopropyl-alcohol [111, 112]. A 0.75M hydrochloric acid solution in 90% acetone [167] is a better eluting agent for Mn(II) than 1.0M HCl in 92% acetone [113], also because of less tailing. The improved kinetic seems to be

connected with the amount of water present relative to the solvation requirements of the ions. Almost water-free organic solvent solutions generally
seem to yield unfavorable exchange kinetics.

Vanadium(IV) will accompany Mn(II) partially, in the described elution
sequence, and a part will be found with the Ni(II). Other elements, such as
Be, Mg, Ca, Sr, Ba, Al, Ti(IV), Zr, Hf, Th, Sc, Y, the rare earths, Na,
K, Rb, and Cs will be retained quantitatively, together with Ni(II) [167].
Lithium will also be retained, provided the column is long enough [167].

E. Separations in Other Mineral Acid Systems

1. Hydrobromic Acid

Korkisch et al. [116] have published cation exchange distribution
coefficients for 19 elements in HBr combined with 8 different organic
solvents. While quite a number of potentially useful separations are indicated
by the survey, no elution curve or examples of applicable quantitative separations were included in this study. The system provides a very large separation factor for the Cd/Zn pair in 0.2M HBr containing 60% acetone, and a
separation factor larger than 1000 for the In(III)/Ga pair in 0.2M HBr containing 80% acetone.

The coefficients of U(VI) are much higher in HBr-acetone systems than
in the corresponding HCl systems. Thus, an excellent separation of U(VI)
from Cu(II) and Fe(III) appears to be possible by eluting these elements with
0.80M HBr in 80% acetone, while U(VI) is retained. Again the separation
factor is very large.

The HBr-acetone cation exchange system, however, generally seems to
tend much more to tailing than does the HCl-acetone system, and many
separations apparently attractive because of large separation factors may
prove to be much less attractive, when the elution experiments are carried
out.

Even less is known about anion exchange in HBr-organic solvent systems.
Korkisch et al. [124] have published coefficients for 23 elements in HBr-
methanol and for 18 elements in other solvents, but only at a single
concentration of HBr (0.45M) and organic solvent (90%). At this

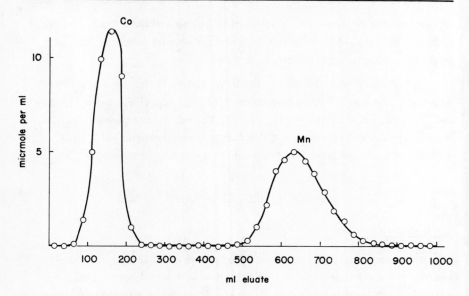

FIG. 8. Elution curve for Co(II)/Mn(II) pair with 1.0M HCl in 80%
acetone. Column of 60 ml (2.0 x 20 cm) AG50W-X8 resin, 200 to 400 mesh.
Flow rate 3.0 ± 0.3 ml/min. One mmole of each Co(II) and Mn(II).

concentration Zn, Ga, In(III), Cd, Po(II), Cu(II), and Bi(III) are retained by
the resin in HBr-methanol mixtures, and apparently can be separated from
Mg, Ca, Sr, Al, La, Yb, Ti(IV), Zr, Th, V(IV), U(VI), Mn(II), Fe(II),
Co(II), and Ni(II), which are not. Zinc, Ga, and In(III) are eluted with 0.45M
aqueous HBr, and can be separated from Cd and Pb(II), which are retained
by the column. More detailed investigations without doubt will reveal many
more useful separations in this solvent system, but again the kinetics do not
always seem to be favorable.

2. Nitric Acid

Distribution coefficients for 19 elements in nitric acid combined with 8
different organic solvents have been published by Korkisch et al. [115]. Of
the elements investigated only Bi(III) and U(VI) show an effect of nitrate
complex formation at high organic solvent concentration. No outstanding
new possibilities for separations are indicated.

Information about anion exchange in HNO_3-organic solvent mixtures is sporadic, concentrated mainly on such elements as the alkaline earths, the rare earths, U(VI), Th, Bi(III), and Pb(II). In the alkaline earth group, Mg can be eluted with 0.5M HNO_3 in 90% isopropyl alcohol, followed by Ca with 0.25M HNO_3 in 95% methanol or 85% ethanol, while Sr and Ba are retained. Unfortunately, the exchange rates are quite slow, especially for the Ca/Sr pair, and satisfactory separations require the use of macroporous resins [152, 155]. Furthermore, Sr, and, especially, Ba have a low solubility in the eluting agent. Kurokawa [153, 168, 169] has used HNO_3-KNO_3 mixtures with organic solvents to obtain better column kinetics; but the exchange rates still remain fairly slow.

A considerable amount of information is available on the behavior of the rare earth elements. All the rare earth elements can be eluted with 0.6M HNO_3 in 55% acetone, and separated from thorium, which is retained by the column [170, 171]. Uranium (VI), Mg, Ca, Sr, Cu(II), Zn, Cd, Fe(III), Co(II), Ni(II), Al, Ga, In(III), Mn(II), Ag, Zr, and Cr(III) accompany the rare earths, and Bi(III), Pb(II), Au(III) and Pd(II) accompany thorium. With 0.25M HNO_3 in 95% methanol, the lighter rare earths are retained, together with Th, U(VI), Bi(III), and Pb(II), while Fe(III), Co(II), Ni(II), Mn(II), Cr(III), Mo(VI), V(V), Ti(IV), Zr, Al, Ga, In(III), Mg, Ca, Sr, Zn, Cd, and Cu(II) are eluted [173]. A technique for the separation of the rare earths from each other in HNO_3-methanol media has been described by Faris et al. [173]. It has been claimed by Molnar et al. [174] that $LiNO_3$ in methanol at elevated temperature provides better separation factors and separation kinetics than HNO_3 in methanol.

Fritz et al. [175] have published distribution coefficients for 28 elements, including the rare earths, in 1.5M HNO_3 containing 85% isopropyl alcohol. Magnesium, Ti(IV), V(IV), Mn(II), Fe(III), Co(II), Ni(II), Zn, Al, Ga, and In(III) are eluted with this reagent, and can be separated from the rare earths, which are retained. Calcium, Sr, Cd, Hg(II), Pb(II), and Bi(III) accompany the rare earths. Au(III) and Pd(II) have not been investigated, but probably will also accompany the rare earths. The separation of the rare earths from Cu(II), Ag, and Zr is not complete, while Sc has a rather low distribution coefficient of 22, and elutes prematurely. The exchange rates are also quite slow, and macroporous resin and slow flow rates need to be used for reasonably good separations.

Further information about the anion exchange behavior of rare earths in HNO_3-organic solvent media includes work on group separations [176, 177], and more complete distribution data in seven different alcohols [126].

A comparatively large amount of information is available on the anion exchange behavior of uranium and thorium in HNO_3-organic solvent mixtures. Most of it is due to the work of Korkisch and his coworkers, and has been summarized by them [171, 178].

Lead can be adsorbed from 0.5M HNO_3 in 90% tetrahydrofuran, while U(VI), Th, Bi(III), Tl(I), the lanthanides from Sm to Lu, Fe(III), Mg, Ca and many other elements can be eluted quantitatively [123]. The rare earths from La to Nd are retained, together with lead. On the other hand, with 0.5M HNO_3 in 90% methyl glycol, Bi(III) is retained by Dowex 1 resin, while Pb(II), Cu(II), Cd, Zn, Al, Ga, In(III), Mn(II), Fe(III), Co(II), Ni(II), Zr, Hf, Mg, Ca, Sr, La, Yb, and U(VI) can be eluted quantitatively [179]. The origin of this selectivity reversal of lead and bismuth has not been examined seriously, but seems to be connected to differences in a specific solvent action. Thorium, La, and the lighter rare earths accompany Bi(III).

Cadmium can be separated from Zn, Al, Cu(II), Fe(III), and Ni(II) by eluting these elements with 0.5M HNO_3 in 90% ethanol, while Cd is retained. Lead (II) accompanies Cd [180]. Some other elements, such as Th, Bi(III), U(VI), Sr, La, and the light rare earth elements, which have not been investigated, should behave similarly.

Many other separations involving such elements as Bi(III), Hg(II), Cd, Zn, Cu(II), Ag, Pd(II), Au(III), and Zr appear to be possible in this system. A systematic study of distribution coefficients and elution behavior will be required to explore the possibilities and to select optimum conditions. A fairly general disadvantage is that exchange rates are rather slow, and tend to be very slow at high concentrations of HNO_3 and/or organic solvent.

3. Sulfuric Acid

Practically no information seems to be available about cation exchange distribution coefficients in H_2SO_4-organic solvent mixtures. Anion exchange distribution coefficients for 10 elements have been published by Korkisch et al. [119]. The only elements which have been investigated in some detail seem to be U(VI) and Th(IV) [178, 181]. Generally, the presence of

the organic solvent increases the distribution coefficients of an element. In
the case of thorium, which has low coefficients in aqueous H_2SO_4, this is of
value. Unfortunately, the organic solvent severely decreases the solubility
of thorium sulfate. Separations of limited amounts of thorium from elements
such as Zn, Cd, Mn(II), Co(II), and Ni(II), by eluting these elements with
0.05M H_2SO_4 in 80% methanol, while thorium is retained, are feasible; but
other more selective and attractive methods for the separation of thorium
from other elements are available [170, 171, 182-184].

F. Separations Using Mineral Acid-Organic Solvent Mixtures Containing Chelating Agents

It has been shown that in HCl-acetone solutions, a "solvent extraction"
effect can be superimposed on the ion exchange equilibrium to reverse
completely the expected selectivity sequence [164]. For example, Fe(III)
is eluted from an anion exchange resin in the chloride form, while Ni(II) and
Co(II) are retained. A logical extension of this is the addition of a chemical
agent which will enhance this solvent extraction effect. For example, a
chelating agent which reacts with one or several elements, to form complex
species which are strongly extractable into water immiscible organic solvents,
would be likely to produce a strong "solvent extraction" effect with water
miscible organic solvents of the same homologous series. At present, little
systematic information is available on ion exchange systems taking advantage
of this approach.

Korkisch et al. [127, 128], using Dowex 50-X8 cation exchange resin,
have determined distribution coefficients for 20 elements in 0.6M HNO_3
containing 95% of various organic solvents, and 0.1M trioctylphosphine oxide
(TOPO). Some coefficients for 5 elements in other HNO_3-TOPO mixtures
with various organic solvents, in mixtures of HNO_3 with tributyl phosphate
(TBP) and bis(2-ethylhexyl)orthophosphoric acid (HCEHP) in various organic
solvents and in HCl mixtures, were included in these studies as well. Very
high separation factors are obtained for the separation of thorium from the
rare earths in 0.5M HNO_3-95% methanol-0.1M TOPO, with about 1000 for the
Yb/Th and about 40,000 for the Ce/Th pairs. Even though neither sufficient
quantitative distribution coefficient data nor a complement of elution pattern
studies has been presented in this literature, the following separations are

predictable, even if the kinetics of exchange should be slow. Americium(III), Ti(IV), Mn(II), Fe(III), Co(II), Zn, Cd, Ca, Sr, Na and Cs should be retained, together with the rare earths, according to their distribution coefficients, while U(VI), Pu(IV), Zr and Hf should be eluted, together with Th.

Coefficients for Sc and various rare earths in HCl containing 95% of various organic solvents, and 0.1M TOPO, TBP or HDEHP, are also available [185]. According to these data, Sc can be eluted from a column of Dowex 50-X8 resin with 0.3M HCl in 95% tetrahydrofuran containing 0.1M TOPO, while the rare earths are retained. The separation factor is larger than 4000 for the Yb/Sc pair. Yttrium, La, and the rare earths, the alkali metals, Al, Cr(III), Ni(II), and the trivalent transplutonium elements should accompany Yb; and Zr, Hf, Mn(II), Ga, In(III), Cu(II), Fe(III), Co(II), Au(III), U(VI), Zn, Cd, Hg(II), Bi(III), Sn(IV), Pb(II), Ge(IV), V(V), Mo(VI), and the platinum metals should accompany Sc.

Distribution coefficients for 13 elements in HCl-organic solvent-thenoyltrifluoroacetone (TTA) mixtures have been presented by Korkisch et al. [129], and it has been shown that carrier-free cesium-137 can be separated from Sc, Y, Sr, Zr, Nb(V), U(VI), Th, Ru, Te, Am, Pu, Np, Hf, Mn(II), Co(II), Ni(II), Fe(III), Cu(II), Ir, Zn, Cd, Ti(IV), Ca, and Mg by eluting these elements with 0.1M TTA in pyridine. In the presence of chlorides and other salts of sodium, potassium, the alkaline earths, and some other elements which have a low solubility in TTA-pyridine mixtures, absorption should be carried out from 0.1M TTA in pyridine diluted to 50% with water.

While the separation factors in these systems are potentially very large, there is the disadvantage of very slow exchange rates, which lead to unfavorable column behavior. Furthermore, the removal of the eluting agent, which may be required for further work, is relatively difficult and time consuming. For these reasons more simple systems are often more attractive. Nevertheless, numerous interesting possibilities, which may have special application, remain unexplored in this field.

IV. APPLICATION TO ROCK ANALYSIS

A. Silicate Rock Analysis

The first ion-exchange procedure for the separation of the major constituent elements in silicate rocks, is believed to have been presented by Yosimura et al. [186]. The method is lengthy and cumbersome, consisting of four different column operations for the separation of nine different elements, and has several weaknesses. First, the distribution coefficient for the anion exchange absorption of Mn(II) as the chloride complex from 10.5M HCl (D ≈ 7) is rather low. Losses due to leakage can occur easily, even with fairly large columns. Second, the separation factor for the calcium-magnesium pair in 1M ammonium acetate ($\alpha \frac{Ca}{Mg}$ = 2.2) is rather low [97]. This severely limits the amounts of these elements, which can be separated. Third, aluminum does not appear quantitatively in the desired eluate fraction, because of partial hydrolysis in the ammonium acetate eluent. Because of the above, the sample size must be limited to 0.1 g, and the results obtainable with the method provide only moderate accuracy.

The method devised by Oki et al. [187] is somewhat shorter. Iron(III) is separated, by extraction from 6M HCl, into ethyl ether, and the other elements are then separated by elution from a column of Amberlite IR-120 cation exchange resin (1.0 x 18 cm), using the following elution sequence: 160 ml of 0.4M HCl for Na, another 150 ml of 0.4M HCl for K, 80 ml of 0.4M H_2SO_4 for Ti(IV), 200 ml of 0.8M HCl for Mg and Mn(II), a further 180 ml of 4M HCl for Al.

The results which are obtained by this method seem to be more accurate than those obtained with the previous one, but still do not satisfy the requirement for accurate reference analysis. The separation factors for the K/Na, Ca/Mg(Mn) and Al/Ca pairs are rather low, between 2.0 and 2.5, and only limited amounts may be present. This restricts the sample size to 0.1 g in the length of column used.

Maines [188] has described for silicate analysis, an ion exchange procedure which can be applied to 1 g samples, and has been shown to give fairly accurate results for five elements. Adsorption of the sulfoxalicylate complexes of Fe(III), Ti(IV), and Al on Dowex 1 anion exchange resin, is used to separate the elements from Mn(II), Mg and Ca, (also K and Na). The operating distribution coefficient for Al is, unfortunately, rather small, and large columns (50 cm resin bed) are required to avoid losses. On continued use of columns, erratic and low results for Al are obtained, and fresh resin has to be used for each analysis. Furthermore, the destruction of the organic reagents used is time-consuming and unattractive, and sodium and potassium are not analyzed.

By starting with an anion exchange group separation in HCl-oxalic acid, a separation scheme for silicate analysis has been developed [189], which is highly accurate for the major elements, and is able to produce results, for minor elements, which are superior to those obtained by other known routine methods. Only the volatile inorganic acids HCl and HNO_3, and the solvents ethanol and acetone, which can be removed very easily by evaporation, are used for separating the group into fractions containing single elements. Iron(III), Al, Ti(IV), V(V), Zr, and Mo(VI) are strongly absorbed on a 46 ml (2.4 x 11 centimeter) column of AGl-X8 or Dowex 1-X8 resin "A", from a solution containing up to 0.25M mineral acid (HCl and H_2SO_4), between 0.05 and 0.25M oxalic acid, 0.03% hydrogen peroxide, and 12 g boric acid in a total volume of about 200 ml. Manganese(II), Mg, Ca, Na, and K are not absorbed, D < 0.5, and excellent separations are obtained. The separation factors for the most critical pairs, Al/Mn(II) and V(V)/Mn(II), are larger than 200. A typical elution curve is shown in Figure 9.

1. Mn(II), Mg, Ca, Na, K

These elements pass through the anion exchange column "A" and are adsorbed on a 60 ml (2.4 x 15 cm) column of AG50W-X8 cation exchange resin "B", which is connected in series to the anion exchange column. A solution of 0.1M hydrochloric acid containing 0.05M oxalic acid and 0.03% H_2O_2 is used to wash these elements through the anion exchanger and onto the cation exchange column. After the columns have been disengaged, the oxalic acid is washed from the cation exchange column, and the adsorbed elements are separated with the following elution sequence: 800 ml of 0.5M HNO_3 for Na plus K, 400 ml of 0.75M HCl in 90% acetone for Mn(II), 400 ml of 3.0M HCl in 60% ethanol for Mg, 400 ml of 3.0M HCl for Ca. A typical elution curve is shown in Figure 10.

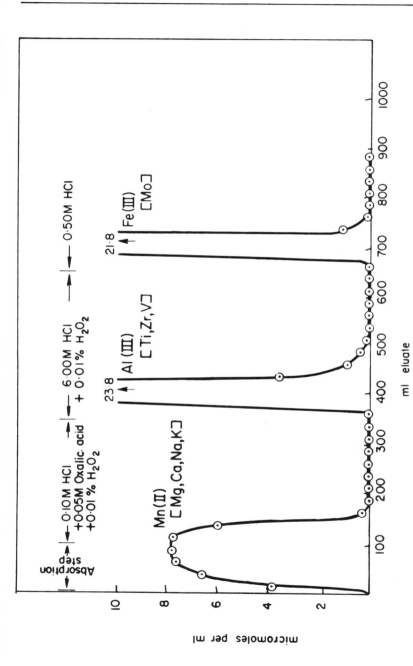

Fig. 9. Elution curve for Mn(II)–Al–Fe(III). Column 23 ml (2.0 x 7.5 cm) AGl-X8, 200 to 400 mesh, resin. Flow rate 3.0 ± 0.3 ml/min; reprinted from Ref. [189], p. 253, by courtesy of Elsevier Publishing Company.

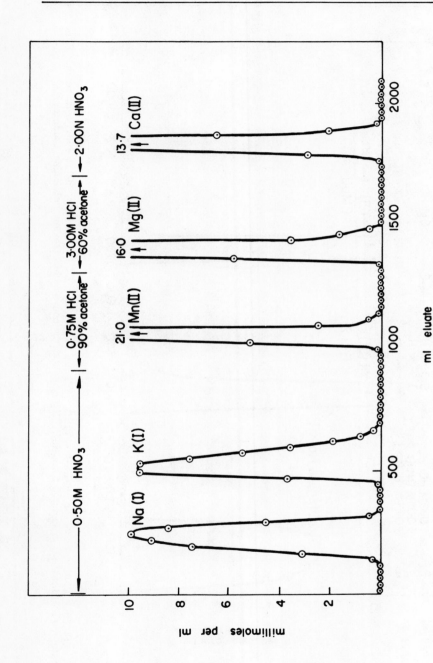

Fig. 10. Elution curve for Na–K–Mn(II)–Mg–Ca. Column 60 ml (2.4 x 15 cm) AG50W-X8, 200 to 400 mesh, resin. Flow rate 3.5 ± 0.5 ml/min for Mn(II) for other elements, 2.0 ± 0.3 ml/min for Mn(II); reprinted from Ref. [189], p. 254, by courtesy of Elsevier Publishing Company.

2. Al, Ti(IV), Zr, V(V)

After cation exchange column "B" is withdrawn, these elements are eluted from the anion exchange column "A", with 100 ml of 0.5M HCl containing 0.05M oxalic acid and 0.02% H_2O_2, followed by 300 ml of 6M HCl containing 0.02% H_2O_2. The oxalate in the eluate is destroyed by nitric acid-bromic acid oxidation, and the elements are readsorbed from dilute acid (< 0.5M) on a 30 ml (2.0 x 9.5 cm) column of AG50W-X8, 200 to 400 mesh, cation exchange resin column "C." The elements are then separated with the following elution sequence: 200 ml of 0.01M HNO_3 containing 0.02% H_2O_2 for V(V), which passes through the column from the beginning of the adsorption step, 325 ml of 1.25M HNO_3 containing 0.02% H_2O_2 for Ti(IV), 250 ml of 2.5M HCl for Al, and 350 ml of 5.0M HCl for Zr. A typical elution curve is shown in Figure 11.

3. Fe(III) and Mo(VI)

Finally, Fe(III) and Mo(VI) are eluted with 250 ml of 0.5M HCl or HNO_3 from column "A". For the separation of these two elements, the eluate, after dilution to < 0.5M acid, can be passed through a column of 30 ml (2.0 x 9.5 cm) AG50W-X8, 200 to 400 mesh, cation exchange resin column "D", and Mo(VI) can be eluted with 150 ml of 0.1M HNO_3 containing 0.03% H_2O_2. Iron(III) is retained, and then can be eluted with 150 ml of 3M HCl. This separation is not required when only major and minor elements are to be determined, because molybdenum normally is present as a trace element.

4. General

With resin of 200 to 400 mesh particle size and flow rates of 3 to 3.5 ml/min, sharp elution peaks are obtained for all the major elements investigated. The method can easily be applied to 1-g samples of silicate rocks after dissolution in HCl, HF, and H_2SO_4 containing mixtures, and removal of the volatile acids by heating to fumes of sulfuric acid. When the separations are followed by selective procedures [189] the results for major elements are at least as accurate as those obtained by the best classic methods of silicate rock analysis, while results for elements present in minor amounts are considerably more accurate, and are also superior to those obtained by x ray fluorescence or atomic absorption spectrometry, which do not require

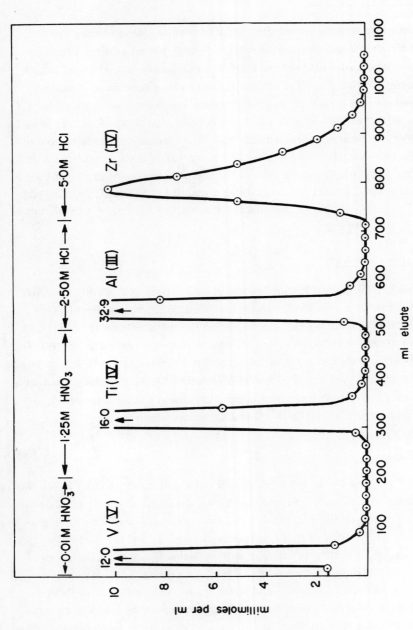

Fig. 11. Elution curve for V(V)–Ti(IV)–Al–Zr. Column 30 ml (2.0 x 9.5 cm) AG50W-X8, 200 to 400 mesh, resin. Flow rate 3.0 ± 0.3 ml/min; reprinted from Ref. [189], p. 255, by courtesy of Elsevier Publishing Company.

resort to separations. To demonstrate the accuracy which is obtainable, 2.595 mg of aluminium, separated from a synthetic mixture containing 26.00 mg Na, 48.30 mg K, 27.61 mg Mg, 39.42 mg Ca, 13.74 mg Mn(II), 64.43 mg Fe(III), 12.63 mg V(V), 12.20 mg Ti(IV), and 29.68 mg Zr, were, after separation, assayed by complexometric titration, using excess DCyTA and back-titration with 0.005M zinc sulfate using xylenol orange as indicator. The 2.588 ± 0.013 mg of Al found, converted to a 1-g silicate rock sample basis, corresponds to an assay of 0.489 ± 0.003% Al_2O_3 for a sample known to contain 0.490% [189]. The coefficient of variation for six analyses at this low concentration level was only about 0.6%.

A deficiency of the described procedure is the low solubility of some metal oxalates. In 250 ml of 0.1M HCl containing 0.1M H_2SO_4 and 60 ml of 0.5M oxalic acid, up to about 50 mg of Ca may be present. Slow precipitation of calcium oxalate, which can lead to losses by retention on the columns, occurs with larger amounts of calcium. No precipitation of calcium oxalate occurs within 90 min, when as much as 200 mg of calcium are present in 250 ml of solution containing the above reagents, if 12 g of boric acid are added. The boric acid needs to be added before the addition of the oxalic acid, heating must be avoided, and the column separation should be carried out immediately. Furthermore, the precipitation of even larger amounts of Sr and Ba, and of up to about 10 mg of rare earths and 3 mg of thorium, is so retarded by the presence of boric acid that such separations can be carried out.

5. Behavior of Other Elements

Nickel(II), Co(II), Sr, and Ba accompany the manganese group quantitatively onto column "B". Cobalt(II) is eluted, together with Mn(II), Ni(II) with Mg, and Sr and Ba together with Ca. Copper(II) cannot be eluted with 0.1M HCl containing 0.05M oxalic acid and elution with 0.2M HCl in 0.05M oxalic acid is quite prolonged. About 500 to 600 ml are required for quantitative elution from a 46 milliliter resin column. Separation from Al is nevertheless complete, because no Al is discovered in the first 1000 ml of eluate [190]. Copper(II), when included in a revised separation scheme, would also appear in the manganese fraction.

Lithium, Rb, Cs, and Be pass through column "A" without adsorption. For the quantitative retainment of Li, the amount of resin in column "B" has

to be assessed very carefully in relation to the mineral acid concentration of
the solution passing through. The heavy alkalies require larger volumes of
0.5M HNO_3 for elution from column "B" than does K, and special procedures
are required for the satisfactory separation of the heavy alkalies from each
other [66] or from beryllium [191].

The elution behavior of Hf, Ga, In(III), Nb(V), Ta(V), U(VI), Cd, Hg(II),
Pt(IV), W(VI), and Sn(IV) has not yet been investigated in detail, but from
the distribution coefficients in Tables 2 and 3 it appears that these elements
should be retained on column "A," while Zn should be retained on column
"B," and finally appear in the manganese fraction.

6. Special Method for Aluminium

The described method can easily be adapted for the direct determination
of Al, which, after the manganese group has been eluted with 0.1M HCl plus
0.05M oxalic acid from column "A," can be eluted selectively with 0.5M HCl
containing 0.05M oxalic acid [192]. The eluate can be absorbed on a 30 ml
(2.0 x 9.5 cm) column of AG50W-X8, 200 to 400 mesh, cation exchange resin,
which is connected in series, and the oxalic acid and V(IV) or V(V) which
partially accompanies Al, can be eluted with 150 ml of 0.01M NHO_3 containing 0.02% H_2O_2. Aluminium can then be eluted with 3.0M HCl. A typical
elution curve is shown in Figure 12. This separation is simple and selective.
Gallium and In(III) are separated and found in the Ti(IV), Fe(III) containing
fraction. Of those that have been investigated (Tables 2 and 3), no other
element accompanies Al. The results of the analysis of synthetic mixtures,
and of standard silicate rocks show a high accuracy and reproducibility,
about 0.5% in samples containing about 1 percent of Al_2O_3, and about 0.2%
for high Al_2O_3 concentrations [192].

7. Special Method for Traces of Alkali Metals

The method of silicate analysis described above does not provide accurate
results for the alkali metals, especially sodium, when these elements are
present in concentrations below 0.1%, because contribution of alkali metals
from reagents and other external contaminants is too high. Some silicate minerals, such as dunites and peridotites, contain very low concentrations of Na and K,

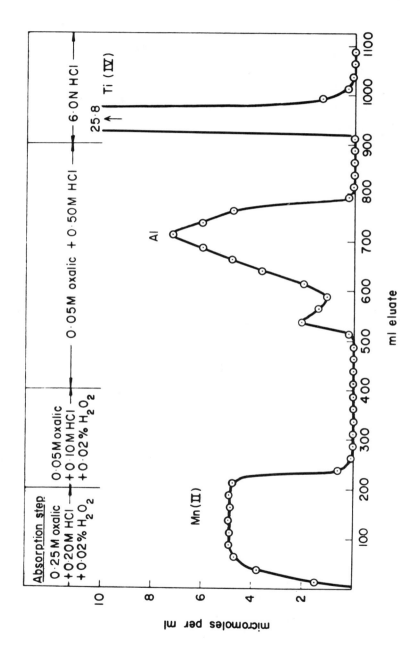

Fig. 12. Elution curve for Mn(II)–Al–Ti(IV). Column 46 ml (2.0 x 14 cm) AGI-X8, 200 to 400 mesh, resin. Flow rate 3.0 ± 0.3 ml/min; reprinted from Ref. [192], p. 2059, by courtesy of American Chemical Society.

together with large amounts of Mg. For such samples a special procedure
for alkali determination provides excellent results [191, 193]. After dissolution the cations are absorbed from about 0.2M HCl on a column of 90 ml
(2.4 x 22 centimeter) AG50W-X8 resin of 200 to 400 mesh particle size, and
the alkali metals are eluted with 0.50M HNO_3. The eluate is received
directly in volumetric flasks, and determined by atomic absorption spectrometry or flame photometry, using standards in 0.50M HNO_3. In the case of
1 gram samples of dunite or peridotite the first 250 ml contain the Li, the
second 250 ml the Na, the 500 to 600-ml fraction is discarded, and the next
250 ml contain the K. Only redistilled water and suprapure HNO_3 are used.
Reagent blank values are about 2 µg Na_2O, <1 µg K_2O, <0.5 µg Li_2O. Very
satisfactory results have been obtained on 1-g samples of silicates containing
between 10 and 500 ppm Na_2O and K_2O [193].

B. Determination of U, Th and Pb for Geochronology

Determination of the amounts of U, Th, and Pb, in order to evaluate the
geological age of rocks and minerals, often requires the most effective
separation procedures available, when these elements are present as minor
or trace components in complex mixtures. Ion exchange chromatography is
extremely well suited for this purpose. One of the problems in this kind of
work is to keep contamination by external lead at an absolute minimum.
Sample dissolution procedures must therefore be approached carefully, from
this point of view. An excellent procedure for the dissolution of tantalo-
niobates in hydrofluoric-hydrochloric acid mixtures, including a preliminary
separation of Pb(II), Th, and U(IV), after reduction of U(VI) with stannous
chloride, has been described [194].

1. Lead

After sample dissolution, the separation of lead is always carried out
first, to keep contamination to a minimum. Probably the most selective
and useful method for this purpose is anion exchange chromatography in
HBr and HBr-HNO_3 mixtures [194, 195]. Adsorption can take place from
between 0.1 and 4.0M HBr. When substantial amounts of other anions, such
as chloride, nitrate, phosphate, or organic anions are present, adsorption

should be carried out from 1M or more concentrated HBr. In 4M HBr even sulfate can be present in substantial amounts. The following elements can be eluted with 0.1M HBr: U(VI), Th, Zr, Hf, Ti(IV), Sc, Y, La, and the rare earths, Al, Ga, In(III), Fe(II), Fe(III), Be, Mg, Ca, Sr, Ba, Zn, Mn(II), Co(II), Cu(II), Ni(II), Cr(III), Sb(III), Ge(IV), Li, Na, K, Rb, and Cs [195-197]. Then lead can be eluted selectively with 0.30M HNO_3 plus 0.025M HBr, while Cd, Hg(II), Pd(II), Bi(III), Tl(III), Au(III), and Pt(IV) are retained by the column [195]. The column kinetics for most of these separations are quite good, and relatively high flow rates (3 to 4 ml/min) can be used without much peak broadening or tailing. Indium(III) and Sb(III) are the only exceptions. Alternative selective methods for the separation of lead from other elements use either cation exchange in HBr [198, 199] or anion exchange in nitric acid-tetrahydrofuran [123]. Unfortunately, in the first method, lead is eluted preferentially, while most of the common bulk elements remain absorbed. This limits the amount of material which can be handled, and makes the method less suitable for the separation of lead from large amounts of such elements as Al, Fe(III), Na, K, Ca, Mg, U(VI), and the rare earths. In the second method [123], the rare earths, which are major constituents of many radioactive minerals, are among the few elements which accompany lead. Furthermore, the behavior of some other elements with tendencies to nitrate complex formations, such as Sr, Ba, Hg(II), and Au(III), have not been investigated. The fairly high distribution coefficient for Ca [123] suggests that Sr and Ba are likely to accompany lead.

Anion exchange separation of lead in aqueous HCl [136, 200] is also quite selective. Unfortunately, the maximum value of the distribution coefficient $D \approx 27$ at about 1.5M HCl is low, and may lead to an early breakthrough of lead, thereby limiting the amount of solution which can be handled by a column. Cation exchange distribution coefficients in HBr containing organic solvents [116] also suggest a possible approach to the selective separation of lead, but at present, a lack of information about the elution behavior prevents evaluation of the most favorable conditions in this system. None of these methods seem to be as selective and generally useful as anion exchange in HBr-HNO_3 mixtures.

2. Thorium

The eluate from the lead separation containing less than 0.5M acid is
passed through a column of AG50W-X12 cation exchange resin. Molybdenum
(VI), W(VI), Nb(V), and V(V) can be eluted with 0.01M HNO_3 containing
H_2O_2, followed by 0.5M HNO_3 containing H_2O_2 for Nb(V) [157, 201-203].
A fraction containing all the uranium, together with many other elements, can
then be eluted with 1.75M HCl, while Zr, Hf, Ba, and Th are quantitatively,
and the rare earths partially, retained by the resin [204]. Barium, Zr, Hf,
Sc, Y, and the rare earths can then be eluted quantitatively with 4.0M HCl,
while only thorium is retained by the resin [182, 183, 194]. This separation
is completely selective for thorium. Only those elements which form insoluble
precipitates interfere. For quantitative recovery the resin must be ashed
[182, 183, 194]. Eluting agents for thorium, such as 3M H_2SO_4 [205-207],
or 0.5M oxalic acid [206], are not satisfactory for the most accurate work.
There is prolonged tailing, and recoveries are only about 98 to 99%.

Anion exchange in 5 to 6M HNO_3 also offers a quite selective method for
the separation of thorium [208, 209], but has the disadvantage that U(VI)
and some other elements show strong tailing. Bismuth(III), Au(III), Pd(II),
Pa(V), and some transuranium elements accompany thorium.

A selective separation of thorium from other elements can also be
obtained by anion exchange in 0.6M HNO_3 containing 55% acetone [171, 172].
Only Bi(III), Pb(II), Au(III), Pd(II), Pt(IV), and Pa(V) accompany thorium,
and the kinetics, though not very good, are considerably better than in
aqueous 6M HNO_3.

Numerous other methods for the separation of thorium by ion-exchange
chromatography have been suggested, and are ably summarized by Korkisch
[171]. None of these seems to be as selective and attractive for application
to complex mixtures as the first method described above.

3. Uranium

The uranium containing fraction from the thorium separation can be
evaporated to fumes of sulfuric acid, after a few milliliters of sulfuric acid
have been added. After dilution to less than 0.25M sulfuric acid, Fe(III),
Al, Ti(IV), Ga, In(III), Be, Mg, Ca, Cu(II), Co(II), Ni(II), Mn(II), Cd(II),

the alkali metals and some other elements can be separated on a column of AGl-X8 or Dowex l-X8 resin in the sulfate form, by eluting these elements with 0.25M H_2SO_4 [204]. Uranium(VI) is retained and can be eluted with 1M HNO_3 or HCl. Elements such as Zr, Hf, Mo(VI), W(II), Ta(V), and Nb(V), which would accompany U(VI), have been separated in the steps taken for the earlier separation of Pb(II) and Th.

Numerous other methods for the separation of uranium are available, and have been surveyed by Korkisch [171].

V. SPECIAL APPROACHES TO ION EXCHANGE SEPARATIONS

A. Cation Exchange in Concentrated Mineral Acids

It has been shown by Djurfeldt et al. [210, 211], that the cation exchange distribution coefficient of Fe(III) has a minimum at about 5M HCl, and then increases to fairly high values. Similar behavior was observed for Ga and Au(III) by Kraus et al. [212]. Since it is known that these elements form the monovalent anions $FeCl_4^-$, $GaCl_4^-$, and $AuCl_4^-$ in concentrated HCl, their strong absorption at first seems to be a bit surprising. According to the interpretation of Diamond et al. [134], this behavior is caused by a combination of two factors. First, the Donnan potential, which excludes co-ions from the resin phase, becomes considerably lowered at high external electrolyte concentrations. The external anions, therefore, are allowed to enter the resin phase, and can form neutral association complexes with the excess of cations present. These anions therefore act as pseudo exchange groups. Second, the large metal chloro-anions disrupt the fairly ordered water structure of the external solution phase more strongly than the smaller chloride anions, and are pushed into the less ordered resin phase for thermo-dynamic reasons. As has been pointed out already, this effect should be included in the ($\Delta G_2 - \Delta G_1$) term of Eisenman's Equations (Equations 6-8).

The long range interaction with the structure of the surroundings also affects the ion exchange equilibrium, in the case of hydrated or solvated cations; in this case the changes in the free energy of hydration or solvation play the more prominent part, except perhaps when very large cations with low charge density are involved.

Because the hydrogen cation is small, and strongly hydrated, it will tend to compete strongly for water molecules when not enough of these are present to satisfy all demands, and thus will tend to influence quite strongly the free energy of hydration of other cations in the aqueous phase. In addition it will tend to change the normal water structure. In concentrated acid solutions, quite a few interesting and novel separations with changed selectivities should, therefore, become possible. The only comprehensive systematic studies of cation exchange distribution coefficients, and cation exchange behavior in such systems, have been carried out in HCl, $HClO_4$, and their mixtures [213], and in HBr [214] by Nelson and his coworkers. Among the interesting separations possible are the elution of barium with 9M $HClO_4$, while strontium is retained and can be eluted with 5M or, even better, 3M HNO_3 [213]. The separation factor is 6.4. Mn(II) is absorbed from 9M $HClO_4$, and can be separated with a separation factor of > 10 from Co(II), Cu(II), and Ni(II), which are not absorbed [213]. Iron(III), Ga(III), Au(III), and Sb(V) are strongly absorbed from 8M or 9M HCl and can be separated, with a separation factor of about 100 or larger, from most elements of the periodic table [213]. In 9M HBr, Mg can be separated from Ca with a separation factor of about 10 [214], while Al, In, and Ga can be separated by the elution sequence 9M HBr for Al, 9M HCl for In(III), 4M HBr or HCl for Ga, with large separation factors [214]. All these separations and many others in the concentrated electrolyte systems, which appear to be attractive because of their relatively high separation factors, have the serious disadvantage of slow and often very slow kinetics. Nelson has tried to overcome this, with good success, in quite a number of cases [214] by using Dowex 50 resin of 4% instead of 8%, cross-linkage, and of very small particle size (20 to 30 μm). In addition he carried out separations in water jacketed columns at elevated temperatures (60°C). Yet alternative procedures in other systems are available in most cases, and are often more attractive because they do not require these special precautions. Nevertheless, separation in concentrated electrolytes may occasionally offer a novel, and sometimes the only solution to a separation problem.

B. Exchange of Cationic Complexes Containing Neutral Ligands

How strongly a cation is adsorbed under a certain set of conditions depends, according to the theory of Eisenman, on its electrostatic interaction with the exchange group, and on the change of its free energy of hydration ΔG_1 when it moves from the external solution into the resin. When the water dipoles in the coordination shell of the cation are replaced by another neutral ligand, which is more strongly bound, but a weaker dipole than water, the outer hydration cloud of the cation will be loosened, and the structure directing influence weakened. As a result the free energy of hydration in the aqueous solution will be lowered, and ΔG_1 will decrease. When this cation is exchanged against another one which does not form a complex with the same ligand, the value of the difference $\Delta G_2 - \Delta G_1$ will increase, and the element forming the complex will be much more strongly absorbed, relative to the uncomplexed element. This effect will be enhanced when the neutral ligands are very large, and the cation is ejected from the water phase, because of its structure disturbing properties.

Elements such as Ni(II), Cu(II), Zn, Cd, and Ag, which do form stable ammine complexes, are much more strongly absorbed from ammonium nitrate solutions containing ammonia, than from ammonium nitrate solutions of the same concentration containing no ammonia. This fact has been known for some time [215], and has found commercial application for the recovery of copper [216]. Based on the stability of the ammine and amine complexes of copper and nickel, Walton has developed a method of ligand exchange chromatography for the separation of organic amines, using cation exchange columns loaded with copper or nickel [217-219](See Chapter by Walton). The reverse application, which uses the strong adsorption of the ammine and amine complexes of some elements by cation exchange resins as a means for the analytical separation of these elements, does not seem to have received much attention. It has been found that Ni(II), Cu(II), Zn, Cd, and Ag can easily be separated, as a group, from Fe(III), Al, Ti(IV), Mg, Ca, Na, K, and many other elements in an ammonium citrate-sulfosalicylate mixture containing excess ammonia [220]. Iron (III), etc. form anionic complexes which are not adsorbed by a column of AG50W-X8 or Dowex 50W-X8 resin in the ammonium form, while Ni(II), etc., form cationic ammine complexes which are considerably more strongly adsorbed than the corresponding aquo complexes, and therefore can easily be separated from the alkali metals, in addition to Fe(III), etc.

By using organic amines which give more stable cationic complexes with a larger number of elements, and carefully selecting the complexing agent

for the anionic complex formation, a large variety of separations should become possible. Another promising reagent which produces cationic complexes
in neutral or acid solutions is thiourea. The separation factors which can be
obtained by using such a selective cation-anion complexing are extremely
high. Furthermore, the ammine and thiourea cations are not excessively
large, and one can expect reasonable kinetics. The approach should be
useful for the concentration of trace elements. It is less attractive for the
total analysis of major elements, because the removal of the complexing agents
and ammonium salts can be troublesome.

REFERENCES

1.   J. I. Bregman, Ann. N. Y. Acad. Sci., 57, 125 (1953).

2.   J. Kennedy, R. V. Davies, and B. K. Robinson, A. E. R. E. Report
       C/R 1896 (1956).

3.   M. Markol, J. Appl. Chem. (London), 16, 191 (1966).

4.   A. Skogseid, Diss. Oslo (1948).

5.   J. Seidl, J. Štamberg, and E. Hrbková, J. Appl. Chem., 12, 500
       (1962).

6.   W. Szczepaniak, Chem. Anal (Warsaw), 8, 843 (1963).

7.   V. A. Klyachko, Doklady Akad. Nauk SSSR, 81, 235 (1951).

8.   G. Manecke, Zeit. Elektrochem., 57, 189 (1953).

9.   J. R. Parrish, Chem. and Ind., 137 (1956).

10.   H. P. Gregor, D. Dolar, and G. K. Hoeschele, J. Am. Chem. Soc.,
       77, 3675 (1955).

11.   H. P. Gregor, M. Taifer, L. Citarel, and E. I. Becher, Ind. Eng.
       Chem., 44, 2834 (1952).

12.   R. C. De Geiso, L. G. Donaruma, and E. A. Tomic, Anal. Chem.,
       34, 845 (1962).

13.   L. D. Pennington and M. B. Williams, Ind. Eng. Chem., 51, 759
       (1959).

14.   E. Bayer, Angew. Chem., 76, 76 (1964).

15. N. Hojo, J. Fac. Textile Sericult., Shinshu Univ., Ser. C, No. 5 (1958).

16. S. B. Savvin, B. F. Myasoedov, and O. P. Eliseeva, Zh. Anal. Khim., 24, 1023 (1969).

17. E. Blasius and G. Olbrich, Z. Anal. Chem., 151, 81 (1956).

18. R. Rosset, Bull. Soc. Chim., France, 59 (1966).

19. E. Blasius and I. Bock, J. Chromatog., 14, 244 (1964).

20. R. Hering, J. Prakt. Chem., 14, 285 (1961).

21. L. Wolf and R. Hering, Chem. Tech. (Berlin), 10, 661 (1958).

22. K. A. Kraus and H. O. Phillips, J. Am. Chem. Soc., 78, 694 (1956).

23. C. B. Amphlett, L. A. McDonald, and M. J. Redman, J. Inorg. Nucl. Chem., 6, 220 (1958).

24. K. H. Koenig and E. Meyn, J. Inorg. Nucl. Chem., 29, 1519 (1967).

25. Y. Inoue, S. Suzuki, and H. Goto, Bull. Chem. Soc., Japan, 37, 1547 (1964).

26. L. Szirtes and L. Zzinka, Chem. Zvesti, 21, 620 (1967).

27. G. Alberti, P. Cardini-Galli, U. Constantino, and I. Torracca, J. Inorg. Nucl. Chem., 30, 639 (1968).

28. K. A. Kraus, H. O. Phillips, T. A. Carlson, and J. S. Johnson, Second Int. Conf. on peaceful uses of At. Energy, Geneva 1958, paper 1832.

29. S. S. Rodin and A. K. Lavrukhina, Radiokhimiya, 4, 623 (1962).

30. M. Qureshi and H. S. Rathore, J. Chem. Soc. A, 2515 (1969).

31. K. A. Kraus, T. A. Carlson, and J. S. Johnson, Nature, 177, 1127 (1956).

32. H. J. Riedel, Ber. Kernforsch., 30, 83 (1962).

33. M. Qureshi and J. P. Gupta, J. Chem. Soc. A, 1755 (1969).

34. A. Clearfield, G. D. Smith, and B. Hammond, J. Inorg. Nucl. Chem., 30, 277 (1968).

35. H. O. Phillips and K. A. Kraus, J. Am. Chem. Soc., 84, 2267 (1962).

36. M. Abe and T. Ito, Nippon Kagaku Zasshi, 87, 1174 (1966).

37.   L. H. Baetsle and D. Huys, J. Inorg. Nucl. Chem., 30, 639 (1968).

38.   M. J. Nunes da Costa and M. A. S. Jeronimo, J. Chromatog., 5, 546 (1961).

39.   A. E. Taylor and C. A. Jensen, J. Am. Chem. Soc., 80, 5918 (1958).

40.   A. Lewandowski and S. Idzikowski, Chem. Anal. (Warsaw), 10, 919 (1965).

41.   J. D. Donaldson, M. J. Fuller, and J. W. Price, J. Inorg. Nucl. Chem., 30, 1083 (1968).

42.   S. Meloni and A. Brandone, Radiochim. Acta, 10, 97 (1968).

43.   H. W. Levi and E. Schiewer, Radiochim. Acta, 5, 126 (1966).

44.   K. A. Kraus and H. O. Phillips, J. Am. Chem. Soc., 78, 249 (1956).

45.   S. Ahrland, I. Grenthe, and B. Noréu, Acta Chem. Scand., 14, 1059 (1960).

46.   R. Prasad and A. K. Dey, Kolloid Z., 183, 71 (1962).

47.   C. B. Amphlett, L. A. McDonald, and M. J. Redman, J. Inorg. Nucl. Chem., 6, 236 (1958).

48.   J. Krtil, J. Chromatog., 20, 384 (1965).

49.   J. Krtil, J. Inorg. Nucl. Chem., 27, 1862 (1965).

50.   V. Kourim, Sb. Ref. Celostatni Radiochem. Konf., 3, Liblice, Czech. (1964) 4.

51.   K. H. Lieser, J. Bastian, and A. B. H. Hecker, Z. Anal. Chem., 228, 98 (1967).

52.   E. V. Kazakov and I. F. Karpova, Vestn. Leningrad Univ. 21, Ser. Fiz. i. Khim. No. 2, 139 (1966).

53.   W. E. Prout, E. R. Russel, and H. J. Groh, J. Inorg. Nucl. Chem., 27, 473 (1965).

54.   L. H. Baetsle, D. Huys, and D. van Deyck, J. Inorg. Nucl. Chem., 28, 2835 (1966).

55.   S. A. Kolesova and V. V. Vol'Khin, Izv. Akad. Nauk SSSR, Neorgan. Materialy, 2, 1110 (1966).

56.   R. B. Hahn and H. C. Klein, Anal. Chem., 40, 1135 (1968).

57.   H. Buchwald and W. P. Thistlewhaite, J. Inorg. Nucl. Chem., 5, 341 (1957).

58. J. van R. Smit, W. Robb, and J. J. Jacobs, J. Inorg. Nucl. Chem., 12, 95 (1960).

59. H. L. Caron and T. T. Sugihara, Anal. Chem., 34, 1082 (1962).

60. W. J. Maek, M. E. Kussy, and J. E. Rein, Anal. Chem., 35, 2086 (1963).

61. V. Kourzhim, A. K. Lavrukhina, and S. S. Rodin, Dokl. Akad. Nauk. SSSR, 140, 832 (1961).

62. E. R. Tompkins, J. X. Khym, and W. E. Cohn, J. Am. Chem. Soc., 69, 2769 (1947).

63. E. R. Tompkins and S. W. Mayer, J. Am. Chem. Soc., 69, 2859 (1947).

64. F. W. Cornish, Analyst, 83, 634 (1958).

65. E. Glueckauf, Trans. Faraday Soc., 51, 34 (1955).

66. F. W. E. Strelow, C. J. Liebenberg, and F. von S. Toerien, Anal. Chim. Acta, 43, 465 (1968).

67. S. Fronaeus, Acta Chem. Scand., 5, 859 (1951).

68. R. I. Walter, J. Inorg. Nucl. Chem., 6, 58 (1958).

69. J. Gillis, J. Hoste, P. Cornand, and A. Speeke, Mededel. Koninkl. Vlaam, Acad. Wetenschap Belg., 15, 63 (1953).

70. M. Herrman, Ind. Chim. Belge, 23, 123 (1958).

71. W. R. Bandi, E. G. Buyok, L. L. Lewis, and L. M. Melnik, Anal. Chem., 33, 1275 (1961).

72. R. K. Preobrazhensky and L. M. Moskvin, Radiokhimiya, 3, 309 (1961).

73. E. P. Tsintsevich, I. P. Alimarin, and L. F. Marchenkova, Chem. Ab., 53, 10898 (1959).

74. Z. Dizdar, Rec. Trav. Inst. Recherches Structure Matiere, 2, 85 (1953).

75. M. R. Zaki and K. Shakir, Z. Anal. Chem., 185, 422 (1962).

76. F. De Corte, P. van den Winkel, A. Speeke, and J. Hoste, Anal. Chim. Acta, 42, 67 (1968).

77. T. Nozaki, O. Hiraiwa, Ch. Henmi, and K. Koshiba, Bull. Chem. Soc. Japan, 42, 245 (1969).

78.   F. W. E. Strelow and C. H. S. W. Weinert, unpublished work,
      N. C. R. L., Pretoria, 1969.

79.   F. W. E. Strelow, Anal. Chem., 32, 1185 (1960).

80.   F. W. E. Strelow, C. R. van Zyl, and C. R. Nolte, Anal. Chim.
      Acta, 40, 145 (1968).

81.   F. W. E. Strelow and C. R. van Zyl, Anal. Chim. Acta, 41, 529
      (1968).

82.   F. W. E. Strelow, Anal. Chem., 40, 928 (1968).

83.   H. Honda, Japan Analyst, 3, 132 (1953).

84.   G. Eulitz, Z. Anal. Chem., 178, 360 (1961).

85.   H. Tsubota, Bull. Chem. Soc. Japan, 33, 770 (1960).

86.   G. M. Milton and W. E. Grummit, Can. J. Chem., 35, 541 (1957).

87.   E. Hantabal, M. Fojtik, V. Rusek, and T. Trnovec, Chem. Zvesti,
      18, 203 (1964).

88.   M. Lerner and W. Rieman, Anal. Chem., 26, 610 (1954).

89.   L. Wish, Anal. Chem., 33, 53 (1961).

90.   F. H. Pollard, G. Nickless, and D. Spincer, J. Chromatog., 13,
      224 (1964).

91.   J. J. Bouquiaux and J. H. C. Gillard, Anal. Chim. Acta, 30,
      273 (1964).

92.   P. Povondra, Z. Sulcek, R. Pr̆ibil, and R. Stangl, Talanta, 8, 705
      (1961).

93.   Z. Sulcek, P. Povondra, R. Pr̆ibil, and R. Stangl, Talanta, 9, 467
      (1962).

94.   P. Povondra and R. Pr̆ibil, Talanta, 10, 713 (1963).

95.   W. E. Bennett and D. O. Skovlin, Anal. Chem., 38, 518 (1966).

96.   J. H. Carpenter, Limnol. and Oceanography, 2, 271 (1957).

97.   F. W. E. Strelow and C. H. S. W. Weinert, Talanta, 17, 1 (1970).

98.   J. Korkisch and F. Feik, Anal. Chem., 37, 757 (1965).

99.   A. Lindenbaum and A. Westfall, J. Phys. Chem., 62, 390 (1958).

100. J. Kennedy and V. J. Wheeler, Anal. Chim. Acta, 20, 412 (1959).

101. D. C. Sutton, USAEC Rept. No. HASL-134 (1963).

102. H. Tsubota, Bull. Chem. Soc. Japan, 38, 159 (1965).

103. N. F. Kember, P. J. MacDonald, and R. A. Wells, J. Chem. Soc., 2273, 1955.

104. O. Samuelson and E. Sjöström, Anal. Chem., 26, 1908 (1954).

105. G. Carleson, Acta Chem. Scand., 8, 1673 (1954).

106. E. W. Berg and J. T. Trümper, Anal. Chem., 30, 1827 (1958).

107. Y. Yoshino and Y. Kurimura, Bull. Chem. Soc. Japan, 30, 563 (1957).

108. M. Kojima, Japan Analyst, 6, 369 (1957).

109. M. Kojima, Japan Analyst, 7, 177 (1958).

110. P. C. van Erkelens, Anal. Chim. Acta, 25, 42 (1961).

111. D. J. Pietrzyk and J. S. Fritz, U. S. At. Energy Comm. Rep. IS-337, Nov. 1960.

112. J. S. Fritz and P. J. Pietrzyk, Talanta, 8, 143 (1961).

113. J. S. Fritz and T. A. Rettig, Anal. Chem., 34, 1562 (1962).

114. J. Korkisch and S. S. Ahluwalia, Talanta, 14, 155 (1967).

115. J. Korkisch, F. Feik, and S. S. Ahluwalia, Talanta, 14, 1069 (1967).

116. J. Korkisch and E. Klakl, Talanta, 16, 377 (1969).

117. L. W. Marple and D. Price, Proc. Iowa Acad. Sci., 73, 74 (1966).

118. D. J. Pietrzyk and D. L. Kiser, Anal. Chem., 37, 233 (1965).

119. J. Korkisch and S. S. Ahluwalia, Z. Anal. Chem., 215, 86 (1966).

120. J. Korkisch and I. Hazan, Talanta, 11, 1157 (1964).

121. K. A. Orlandini and J. Korkisch, Anal. Chim. Acta, 43, 459 (1968).

122. T. Cummings and J. Korkisch, Talanta, 14, 1185 (1967).

123. J. Korkisch and F. Feik, Anal. Chem., 36, 1793 (1964).

124. J. Korkisch and I. Hazan, Anal. Chem., 37, 707 (1965).

125. J. S. Fritz and M. L. Gilette, Talanta, 15, 287 (1968).

126. J. Korkisch, I. Hazan, and G. Arrhenius, Talanta, 10, 865 (1963).

127.   J. Korkisch and K. A. Orlandini, Anal. Chem., 40, 1952 (1968).

128.   J. Korkisch and K. A. Orlandini, Talanta, 16, 45 (1969).

129.   J. Korkisch and K. A. Orlandini, Anal. Chem., 40, 1127 (1968).

130.   J. Korkisch and A. Huber, Talanta, 15, 119 (1968).

131.   F. W. E. Strelow and Cynthia Baxter, Talanta, 16, 1145 (1969).

132.   G. Eisenman, Biophys. J. Suppl., 2, 259 (1962).

133.   G. Eisenman, Membrane Transport and Metabolism, Academic
       Press, New York, 1961, 163-179.

134.   R. M. Diamond and D. C. Witney, Ion Exchange (J. A. Marinsky, ed.),
       Vol. 1, Chapter 8, Marcel Dekker, Inc., New York, 1966.

135.   H. S. Frank and Wen-Yang Wen, Faraday Soc. Disc., 24, 133 (1957).

136.   K. A. Kraus and F. Nelson, Int. Conf. on Peaceful uses of Atomic
       Energy, Geneva, 1955, Paper No. 837.

137.   C. W. Davis and B. D. R. Owen, J. Chem. Soc., 1676 (1956).

138.   H. P. Gregor, D. Nobel and M. H. Gottlich, J. Phys. Chem., 59,
       10 (1955).

139.   J. Korkisch and S. S. Ahluwalia, Anal. Chem., 38, 497 (1966).

140.   J. Korkisch, Nature, 210, 626 (1966).

141.   F. W. E. Strelow and K. G. R. Pachler, Unpublished work, 1962.

142.   F. W. E. Strelow, C. R. van Zyl, and C. J. C. Bothma, Anal.
       Chim. Acta, 45, 81 (1969).

143.   F. W. E. Strelow and C. H. S. W. Weinert, Unpublished work,
       1968.

144.   V. Nevoral, Z. Anal. Chem., 195, 332 (1963).

145.   Z. Šulcek, P. Povondra, and R. Štangl, Chemist-Analyst, 55, 36
       (1966).

146.   R. Ratner and Z. Ludmer, Israel J. Chem., 2, 21 (1964).

147.   F. Nelson, D. C. Michelson, H. O. Phillips, and K. A. Kraus,
       J. Chromatog., 20, 107 (1965).

148.   F. W. E. Strelow and C. H. S. W. Weinert, Unpublished work,
       1968.

149.   R. R. Ruch, F. Tera, and G. H. Morrison, Anal. Chem., 36, 2311
       (1964).

150.   C. Venturello, C. Gualandi, and I. Mazzei, Ann. Chim. (Rome), 49,
       149 (1959).

151.   C. Gualandi, I. Mazzei, and G. Burana, Ann. Chem. (Rome), 49,
       1941 (1959).

152.   J. S. Fritz and H. Waki, Anal. Chem., 35, 1079 (1963).

153.   K. Kurokawa, Nippon Kagaku Zasshi, 88, 188 1967; (J. Chem. Soc.
       Japan, Pure Chem. Sect.).

154.   F. Nelson, J. H. Holloway, and K. A. Kraus, J. Chromatog., 11,
       258 (1963).

155.   J. S. Fritz and H. Waki, Anal. Chem., 36, 900 (1964).

156.   F. W. E. Strelow, Anal. Chem., 35, 1279 (1963).

157.   J. S. Fritz and J. E. Abbink, Anal. Chem., 34, 1080 (1962).

158.   F. W. E. Strelow, J. South African Chem. Inst., 16, 38 (1963).

159.   F. W. E. Strelow and C. R. van Zyl, J. South African Chem. Inst.,
       20, 1 (1967).

160.   J. Korkisch and G. E. Janauer, Talanta, 9, 957 (1962).

161.   J. Korkisch, Mikrochimica Acta, 1964, 816.

162.   F. W. E. Strelow and Cynthia Baxter, Talanta, 16, 1145 (1969).

163.   F. W. E. Strelow, Anal. Chem., 31, 1201 (1959).

164.   I. Hazan and J. Korkisch, Anal. Chim. Acta, 32, 46 (1965).

165.   F. W. E. Strelow, C. R. van Zyl, A. H. Victor, A. J. Gricius,
       and C. Eloff, Unpublished work, 1970.

166.   F. W. E. Strelow and C. H. S. W. Weinert, Unpublished work, 1968.

167.   F. W. E. Strelow and Cynthia Baxter, J. South African Chem. Inst.,
       22, 29 (1969).

168.   Kazuo Kurokawa, J. Chem. Soc. Japan, Pure Chem. Sect., 89,
       1076 (1968).

169.   Kazuo Kurokawa, J. Chem. Soc. Japan, Pure Chem. Sect., 88,
       1171 (1967).

170.   J. Korkisch and S. S. Ahluwalia, J. Inorg. Nucl. Chem., 28, 264
       (1966).

171.   J. Korkisch, Modern Methods for the Separation of rarer metal ions, Pergamon Press, Oxford, 1969.

172.   S. S. Ahluwalia and J. Korkisch, Anal. Chim. Acta, 31, 552 (1964).

173.   J. P. Faris and J. W. Warton, Anal. Chem., 34, 1077 (1962).

174.   F. Molnar, A. Horvath, and V. A. Khalkin, J. Chromatog., 26, 215 (1967).

175.   J. S. Fritz and R. G. Greene, Anal. Chem., 36, 1095 (1964).

176.   R. A. Edge, J. Chromatog., 5, 526 (1961).

177.   R. A. Edge, Anal. Chim. Acta, 29, 321 (1963).

178.   J. Korkisch and G. E. Janauer, Talanta, 9, 957 (1962).

179.   F. Feik and J. Korkisch, Talanta, 11, 1585 (1964).

180.   J. Korkisch and F. Feik, Anal. Chim. Acta, 32, 110 (1965).

181.   G. E. Janauer and J. Korkisch, J. Chromatog., 8, 510 (1962).

182.   F. W. E. Strelow, Anal. Chem., 31, 1201 (1959).

183.   F. W. E. Strelow, Anal. Chem., 33, 1648 (1961).

184.   F. W. E. Strelow, Anal. Chem., 39, 1454 (1967).

185.   K. A. Orlandini and J. Korkisch, Separation Science, 3, 255 (1968).

186.   J. Yosimura and H. Vaki, Japan Analyst, 6, 362 (1957).

187.   Y. Oki, S. Oki, and H. Shibata, Bull. Chem. Soc. Japan, 35, 273 (1962).

188.   A. D. Maines, Anal. Chim. Acta, 32, 211 (1965).

189.   F. W. E. Strelow, C. J. Liebenberg, and F. von S. Toerien, Anal. Chim. Acta, 47, 251 (1969).

190.   F. W. E. Strelow and C. H. S. W. Weinert, Unpublished work, 1970.

191.   F. W. E. Strelow, J. H. J. Coetzee, and C. R. van Zyl, Anal. Chem., 40, 196 (1968).

192.   F. W. E. Strelow, C. J. Liebenberg, and F. von S. Toerien, Anal. Chem., 41, 2058 (1969).

193.   F. W. E. Strelow, F. von S. Toerien, and C. H. S. W. Weinert, Anal. Chem. Acta, 50, 399 (1970).

194. F. W. E. Strelow, Anal. Chem., 39, 1454 (1967).

195. F. W. E. Strelow and F. von S. Toerien, Anal. Chem., 38, 545
      (1966).

196. T. Anderson and A. B. Knudsen, Acta Chem. Scand., 16, 849 (1962).

197. R. H. Herber and J. W. Irvine Jr., J. Am. Chem. Soc., 76, 987
      (1954).

198. J. S. Fritz and B. B. Garralda, Anal. Chem., 34, 102 (1962).

199. J. S. Fritz and R. G. Greene, Anal. Chem., 35, 811 (1963).

200. F. Nelson and K. A. Kraus, J. Am. Chem. Soc., 76, 5916 (1954).

201. J. S. Fritz and L. H. Dahmer, Anal. Chem., 37, 1272 (1965).

202. F. W. E. Strelow, Anal. Chem., 35, 1279 (1963).

203. F. W. E. Strelow, J. South African Chem. Inst., 16, 38 (1963).

204. F. W. E. Strelow and C. R. van Zyl, J. South African Chem. Inst.,
      20, 1 (1967).

205. B. P. Radhakrischna, Anal. Chim. Acta, 6, 351 (1952).

206. O. A. Nietzel, B. W. Wessling, and M. A. de Sesa, Anal. Chem.,
      30, 1182 (1958).

207. J. Korkisch and P. Antal, Z. Anal. Chem., 173, 126 (1960).

208. J. Danon, J. Am. Chem. Soc., 78, 5953 (1956).

209. D. J. Carswell, J. Inorg. Nucl. Chem., 3, 384 (1957).

210. R. Djurfeldt and O. Samuelson, Acta Chem. Scand., 4, 165 (1950).

211. H. Titze and O. Samuelson, Acta Chem. Scand., 16, 678 (1962).

212. K. A. Kraus, D. C. Michelson, and F. Nelson, J. Am. Chem. Soc.,
      81, 3204 (1959).

213. F. Nelson, T. Murase, and K. A. Kraus, J. Chromatog., 13, 503
      (1964).

214. F. Nelson and D. C. Michelson, J. Chromatog., 25, 414 (1966).

215. R. Nelson and H. F. Walton, J. Phys. Chem., 48, 406 (1944).

216. F. Gerstner, Z. Electrochem., 57, 221 (1953).

217. J. J. Latterell and H. F. Walton, Anal. Chim. Acta, 32, 101 (1965).

218.   A. G. Hill, R. Sedgley, and H. F. Walton, <u>Anal. Chim. Acta</u>, <u>33</u>, 84 (1965).

219.   K. Shimormura, L. Dickson, and H. F. Walton, <u>Anal. Chim. Acta</u>, <u>37</u>, 102 (1967).

220.   F. W. E. Strelow and F. von S. Toerien, Unpublished work, 1969.

Chapter 3

PELLICULAR ION EXCHANGE RESINS IN CHROMATOGRAPHY

Csaba Horvath

Yale University
New Haven, Connecticut 06520

I. INTRODUCTION

Ion exchange resins employed in packed beds have traditionally been spherical or irregularly shaped particles whose whole mass is made up of the swollen resin itself. This conventional form of resins has the advantage that a large amount of ion exchanger can be packed into a given bed without drastically reducing its permeability. Therefore, ion exchange resins have customarily been manufactured also in this conventional form, to meet the needs of most technological applications for high bed capacity.

Since the use of ion exchange resins in analytical chemistry began, with the pioneer work of Samuelson [1], such resins from commercial sources have been employed very successfully. The introduction of ion exchange resins in chromatography [2-4] has greatly expanded the scope of such applications, and ion exchange chromatography has become the most prominent branch of liquid chromatography [5]. Resins used for packing chromatographic columns have essentially had the same structure as those used in large scale technological applications, and only their purity and uniformity have been improved, and their particle size range reduced. The high capacity of these resins has been useful also in chromatography, since high column loading capacity is required for separations on the preparative and semipreparative scale, and in analytical work, when the low sensitivity of the effluent monitoring technique demands relatively high solute concentrations in the effluent.

Recently, ion exchange chromatography and liquid chromatography in general have been undergoing a rapid development. On the one hand, this phenomenon is rooted mainly in the broadening of our theoretical and practical approach to chromatography, by experience gained in gas chromatography. On the other hand, the need for fast, reliable, and convenient techniques for the analysis of nonvolatile substances has greatly increased, particularly due to the rapid advancement of the life sciences.

It was recognized some time ago that the full potential of liquid column chromatography, including ion exchange chromatography, has not been exploited by the conventional techniques, and that its speed and efficiency as well as sensitivity could be increased significantly. Thus, the development of suitable instrumentation was initiated in order to provide adequate hardware for controlling eluent flow and column temperature, as well as to facilitate sample introduction at high column inlet pressures, and effluent monitoring with highly sensitive detectors. Since the column is the most important part of the chromatographic system, the design of high efficiency columns became imperative, and a variety of new approaches were explored. In addition, the solution of complex separation problems necessitated the development of novel "software," encompassing column combinations, elution modes and programming techniques. By the incorporation of these features into a liquid chromatograph, a high performance analytical tool has been obtained which can be coupled to suitable readout and data handling devices, and finally automated.

Although this development is still in its infancy, it has already become clear that a new analytical technique is evolving, which is rightfully called high performance liquid chromatography. By virtue of its performance and convenience of operation, this technique is actually closer to gas chromatography than to conventional liquid chromatography. As the attainment of high performance requires the column to be operated at relatively high inlet pressures, the technique is also termed "high pressure liquid chromatography," in order to distinguish it from conventional column chromatography, at low pressures. Modern amino acid analyzers [6-8], which embody sophisticated hardware, detectors, and columns packed with newly developed ion exchange resins, amply demonstrate the potential of high performance liquid chromatography.

This chapter is devoted to a new type of ion exchange resins, which has been developed to meet the specific need of high performance liquid chromatography for suitable column packing. In contrast to conventional resins, this material consists of spherules whose outer shell only is formed of the actual ion exchange resin, and the bulk of the particle consists of a fluid impermeable core such as glass. As the resin layer surrounds the impervious core like a thin skin, these materials have been called pellicular ion exchange resins. Since sensitive detectors have been available, these resins have found increasing use in liquid chromatography, despite their relatively low capacity.

II. NONCONVENTIONAL ION EXCHANGE RESIN PARTICLES

In most processes which involve columns packed with conventional ion exchange resins, the rate determining step is solute diffusion inside the resin particles. Mass transfer across the stagnant liquid film surrounding the particles usually proceeds at rates higher than those of diffusion in the gel [9]. Most commonly, the speed of separation in ion exchange chromatography is limited also by intraparticular diffusion [10], and any significant improvement of the overall column efficiency must be achieved by an increase of mass transfer rates in the resin phase.

We can conceive a number of ways to approach such a goal. Elevated column temperature, for example, would be desirable from the dynamic point of view, but since the temperature coefficient of equilibrium constants is usually greater than that of diffusivity, the net effect of increasing column temperature on the separation efficiency is not necessarily beneficial. In addition, breakdown of the resin can easily occur at high temperatures over an extended period of time. Higher gel diffusivities could be obtained also by lowering the degree of crosslinking. However, the excessive swelling and shrinking, as well as the poorer mechanical properties of low crosslinked resins, make their use in packed beds impractical. A more promising approach is to reduce particle size, thereby increasing mass transfer rates by reduction of intraparticular diffusion path length. However, the pressure drop necessary to maintain a given flow velocity through a column is inversely proportional to the squared particle diameter. Thus, higher inlet pressures are needed with smaller particles, and the available inlet pressure and the instability of the packing at large pressure gradients limit the minimum particle size. Nevertheless, this approach is likely to become important in the development of high-performance liquid chromatography, as technical problems of operating the instrument at several hundred atmospheres are solved, and resins of improved mechanical properties become available. Indeed, the use of columns packed with resin particles of a few microns in diameter has already demonstrated the great potential of this approach [11, 12, 13].

Although the means to increase intraparticular mass transfer rates appear to be exhausted by the above possibilities, the diffusion path length in the resin can be reduced by departing from the conventional resin structure, to increase diffusion rates without decreasing particle diameter. As early as 1952 Pepper [14, 14a] brought forward the idea of confining the actual ion exchange resin to a thin layer on a suitable carrier. This concept has been reduced to practice in three different ways; hence, we can distinguish the following three groups of nonconventional ion exchange resins: (a) superficial, (b) supported, and (c) pellicular resins. The structure of these resin types is illustrated schematically in Figure 1.

Superficial ion exchange resins are obtained by converting only the outer shell of suitable crosslinked polymer beads into ion exchange resin as first suggested by Weiss [15]. Parrish [16] prepared a superficial cation exchange resin having a capacity of 5.3 μEq/ml by sulfonating crosslinked polystyrene beads along a shallow surface layer. According to expectation, rapid separations were obtained with this material in chromatography. A more detailed study of the properties of superficial cation exchange resins was carried out recently by Skafi and Lieser [17]. Resins of different capacities were obtained by partial sulfonation of very highly crosslinked (25 mol % DVB) polystyrene beads. The degree of sulfonation was controlled by varying the time of reaction. Diffusion measurements indicated, however, that film diffusion was controlling only with the lowest capacity resin. The capacity of this resin was about 0.6 μEq/g in comparison to 0.01 and 5000 μEq/g capacities calculated for a sulfonated monolayer and measured with conventional Dowex 50 x 12 resin, respectively. Since a very highly crosslinked polymer was selected in order to obtain an ion exchanger layer of uniform thickness

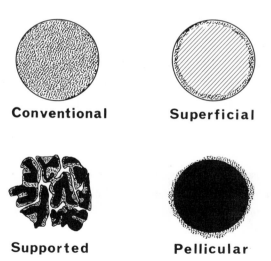

Conventional   **Superficial**

Supported   **Pellicular**

FIG. 1. Schematic illustration of nonconventional ion exchange resin particles.

and sharp boundary, solute diffusivity in the superficial layer was obviously very low to explain the fact that resins of layer thickness greater than a few monolayers showed gel diffusion control despite the superficial structure. Skafi and Lieser [18] found that the selectivity of their resin was similar to that of corresponding conventional resins. They also demonstrated [19] that rapid separations could be obtained with superficial resins in chromatography, although the very low capacity of their resin can be a serious handicap in most applications. Recently Fricke et al. also described a technique for making superficial ion exchange resins [19a].

Supported ion exchange resins are obtained by forming ion exchange resin in the cavities of porous carriers. Boardman [20, 21] prepared such resins in a sealed tube by precipitation copolymerization of suitable monomers in methanol solution in the presence of Celite. Thus, the copolymer was deposited in the porous structure of the support material. A weak cation exchange resin was made from methacrylic acid and divinylbenzene (10% crosslinking). The capacity of this resin was 0.69 mEq/g, compared to the 9.2 mEq/g capacity of Amberlite IRC-50. For the preparation of a strong cation exchanger, styrene and divinylbenzene (5%) were polymerized onto silanized Celite in a similar procedure, and the product was subsequently sulfonated. The capacity of this resin was 0.28 mEq/g. The reason for preparing such resins was to obtain higher resin capacities for proteins than those of conventional resins. Since large molecules cannot penetrate resins having the usual degree of crosslinking, the increased surface to volume ratio of supported resins was expected to give higher protein adsorption values than those obtained with conventional resins. The chromatographic studies of Boardman [22] have indeed shown that proteins have relatively high adsorptiv-ity on supported resins. However, such effects can now be obtained conveniently with macroreticular resins which were developed after this study was completed. As the support material can impart adequate mechanical stability to the resin, an extra advantage of supported ion exchange resins is that they can have a much lower degree of crosslinking than usual conventional resins, and can still be used in columns. By using Boardman's technique, Feitelson and Partridge [23] prepared a supported strong cation exchange resin with crosslinking of the order of 0.5 to 1.0%. This material was used for the separation of large peptides by elution chromatography.

Liquid ion exchangers on porous support have also been used in liquid-liquid chromatography [24, 25]. Such supported ion exchangers appear to be particularly promising in chromatographic separation of large molecules. It is worth mentioning that supported ion exchangers have also been employed in chromatographic techniques other than column chromatography. Since Flood [26] first employed aluminum hydroxide to impart ion exchange properties to paper, a variety of ion exchangers has been used on paper support in paper chromatography. In thin layer chromatography polyethylene imine impregnated cellulose has frequently been used since Randerath [27] demonstrated the advantages of this cellulose supported anion exchanger.

Pellicular ion exchange resins combine properties of both superficial and supported resins. Here the resin has the same spherical annulus configuration as superficial resins but the resin layer is formed by deposition onto the surface of the support, rather than from the core material itself. Thus, similarly to supported resins, neither the degree of crosslinking nor the chemical structure of the resin are limited, while the favorable physical configuration of superficial resins is retained. A photomicrograph of pellicular anion exchange resin particles is shown in Figure 2. Pellicular ion exchange resins were introduced by Horvath et al. [28] in high performance liquid chromatography, and found application rapidly in nucleic acid analysis. Later Kirkland [29] developed similar resins having pellicular structure, which are sometimes called "controlled surface porosity ion exchange resins."

III. PELLICULAR RESINS

A. Preparation

The formation of a well defined and stable resin layer on the surface of tiny spherules requires a more complex procedure than the preparation of conventional resins. As the support particles are usually smaller than 50 µm, the difficulties in making a uniform resin layer on their surface without agglomeration of the particles can be easily appreciated. A great deal of experience is required to obtain reproducible products, and details of the processes used by the manufacturers have not been published.

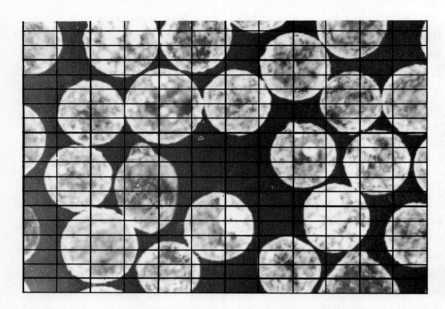

FIG. 2. Photomicrograph of pellicular strong anion exchange resin beads. Particle diameter range 44-53 μm.

In the author's laboratory, the following three methods have been investigated and found to give pellicular resins but none are sufficiently refined to provide batch to batch reproducibility. So far the chemistry of preparation has been essentially the same as that used in the preparation of conventional ion exchangers [30].

1. Layer Formation by Colloidal Particles

This method resembles the preparation of ion exchange membranes by using finely ground resins [31]. Actually, pellicular resins can be considered as thin spherical ion exchange membranes supported by glass beads; thus, concepts used in the preparation of membranes may be applied to making pellicular ion exchangers. Submicron sized ion exchange resin powders can be obtained, for example, by grinding a mixture of commercial resins and salt in a vibrating mill, and then removing the salt by washing. In order to obtain a pellicular resin, glass beads are coated with a paste or slurry containing the resin powder and a suitable binder in a volatile solvent.

Then, the solvent is evaporated while the beads are agitated to avoid agglomeration. The selection of a proper binder plays a crucial role in this process. Dispersions obtained by kneading finely ground ion exchange resins with colloidon have been successfully used in this procedure, in agreement with earlier findings that colloidon serves as suitable matrix for ion exchange membranes [32].

A refinement of this method has been described by Kirkland [33]. The resin coating on glass beads is formed by layers of fine ion exchange resin particles alternating with interlayers of still smaller particles of silica. The coating is held together by opposite electrical charges of the adjacent layers. For example, an anion exchange resin can be prepared by treatment of glass beads, first with a suspension of 100-500 mμ particles of Amberlite XE 255, then with a suspension of Ludox AM, a very fine silica modified with alumina. The product is dried after each treatment and the procedure is repeated until a sufficiently thick layer is built up. The alternating layers of the positively charged resin and the negatively charged silica particles form a uniform and coherent coating.

2. In Situ Resin Formation in the Cavities of a Porous Surface Layer

A number of methods have been described for forming a porous layer of an inert support, or adsorbent on the surface of glass beads for use as column packing in gas chromatography [34]. Recently, porous layer coated beads have found application also in high performance liquid chromatography [35-37]. Glass beads with etched surface are available commercially, and have been used as support in liquid chromatography [38].

When the porous surface layer of such materials is impregnated with a suitable monomer mixture containing an initiator, crosslinked polymer can be formed in the cavities of the layer in situ.

Ionogenic groups are either introduced into the polymer by subsequent chemical reaction, or they are already present when ionogenic monomers are used. An advantage of this method is that polymerization can be carried out under a variety of conditions. For example, the impregnated beads are suspended in a liquid which is not a solvent of the components in the monomer mixture, and the polymerization is carried out by heating and stirring the suspension. The polymerization may also be carried out in a sealed container without a suspending liquid, by heating or irradiation. In a similar fashion the porous layer can be impregnated with a soluble polymer which is then crosslinked in situ.

A disadvantage of this method is that swelling of the resin in the cavities may result in the destruction of the membrane layer, with subsequent peeling from the glass support. The amount of polymer therefore has to be limited, to coat only the pore walls, so that it can swell without restriction in the cavities of the porous layer. This is conveniently achieved by using a solution of the monomers in a volatile solvent such as ether, for impregnation, and by evaporating the solvent prior to polymerization.

3. Resin Formation in Situ Directly on the Support Surface

The sorbent layer of pellicular resins obtained in the above procedures does not consist of ion exchange resin entirely. Thus, the sorption properties of such resins are influenced by the binder, or the material which forms the primary porous surface layer. The effect of these ingredients on the chromatographic properties of pellicular resins thus prepared has not yet been investigated, and it may be beneficial in special applications. Nevertheless, a resin layer of uniform chemical structure offers the advantages of greater uniformity, as well as stability, because the resin can swell unhindered and uniformly.

When fine glass beads, whose surface has been treated to procure satisfactory adherence of the resin, are coated with the monomer mixture, it is possible to carry out the polymerization so that a resin layer is formed in situ on the support surface. The surface treatment of glass can be carried out with a silanizing agent such as dichlorodimethyl silane, used for inactivation of support in gas chromatography. Depending on the polymer to be formed one of the following coupling agents may also be used: γ-aminopropyl triethoxy silane, β-(3,4-epoxycyclohexyl) ethyltrimethoxysilane and γ-methacryloxypropyltrimethoxysilane.

In one process, surface treated glass beads are first coated with a mixture of styrene, divinyl benzene, and an initiation, and the polymerization is carried out in an aqueous slurry of these beads in a fashion similar to the suspension polymerization process used in the manufacture of conventional resins [28, 39]. Alternatively, the monomers and initiator are dissolved in a solvent which does not swell the polymer. The polymerization is carried out in a slurry of glass beads in this solution, under vigorous stirring so that the polymer precipitates onto the surface of the beads. The control of the thickness of the polymer layer formed by these processes requires very precise adjustment of the conditions, i.e., stirring, temperature, and the relative amounts of monomers, glass beads, and solvent or dispersing agents. In order to obtain a sufficiently thick layer, it may be necessary to repeat the procedure. The precipitation copolymerization process has a greater flexibility but gives a less well defined and more inhomogeneous resin coating than suspension polymerization.

In the case of crosslinked polystyrene coating, strong pellicular cation and anion exchange resins are obtained by sulfonation, and by chloromethylation followed by amination with a tertiary amine, respectively. Although the chemistry involved in performing these reactions is essentially the same as that used in making conventional resins, less severe conditions are needed because the diffusion of the reactants in the polymer is facilitated by the shell structure. On the other hand, vigorous stirring has to be avoided because attrition of the polymer may occur, due to the ball mill effect. Generally, the handling of the materials requires great care to avoid removal of the resin from the glass by mechanical action.

B. Characterization

The properties of pellicular resins are determined by the chemical structure and degree of crosslinking of the actual resin, the thickness and composition of the resin layer, and by the core material and its particle size. Although the final test for these resins is the performance of the chromatographic column in a given application, valuable information can be obtained concerning their behavior by the methods described in the following sections.

1. Capacity

The ion exchange capacity of pellicular resins depends primarily on their actual ion exchange resin content, but other components, e.g., silica, may also contribute. The standard methods employed with ion exchange resins [40, 41] can often be used also to determine the exchange capacity

of pellicular resins. In the author's laboratory, direct titration with added
salt has been found a reliable and rapid method when the resin coating is free
of interfering ingredients. It can conveniently be carried out with a potentiometric titration, and if the titrator can be used for pH-stat measurements, the
rate of neutralization can also be studied.

For determining ion exchange capacities, cation and anion exchange
resins are first conditioned in the regular fashion. They are then converted
into the hydrogen and hydroxyl form, respectively. Then the resins are
dried in air at room temperature. Strongly acidic cation exchangers are
titrated directly with sodium hydroxide, but other resins have to be titrated
in salt solution with an appropriate titrant. In most cases correct data are
obtained in less than one hour. From the titration curve, the ion exchange
capacity is calculated as usual, and expressed in microequivalents per gram
air dry resin. Figure 3 shows titration curves of strong anion and cation
exchange resins both of the polystyrene type which were, according to the
manufacturer, made by resin formation directly on the glass bead surface.
The cation and anion exchange resins contained sulfonic acid and dimethyl-
benzylamino groups, respectively. It is seen that at least two different
cationic groups are present in the anion exchanger. It has been found that
the chromatographic properties of such material are determined usually not
only by the total ion exchange capacity but also by the relative amounts of
the weaker and stronger basic groups.

According to Kirkland [35], standard methods are not applicable to the
determination of the ion exchange capacity of Zipax cation exchangers because
the siliceous core interferes in the analytical procedure, due to the acidity
of the silanol groups. Kirkland, therefore, first converted this resin into a
zinc salt which is formed only via the sulfonic acid groups. After removing
the zinc ions by treatment with hydrochloric acid, the ion exchange capacity
was calculated from the zinc concentration in the eluent, as measured by
atomic absorption spectroscopy. When very low ion exchange capacities are
encountered, it may be necessary to use similar microanalytical techniques.
Resort to radioactive tracer measurements [18, 19] may even be necessary.
However, with pellicular resins of higher capacity the titration curve method
is preferred because it provides information also about the capacities of
various ionic groups with different pK values that may be present in the
resin.

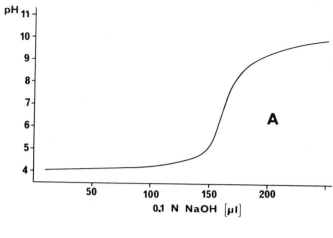

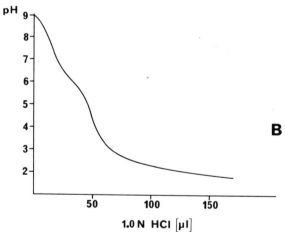

FIG. 3. Titration curves of pellicular ion exchange resins. A. Direct titration of 2 g of strong cation exchanger. B. Titration of 5 g of strong anion exchanger in 5% NaCl solution. The potentiometric titrations were carried out in 50 min using a Radiometer automatic titrator.

A variety of pellicular resins having average particle size in the range 20 to 100 μm have been investigated by the titration method, and their ion exchange capacity was found to range between 5 and 60 μEq/g. These capacity values are 200 and 1000 times smaller than those of conventional resins. For columnar applications, however, it is more meaningful to compare

capacities of wet resins on a volume basis. Then the discrepancy is, of
course, smaller because of the relatively high density of pellicular resins.

In chromatographic applications the adsorption capacity of the resin for
given substances would be of interest because it can be better correlated to
the chromatographic behavior than can ion exchange capacity. Since adsorption capacities greatly depend on the experimental conditions, and their
measurement requires an elaborate procedure, the chromatographic evaluation of the resins is preferably carried out with packed columns, as discussed
in Section B. 6.

2. Density

The density of pellicular resins is close to the density of the core
material which frequently makes up more than 98 weight percent of the
product. Since the density of soda lime glass is 2.4 to 2.6 g/cm^3, pellicular
resins have a much higher density than conventional resins. The high density
is advantageous because it facilitates dry screening and the packing of
columns with dry resin. The void fraction in dry packed beds was found to
be about 0.4, but a significant decrease of interparticular porosity has been
observed after filling the columns with liquids which swell the resin.

3. Layer Thickness and Uniformity

Visual observation of the beads under the microscope is the most
convenient method for estimating the thickness and uniformity of the resin
layer. Staining the resin greatly facilitates this examination. A variety of
dyes may be used [42], but acid fuchsin, and Rhodamine B give the most
satisfactory staining of the anion and cation exchange resins, respectively.
First, the beads are immersed in the dye solution, then the excess dye solution is removed by filter paper, and the beads are dried. After placing the
beads on a microscope slide, a drop of immersion oil is added. Thus, the
glass spheres are invisible, and the colored resin coating is examined for
uniformity and thickness under the microscope at substage illumination.
Black spots often observed under such conditions in the beads are caused by
air bubbles included in the glass.

4. Particle Size

The particle size range of pellicular resins often can be determined by
sieve analysis of the dry product. The effectiveness of the screening

procedure is influenced by the moisture content of the material. Both high and low moisture content may lead to agglomeration due to liquid film formation on the one hand, the buildup of electrostatic charges on the surface of particles, on the other. It is therefore recommended that the resin be conditioned before screening, by keeping it in an atmosphere of controlled humidity, as, for example, in a dessicator, over salt solutions. Since free flowing resin is needed also when columns are packed in a dry procedure, the same treatment should precede the packing of columns.

5. Stability

Pellicular resins have been designed for use in packed beds, in which the particles are fixed in the packing and no attrition occurs. Under such conditions the material should be stable, even if the resin layer undergoes frequent expansion and contraction. Indeed, column life longer than one year has been observed under continuous and continual use in chromatography. On the other hand, when pellicular resins are subjected to mechanical action, such as stirring, vibrating, rubbing, etc., the resin layer may be damaged and peel, particularly when it is swollen.

The stability of pellicular resin is therefore best investigated in a packed column. A sufficiently severe test consists of consecutively pumping eluents, such as water and a concentrated salt solution, through the column to cause the resin layer to alternately swell and shrink. In addition, the column temperature is varied. Pellicular resins of unsatisfactory stability cannot withstand such swelling and shrinking cycles without fragmentation of the layer. This results in a decrease in the permeability of the column, because the released resin particles gradually plug the interstitial channels of the packing. Such instability is readily detected by an increase of the column inlet pressure, after returning to some arbitrarily selected standard conditions with respect to eluent composition, flow rate, and temperature. The permeability of columns packed with a stable resin should be unchanged, even after a great number of cycles, although a slight decrease of permeability may occur at the initial stages of the testing procedure. The instability of the resin usually reveals itself in the first cycles by a continuous rise in the inlet pressures at constant flow rate of the strongly swelling eluent. It must be pointed out, however, that the instability of the column depends on the

packing and conditioning procedure, and changing column permeability has
been observed with stable resins when the column has been packed improperly.

6. Chromatographic Properties

The efficiency of the column is best evaluated by making a chromatographic
run with the sample of interest under standard conditions. For the testing of
the resin, a two component sample is adequate, and the measured column
loading capacities, distribution ratios and plate numbers are compared to
standards. These measurements are carried out in the same manner as in
gas chromatography [43]. These values are, however, also influenced by
the quality of packing; hence, proper column packing is essential for evaluating the resin properties. Column "bleeding" due to the leakage of soluble
substances from the resin may sometimes be of interest. The magnitude of
"bleeding" at different temperatures and eluent compositions is measured by
a differential refractometer or a uv detector, using the effluent from a
column packed with glass beads as reference. Preferably the same eluent is
pumped through both the ion exchange column and the reference column at the
same rate of flow. The "bleeding" from pellicular resin columns is generally
much smaller than that obtained with conventional resins under similar
conditions.

IV. UTILIZATION OF PELLICULAR ION EXCHANGERS IN CHROMATOGRAPHY

Pellicular resins have been developed for use in high performance liquid
chromatography to facilitate rapid analyses at moderately high column inlet
pressures under a variety of conditions, including gradient elution, and to
give columns of reproducible performance and long life.

Ion exchange resins are particularly suitable stationary phases because
of their versatility and stability. They can be prepared in a great variety
of chemical structures and their degree of crosslinking or porosity can be
varied at will. Their versatility is also greatly enhanced by the fact that
solute distribution in the column can take place by ionic interaction, by
adsorption on the polymer matrix, or by partition between the pore fluid and
moving eluent. Although their application has been mostly in aqueous systems,
it is not so restricted, and it is safe to say that ion exchange resins represent

the most universal class of stationary phases in liquid chromatography [5].

The favorable chromatographic properties of ion exchange resins are enhanced by the pellicular structure, although at the cost of reduced column loading capacity. Thus, their employment has been restricted so far to analytical work using sensitive detectors. In the following discussion the most important features with respect to their utilization in chromatography are detailed. To facilitate this discussion, conventional resin beads are compared with pellicular resin particles of the same ion exchange resin material and particle diameter. Most of the conclusions that evolve are applicable to other pellicular sorbents which find increasing use as column materials in high performance liquid chromatography. It should be pointed out, however, that except for certain theoretical considerations, the comparison of pellicular and conventional resins is quite difficult, as many practical aspects whose importance varies from one application to another must also be taken into account.

A. Column Efficiency

The efficiency of a chromatographic column is usually expressed by the plate height H. It is a measure of the dispersion of a solute band which occurs in the column, in terms of variance per unit length. The dimension of the plate height is length. By dividing the column length by the plate height we obtain a dimensionless measure of performance which is called plate number. In addition, useful information about column efficiency is given by the plates per second, and plates per atmosphere values, which are calculated by dividing the plate number by the retention time and by the pressure drop across the column, respectively.

The plate height in an ion exchange column can be written as the sum of two plate height increments, which are related to nonequilibrium phenomena caused by mobile and stationary phase processes, that is, $H = H_M + H_S$, where H_M and H_S are the respective mobile and stationary phase plate height contributions. The value of H_M depends on the geometry and dimensions of the column packing, on the flow velocity, and on the diffusivity and the distribution ratio of the solute, but the exact relationship is not known. On

the other hand, H_S can be calculated for spherical ion exchange beads [44]
as

$$H_S = \frac{1}{30} \frac{D_m}{(1+D_m)}2 \frac{d^2 u}{\mathscr{D}_S} ,$$ (1)

where D_m is the mass distribution ratio of the solute, d is the particle
diameter, $\mathscr{D}_S$ is the effective solute diffusivity in the resin, and u is the
mobile phase flow velocity.

For comparison of the effectiveness of conventional and pellicular resins
the H_S values are of main interest, since the differences between these resin
types lay within the particle boundary. It is convenient to introduce dimensionless groups such as the reduced stationary phase plate height increment

$$h_S = H_S/d,$$ (2)

and the reduced velocity

$$\nu = ud/\mathscr{D}_M ,$$ (3)

where $\mathscr{D}_M$ is the solute diffusivity in the mobile phase. We obtain from
Equation (1) that for conventional beads h_S is given by

$$h_S = \frac{1}{30} \frac{D_m}{(1+D_m)}2 \frac{\mathscr{D}_M}{\mathscr{D}_S} \nu = C_{sphere} \nu$$ (4)

where C_{sphere} is the chromatographic mass transfer coefficient for conventional resin beads.

It has been shown [45] that for pellicular resins, h_S is given by a similar
equation, but the numerical factor 1/30 in Equation (4) is replaced by q/30,
where the value of q is given by

$$q = \frac{1-5(1-\delta)^3 + 9(1-\delta)^5 - 5(1-\delta)^6}{1-(1-\delta)^3} .$$ (5)

Here δ is the dimensionless shell thickness,

$$\delta = (R_o - R_i)/R_o, \tag{6}$$

where R_o and R_i are the outer and inner radii of the spherical annulus.

Thus, for otherwise equivalent chromatographic conditions, and at fixed D_m, the ratio of the chromatographic mass transfer coefficients of a conventional resin C_{sphere} to that of a pellicular resin C_{shell} is given by

$$C_{sphere}/C_{shell} = 1/q, \tag{7}$$

and at the same reduced velocity the ratio of the corresponding stationary phase plate height increments is also equal to $1/q$. When band spreading is controlled by diffusion in the resin, the respective ratio of the overall efficiencies of the two columns is given also by $1/q$. This condition may exist at high reduced velocities, which are preferred to obtain fast separations. Figure 4 shows the variation of $1/q$ with the dimensionless shell thickness δ. It is seen that significant improvement in column efficiency can be expected by using pellicular resins instead of conventional ones. For example, h_S can be reduced more than 1000-fold by confining the resin to a surface layer having a thickness 1% of the radius. However, a lower limit for shell thickness is set by the required D_m values and column loading capacity. Both are related to the so-called phase ratio Γ, which is given by the ratio of the mobile phase volume to the stationary phase volume in the column. The mass distribution ratio is directly proportional to the phase ratio:

$$D_m = D_c \Gamma,$$

where D_c is the usual concentration distribution ratio of a particular solute which can be adjusted within limits by varying the eluent strength. The ratio of the Γ values in conventional resin columns Γ_{sphere} to that in pellicular resin columns Γ_{shell}, assuming the same interparticular porosity in both columns, is given by

$$\Gamma_{sphere}/\Gamma_{shell} = 1/\beta, \tag{9}$$

where

$$\beta = 1 - (1-\delta)^3. \tag{10}$$

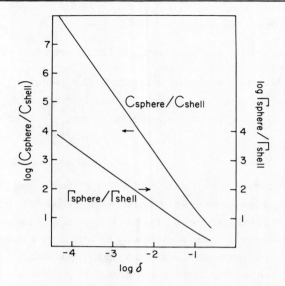

FIG. 4. Dependence of C_{sphere}/C_{shell} (at fixed D_m), and of $\Gamma_{sphere}/\Gamma_{shell}$ on the shell thickness [45].

That is, β is actually that volume fraction of a sphere which is occupied by the resin shell of thickness δ. Figure 4 also shows the dependence of $\Gamma_{sphere}/\Gamma_{shell}$ on the shell thickness. It is seen that the improvement in column efficiency due to the reduction of the C_{shell} values by reducing shell thickness, is significantly greater than the corresponding decrease of the phase ratio. For illustration of the situation cross sections of three beads are depicted in Figure 5. The two equidiametral beads represent conventional and pellicular resin beads, the latter having $\delta = 0.04$. The smaller bead has the same volume as the shell of the pellicular resin bead, which equals 12% of the volume of the large conventional resin bead. It shows that a given reduction of the diffusion path length represents a much lesser reduction in the actual volume of the resin. As the advantages of the pellicular structure are actually related to the high surface-to-volume ratios thus obtained, it is interesting to compare these values for the above beads. Assuming 100 μm diameter for the large beads, we obtain surface-to-volume ratios of 60, 500, and 121 nm^{-1} for the large conventional, the pellicular, and the small conventional beads, respectively.

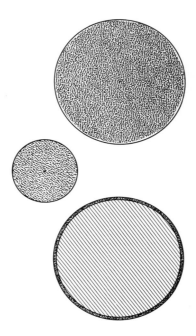

FIG. 5. Cross sections of a conventional and an equidiametral pellicular resin bead (δ = 0.04). The volume of the smaller bead equals the shell volume.

So far we have assumed that D_m of a particular solute was kept the same in both conventional and pellicular resin columns by adjusting D_c, that is, the strength of the eluent in the latter. Thus, the solute is eluted in the equal retention mode. When the eluent strength, that is, D_c is the same in both columns, the D_m values are assumed to be reduced in the pellicular resin column by a factor β with respect to those obtained in the conventional resin column. This affects the corresponding C_{shell} values, so that the C_{sphere}/C_{shell} ratio depends not only on δ but also on D_c. If the interparticular porosity is taken as 0.4, this ratio is calculated by the following equation:

$$C_{sphere}/C_{shell} = (2+3\beta D_c)^2/q\beta(2+3D_c)^2. \tag{11}$$

This relationship is illustrated in Figure 6. It should be kept in mind, however, that in this equal eluent strength mode of elution, the great reduction

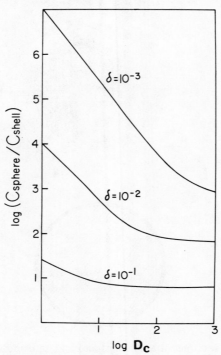

FIG. 6. Curves relating C_{sphere}/C_{shell} to the equilibrium constant (D_c) for different shell thickness, at fixed eluent strength [45].

in C_{shell} relative to C_{sphere} is of no practical value when D_c is small, because of the too small D_m values thus obtained. Under such conditions the actual gain is expressed by

$$C_{sphere}/C_{shell} = 1/\beta q, \tag{12}$$

rather than by Equation (11).

Theoretically, the mobile phase plate height contribution is expected to be the same in both pellicular and conventional resin columns, but in practice the h_M values obtained with pellicular resins are probably lower, because of the greater uniformity and stability of such packings. Actually the relative magnitudes of h_S and h_M determine whether the pellicular structure offers any significant improvement in column efficiency. According to

Giddings [46], h_M values are expected to differ only slightly from the reduced plate height of an unsorbed solute obtained under the same conditions. Such data are available from the literature [47-50], so that we can compare h_S values calculated by equations (4) and (5) with experimentally measured h_M values at different reduced velocities, as shown in Figure 7. The experimental h_M values are scattered through the shaded area and the h_S values calculated at different diffusivity ratios $\mathscr{D}_M / \mathscr{D}_S$, for conventional and pellicular resins having different layer thickness δ are represented by the lines.

It is seen that h_S increases generally at a higher rate with the reduced velocity than does h_M. Therefore, when fast separation is the goal, the column is operated preferably under such conditions that h_M and h_S are of about the same magnitude. Then the corresponding ν values represent a preferred reduced velocity range for a given column and type of solute. From Figure 7 we see that these preferred reduced velocities are invariably higher with pellicular resin columns than with conventional resin columns. For example, by substituting conventional resin with pellicular resin having $\delta = 0.01$, the reduced velocity range, where $h_M \approx h_S$, increases by a factor of 1000. The increase of the reduced velocity, in practice, is tantamount to either (1) an increase in the flow velocity, and consequently in the speed of separation; (2) an increase of the particle diameter, and thus a reduction of the column inlet pressure; or (3) a decrease of the solute diffusivity; with (3) the possibility of separating higher molecular height substances with the same efficiency is provided. Figure 7 also shows that the overall reduced plate height (h_M plus h_S) is significantly smaller with pellicular resins than with conventional resins at any given reduced velocity, thereby providing superior column performance over a wide range of conditions.

In traditional ion exchange chromatography, flow velocities of 10^{-1} to 10^{-2} cm/sec have been commonly used in the separation of slowly diffusing species. We see from Figure 7 that for conventional resins the preferred reduced velocity at diffusivity ratio of 10 is between 10 and 100. Since, at particle diameters of 100 micron and $\mathscr{D}_M$ of 10^{-6} cm^2/sec, this reduced velocity range corresponds to flow velocities between 10^{-1} and 10^{-2} cm/sec, Figure 7 reflects correctly the optimum chromatographic situation.

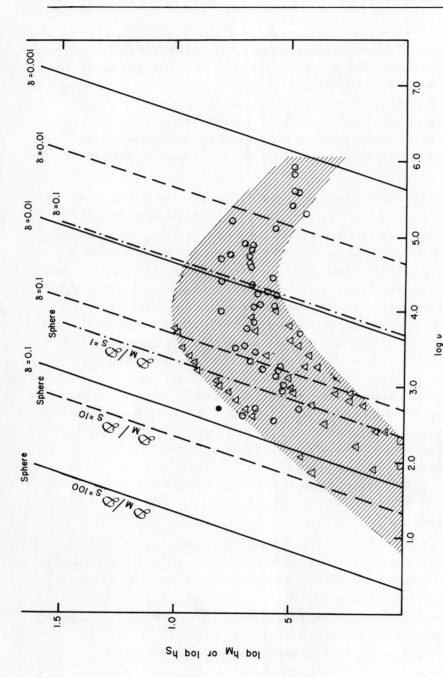

FIG. 7. Plot of calculated h_S and experimental h_M values against reduced velocity. The h_S values were calculated at $D_m = 5$ for spheres and shells representing conventional and pellicular resins, respectively. Solid, broken and dash-dot lines represent diffusivity ratios of 100, 10, and 1, respectively [45]. Experimental data were obtained with unsorbed solutes: △ Knox [47]; □ Brigham, Reed and Dew [49]; ○ Eback and White [48].

The comparison of conventional and pellicular resins both having different particle size has become interesting since the recent introduction of very fine resins (d < μm) into liquid chromatography [11, 12]. As the plate height decreases with the squared particle diameter, small conventional resin particles can give higher column efficiency than that obtainable with relatively large pellicular resin particles. Thus, the necessary column length can be drastically reduced, and as a result, fast separation and relatively high solute concentrations in the effluent can be obtained with very fine conventional resins. Table 1 shows column performance data measured with nucleoside samples using conventional or pellicular cation exchange resin columns. The values pertaining to conventional resins have been calculated from the data of Burtis et al. [13]. The conditions were optimized to achieve rapid separations; thus, the results can give insight into the behavior of these columns in practical applications.

It is seen that conventional resins having five to ten times smaller particle diameter than the pellicular resin, give columns of much higher efficiency, as measured by the plate height. The plates per second values expressing the speed of separation compare also in favor of the conventional resins. However, the plates per atmosphere values, which are related to the column inlet pressure required to achieve that speed of separation, are an order of magnitude higher for the conventional resins than for pellicular resins. These observations, supported by theoretical considerations, suggest that while both column types facilitate equally rapid separations, pellicular resin columns require less column inlet pressure. On the other hand, solute concentrations can be greater in the effluent of conventional columns, and can be operated with less sensitive detectors.

Although this comparison does not suggest any net advantage for pellicular resins over the final conventional resins, some features of pellicular resins, which are not related directly to column efficiency, still make them preferable in many chromatographic applications. Before these features are discussed, it should be pointed out that there is no reason why pellicular resins having particle diameter less than 10 microns cannot be prepared. Such resins would not only be superior to equidiametral conventional resins, as discussed previously, but also would give higher column loading capacity than the present pellicular resins, since this parameter is inversely related to the particle diameter at a constant dimensionless layer thickness.

TABLE 1

Typical Performance Values Obtained with Conventional and Pellicular
Resin Columns in the Analysis of Nucleosides

Resin	Particle size (μm)	Plate height (mm)	Plates/sec	Plates/atm
Conventional[a]	3–7	0.29	6.2	2.9
Conventional[b]	7–14	0.74	4.6	1.0
Pellicular	44–53	1.94	3.1	22.3

[a] DC-X resin, Durram Chemical Co.

[b] VC-10 resin, Sondell Scientific Instruments

The practical benefits of the pellicular structure are due to the favorable
handling characteristics and stability imparted to the material by the
combination of the resin with the heavy and rigid glass support.

1. Columns can be packed with dry pellicular resins so that long and
narrow bore columns (inside diameter down to 0.5 mm) can be easily prepared.
The use of small bore columns in analytical work is not only economical,
because of the low eluent consumption, but is also particularly advantageous
when only minute samples are available and high sensitivity analysis is
required. The dry packing procedure has been found applicable at particle
diameters down to 50 microns. Smaller resin particles may require a wet
packing procedure.

2. Pellicular resin columns withstand large pressure gradients without
changes in the packing structure. Figure 8 shows that a column packed with
conventional resin (4% crosslinking) is easily compressed, and its permeability
decreases with increasing pressure gradient. Thus, such columns are unsuitable for use in high pressure liquid chromatography. On the other hand, the
dependence of flow rate on the pressure gradient was completely linear with
columns packed with pellicular resins of similar particle size and degree of
crosslinking, even at higher pressure gradients than those shown in Figure
8. Another practical consequence of the stability of pellicular resin columns

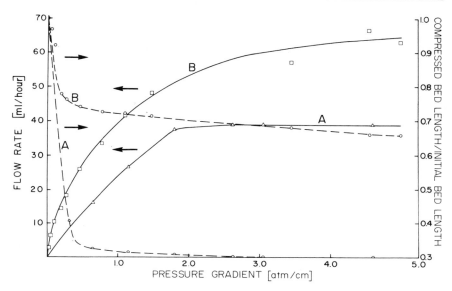

FIG. 8. Plots of flow rate and bed compression against pressure gradient for columns packed with conventional ion exchange resin (Bio Rad AG 50 W-X4, wet mesh range 200-400). Column A: 1.0 mm i.d.; Column B: 1.6 mm, i.d. Solid lines: flow rate. Broken lines: compressed bed length/initial bed length [45].

is that the use of reciprocating pumps is permitted because the pressure pulsations do not cause channeling, or breakdown of the packing. Figure 9 shows that plate heights in pellicular resin column are equal with both pulsating and smooth flow in a wide range of flow velocity. It is noteworthy that neither the frequency nor the amplitude of the pulsation appear to affect band spreading in such columns.

3. Columns packed with pellicular resins are usually stable toward changes in eluent composition or column temperature, and have long life even under greatly varying elution conditions, unlike many conventional resins. The reconditioning of pellicular resin columns can be performed rapidly at high flow rates; thus, the overall analysis time is reduced.

4. The pellicular structure permits the use of slightly crosslinked resins, so that high-performance liquid chromatography can be extended to the analysis of large molecular weight substances, while conventional resins with less than 8% cross linking do not give stable columns [51]. On the

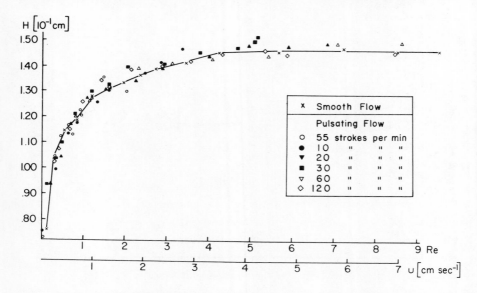

FIG. 9. Plot of plate height against time average flow velocity, as
measured with smooth flow and with pulsating flow, generated by a syringe-
type high-pressure pump and by a reciprocating metering pump having
variable stroke frequency, respectively. Column: 150 cm, 2 mm i.d.,
packed with pellicular cation exchange resin, 120-μm average particle
diameter.

other hand, highly crosslinked resins of high selectivity can also be utilized
in pellicular form because acceptable column efficiencies can be obtained,
despite the relatively low resin diffusivities.

     5. The relatively low phase ratio in pellicular resin columns is of
advantage when otherwise strongly retarded solutes are separated, because
they can be eluted without resorting to extreme eluent concentrations or
temperature.

B. High-Pressure Liquid Chromatograph

     The potential of pellicular ion exchange resins can only be fully exploited
by a liquid chromatographic system which features suitably accurate flow
and temperature control, as well as a sensitive detector. Such systems can
be assembled in the laboratory, but a variety of instruments is also

commercially available which can be operated at high column inlet pressures.

The Varian LCS 1000 liquid chromatography is here described briefly. This instrument was designed originally for narrow bore columns packed with pellicular resins. The flow sheet of the chromatograph is shown in Figure 10. It consists of three major parts: (1) flow generating and control unit; (2) column and injection port enclosed in a temperature controlled oven; and (3) uv detector and strip chart recorder. All wetted parts are made of stainless steel, glass or Teflon.

Chromatographic runs can be performed either by isocratic elution, that is, at constant eluent strength, or by gradient elution. The eluent is pumped by a reciprocating high pressure metering pump from a glass chamber in which the eluent is stirred, and deaerated by heating. When a single eluent is used the chamber is filled by transferring Eluent I from the reservoir pneumatically. In gradient elution, the chamber is filled only partially with the starting eluent (Eluent I) and the stronger eluent (Eluent II) is pumped with a low pressure metering pump into the chamber during the gradient run, in order to change the eluent composition continuously. A variety of gradient schemes can be devised by adjusting the composition of the eluents, the starting volume of Eluent I in the chamber, and the flow rates into and out of the chamber [52].

The flow rates through the column can be varied between 6 and 100 ml/h at column inlet pressures up to 3000 psi. With 1 mm inside diameter columns, the flow rate is usually 10 to 30 ml/h. Higher flow rates are used in purging or reconditioning the column after a gradient run. The uv detector of the instrument monitors the column effluent by measuring its absorbance at 254 mμ.[*] The detector features two identical flow cells, one for the column effluent, and another for the reference. Each cell is 10 mm long and one mm in diameter, and due to the small cell volume (8 μl), no peak distortion occurs under usual operating conditions.

---

[*] A similar uv detector is available from Laboratory Data Control, Inc., Riveria Beach, Florida.

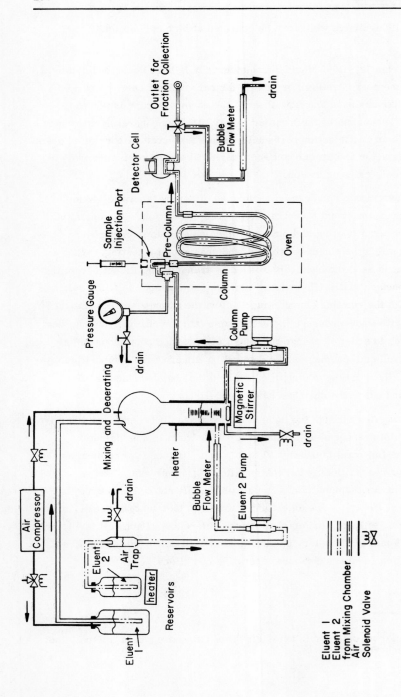

FIG. 10. Flow sheet of an ion exchange chromatograph, Model LCS-1000 of Varian Aerograph. (From Horvath in F. Glick ed., *Methods of Biochemical Analysis*, to be published by John Wiley & Sons, Inc. in October, 1973. Preprinted by permission of the author and publisher.)

C. Applications

The development of high-performance liquid chromatography is still in its infancy. Sensitive detectors and instruments that perform well at high pressures have been made available commercially only recently. High-efficiency column materials such as the very fine conventional ion exchange resins and pellicular resins also represent very new developments. These products were available earlier only in restricted quantities and varying qualities. Only now do Reeve Angel (Clifton, N. J.), and DuPont, Instrument Division (Wilmington, Delaware) begin to market a variety of pellicular resins and packed columns. The resins manufactured by Reeve Angel and DuPont are sold under the trade names Pellionex and Zipax, respectively. So far, the use of pellicular ion exchange resins has already been well established in the analysis of nucleic acid constituents, and the experience gained in this field permits one to draw conclusions for its application in other areas of ion exchange chromatography.

The sorption properties of both pellicular and conventional resins having similar chemical compositions appear to be alike. That is, the fundamental chromatographic process is essentially the same with both resin types. Thus, the literature of ion exchange chromatography can serve as a guide for the design of a suitable column and eluent system, and for the interpretation of a particular retention pattern. Therefore, only the practical aspects of the employment of pellicular resins in chromatography are discussed, with emphasis on the different handling characteristics of conventional and pellicular resin columns.

1. Column Packing

The column efficiency, particularly in liquid chromatography, depends greatly on proper packing. The preparation of columns with conventional resins for high pressure chromatography often requires elaborate procedures [51]. On the other hand, many pellicular resins can be packed dry, and this technique is not only very convenient, and facilitates making narrow bore columns, but also is expected to give superior column efficiency [50]. The following procedure has been found to be applicable to Pellionex resins.

Usually No. 316 stainless steel is the preferred tubing material because it is resistant to most eluents, and can be connected with high pressure

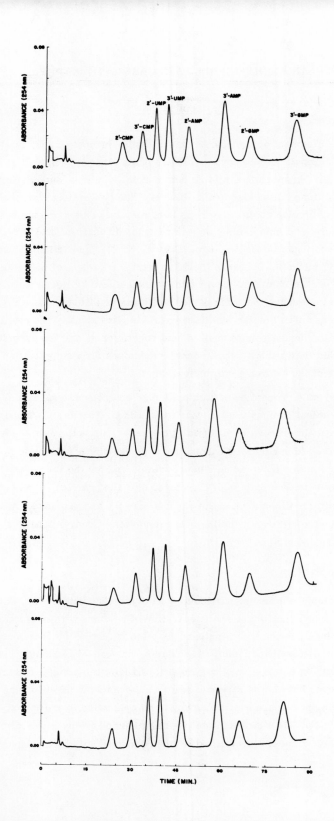

fittings. Tubing up to three meters long can be packed in one length, and long columns can be made by connecting individually packed segments. Before packing, the outlet end of the tube is plugged, e.g., with a porous Teflon disc. The pellicular resin is then fed into the tube in a vertical position while it is tapped or vibrated, but only slightly, to avoid the possibility of resin damage by attrition. The moisture content of the resin has to be controlled in order to provide a free flowing powder. When the resin is either too dry or too moist the particles tend to stick to each other either by electrostatic forces, or because the sorbed moisture renders their surface sticky. After the column is packed and still in vertical position, the packing is compacted by pumping through the column, at the maximum possible flow rate, an eluent, which wets the resin but does not make it swell appreciably. The pressure is then released through the column outlet and the inlet end is disconnected and inspected. If the initial part of the column is void of resin, it is repacked or cut off. Following the above, the column is conditioned first with an eluent which causes the resin to swell strongly. Then the column is coiled, if necessary, and placed into the instrument. The conditioning process is completed by purging the column with suitable eluents to remove impurities, and finally with the eluent used for separation. These steps are performed preferably at elevated temperature. When gradient elution is planned, the conditioning is completed by making a few blank gradient elution and reconditioning runs. Generally, column conditioning or reconditioning can be performed without detrimental effects at flow rates much higher than those used during the chromatographic runs. Figure 11 shows that excellent reproducibility of column packing and column efficiency can be obtained by this dry packing procedure.

2. Eluents

The eluents employed with pellicular resin columns have generally been much more dilute than those used in conventional ion exchange chromatography. Because the ratio of the stationary phase volume to mobile phase volume is

FIG. 11. Reproducibility of column packing with pellicular resins. The chromatograms were obtained on five columns under the same elution conditions. The 1 mm i.d. columns were packed by the dry procedure with pellicular strong anion exchange resin (sieve fraction #270-325). Column length: 300 cm. Eluent: phosphate gradient. Temperature: 70°C. Sample: 2', 3' ribonucleosides [12a].

smaller with pellicular resins, weaker eluents suffice to elute solutes at
mass distribution ratios comparable to those obtained with conventional
resins using stronger eluents. The selection of the proper eluent or eluent
system is probably the most difficult task in ion exchange chromatography,
and usually is achieved by a trial and error approach. Nevertheless, such
screening of eluents is simplified when using pellicular resin columns,
because both the eluent composition and column temperature can be quickly
changed to find optimum conditions, by performing a few rapid trial runs at
high flow velocities. Both salt elution and elution with acids or bases have
been employed, but salt elution is preferred for longer column life and milder
conditions. In addition, the compatibility of eluents with stainless steel has
also to be considered, eluents of pH less than two needing to be excluded.
Since the column effluent is continuously monitored, an eluent has to be
selected which does not upset the proper functioning of the detector. In many
instances acidic phosphate solutions proved to be satisfactory, with both
anion and cation exchange resins using isocratic or gradient elution. The
advantage of such solutions is that they possess buffer properties, do not
absorb light significantly at the operating wavelength of the standard uv
detector (254 mm), and do not attack No. 316 stainless steel. When higher
ionic strength is required than that obtainable with moderately soluble acidic
phosphates, the addition of neutral salts such as KCl can be considered. The
addition of organic solvents, such as low molecular weight alcohols, was
found to have influence on the selectivity of the resins. It may offer the
possibility of achieving the separation of critical solute pairs in specific
cases, or of reducing solute adsorption by the matrix in general.

The column temperature and the pH of the eluents often play the most
important role in determining retention values in isocratic elution. Figure
12 illustrates the effect of temperature and pH on the retention volumes of
nucleosides as measured on a pellicular cation exchange resin column. It
is seen that in this case, the analysis is best carried out at 30°C and at a
pH of about 5.

Gradient elution is preferred in the analysis of samples containing many
components because it provides higher peak capacities than isocratic elution.
Thus, late peaks can be eluted faster and evaluated more easily. Linear
increase of the salt concentration for the eluent during elution is the most

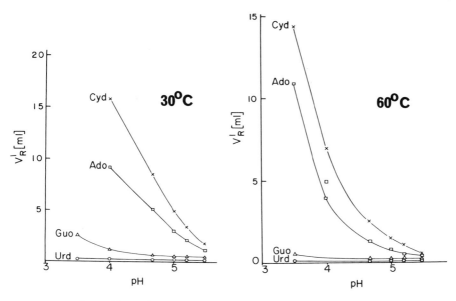

FIG. 12. Effect of pH and temperature on the adjusted retention volumes of nucleosides. Column: pellicular strong cation exchange resin. Eluent: 0.02 M KH_2PO_4; pH adjusted with H_3PO_4 or KOH. Cyd: cytidine; Ado: adenosine; Guo: guanosine, Urd: uridine [39].

convenient method for obtaining fast separations and easily resolvable late peaks, although pH gradient or the combination of concentration gradients and pH gradients have been also employed.

3. Sample Introduction and Elution

The sample is most commonly injected into the column with a syringe at arrested flow. The stability of pellicular resin columns permits stopping the flow and releasing the pressure a great many times without affecting the packing structure adversely, that is, without deterioration of efficiency. Thus, the use of high pressure sampling valves can be avoided. Although at pressures less than 1000 psi septum injection is possible, it is the author's experience that direct on-column sample injection at arrested flow gives more accurate and reproducible results.

The flow velocity of the eluent in columns packed with 30- to 50-μm size pellicular resins is usually 1 to 2 cm/sec. This is about 20 to 50 times

higher than eluent velocities customarily used in conventional ion exchange
chromatography with similarly sized particles. Such high flow velocities
afford rapid separation, even with long columns. However, significantly lower
flow velocities may be necessary in the separation of sample components
having large molecular weights, or when high column efficiency or system
sensitivity is required. The flow velocity may also be limited by the attainable
column inlet pressure. According to the need of a particular separation, the
column temperature can be varied considerably without column deterioration.
Pellicular columns withstand not only rapid changes in temperature, but also
can be used at temperatures as high as 80°C for an extended period of time.
Many separations can be performed more efficiently with pellicular resins at
temperatures higher than ambient, despite their relatively low phase ratio.
It is noteworthy that many relatively unstable compounds can be analyzed at
high temperatures on pellicular resin columns, without loss of recovery when
the eluent is properly deaerated and the chromatographic run is performed
rapidly at high flow velocities, because of the short retention times thus
obtained. The chances are that much more "labile" substances can be
analyzed under such conditions than is inferred from experience gained in
conventional ion exchange chromatography.

4. Analysis of Nucleic Acid Constituents

The analysis of nucleic acid hydrolysates, an important area of biochemical research, has been greatly facilitated by the introduction of pellicular
resins and sensitive uv detectors. Since then, it has been possible to
increase the speed and sensitivity of analysis by orders of magnitude with
respect to that of previous column chromatographic methods which utilized
conventional resins. Details of the use of pellicular resins in this field can
be found in the original papers [31, 28, 29, 39, 53-58]. The chromatographic
systems employed are essentially the same as those developed with conventional resins for elution with acidic salt solutions: (1) purine and pyrimidine
bases or nucleosides are separated on strong cation exchanger columns;
(2) nucleotides, i.e., the mono-, di-, and triphosphoric acid derivates of
nucleosides are separated on strong anion or cation exchanger columns; and
(3) oligo- and polynucleotides are separated on strong or weak anion
exchangers. In most applications, narrow bore columns of one or two
millimeter inside diameter have been used with pellicular resins of 30 or

50 μm average particle diameter. Commercial instruments, such as the LCS 1000 (Varian Aerograph) and the high-performance liquid chromatograph of DuPont, have been found particularly suitable for working with such columns.

The separation of the bases on Zipax strong cation exchange resin is illustrated in Figure 13. This pellicular resin is made from a fluoropolymer sulfonic acid and has a low capacity, permitting the bases to be eluted with 0.01M nitric acid in the absence of added salt. The four major bases of ribonucleic acid have been separated on polystyrene sulfonic acid type pellicular resin as shown in Figure 14. The great affinity of these solutes for the polyaromatic matrix and the slightly higher resin capacity, required the use of 0.02M ammonium phosphate eluent, even at pH 5.5. The same conditions but lower temperature were used for the separation of the four major ribonucleosides in Figure 15. Here each peak represents 300 pmole. The determination of the base composition is greatly simplified by degrading RNA enzymatically, and by analyzing the nucleoside mixture. The high speed and sensitivity of analysis as demonstrated in Figure 15 makes this method, which has been introduced by Uziel et al. [59], particularly attractive.

Nucleotides have been separated mostly on strong anion exchange resins. Samples consisting of few components only are eluted isocratically as shown in Figures 16 and 17. The separation of the four 5'-nucleoside monophosphates on a strong Zipax anion exchanger, which is acrylic based, required a very dilute eluent, probably due to the absence of an aromatic resin matrix. The mixture of the biologically very important adenosine mono-, di-, and triphosphates was separated on a polystyrene based strong anion exchanger containing dimethylbenzylammonium groups, and the chromatogram is shown in Figure 17. The elution of these substances, which have strong affinity to such resin, required a 0.75M KH_2PO_4 solution even at 80°C column temperature. Therefore, gradient elution appears to be a more suitable method for this particular analysis, as higher efficiency is obtained and lower flow rates are required [56].

For the rapid analysis of samples which contain many components, gradient elution is mandatory. The eight 2' and 3' isomers of the major ribonucleotides can be analyzed at subnanomole level in about a half hour by using a linear concentration gradient of KH_2PO_4 in the pH range 3 to 4. The

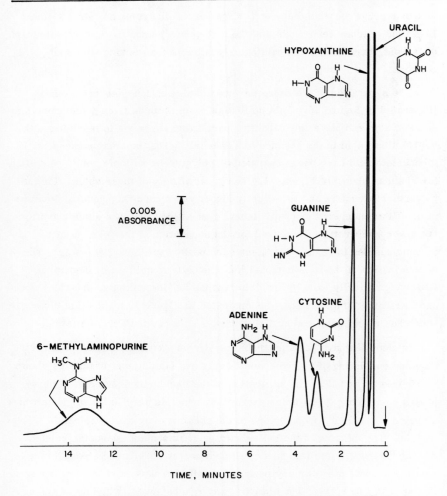

FIG. 13.   Chromatogram of nucleic acid bases.   Column: Zipax strong
cation exchange resin, 20-37 μm; 2.1 mm i.d., 100 cm.   Eluent: 0.01 N
HNO3.   Inlet pressure: 735 psi.   Flow rate: 120 ml/h.   Temperature: 63°C.
Sample: 3 nmole per component [29].

chromatogram shown in Figure 18 has been obtained with a strong anion

exchange resin which has a structure similar to that of the resin used

for the separation of adenosine phosphates.   A similar column and a

linear gradient elution with ammonium formate buffer were used to

separate ribonucleosides mono-, di-, and triphosphoric acids as shown

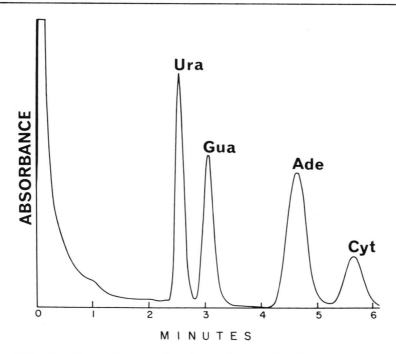

FIG. 14. Chromatogram of purine and pyrimidine bases. Column: pellicular strong cation exchanger, 44-53 μm, 1 mm i.d., 300.7 cm. Eluent: 0.02M NH$_4$H$_2$PO$_4$, pH 5.5. Inlet pressure: 2480 psi. Flow rate 33.4 ml/h. Temperature: 68°C. Sample 0.8 nmole of each. Ura: uracyl, Gua, guanidine, Ade: adenine, Cyt: cytosine [39].

in Figure 19. Better resolution can be obtained with phosphate solutions, but the analysis takes a longer time.

The 2'- and 3'-ribonucleoside monophosphates have also been separated on a polystyrene sulfonic acid type pellicular cation exchanger using a 0.01M NH$_4$H$_2$PO$_4$ solution whose pH was adjusted with phosphoric acid to 2.5. Chromatograms obtained by isocratic elution at different column temperatures are depicted in Figure 20. Although the separation is inferior to that obtained on the anion exchanger column by gradient elution, this system offers a simple procedure when the isomers of the various nucleotides do not have to be separated. As seen, the isomer pairs can be eluted as single peaks by adjusting column temperature.

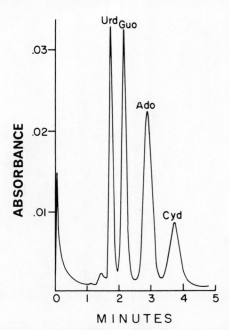

FIG. 15. Chromatogram of ribonucleosides. Column: pellicular strong cation exchanger, 44-53 micron, 1 mm i.d., 151.7 cm. Eluent: 0.02M $NH_4 H_2 PO_4$, pH 5.6. Inlet pressure: 1920 psi. Flow rate: 25.5 ml/h. Temperature: 39°C. Sample 0.3 nmole per component. Symbols: See Figure 10 [39].

Pellicular ion exchange resins are very promising for the separation of larger nucleic acid fragments but, at the present time, little experience has been gained in this field. It is believed that polyaromatic ion exchange resins are unsatisfactory because of the strong adsorption of these species on the resin matrix. Nevertheless, small oligonucleotides can be separated on strong polystyrene based anion exchanger, as is shown by the chromatogram in Figure 21. It appears that the use of aliphatic low crosslinked pellicular anion exchangers of small particle size to obtain high column efficiency, would be necessary to resolve complex oligonucleotide mixtures or to separate polynucleotides. Preliminary results from the author's laboratory with pellicular resins prepared by the polymerization on N, N-diethylaminoethylacrylamide onto 10-μm glass beads indicate that this approach is indeed promising.

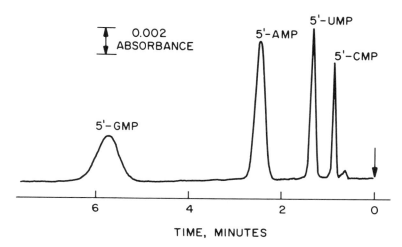

FIG. 16.   Chromatogram of 5'-ribonucleotides.   Column: Zipax strong anion exchange resin, 20–37 μm; 2.1 mm i.d., 100 cm.   Eluent: 0.006 M $H_3 PO_4$, 0.002 M $KH_2 PO_4$, pH 3.75.   Inlet pressure: 900 psi.   Flow rate: 114.6 ml/h.   Temperature: 60° C.   Sample: about 1 nmole of each component. AMP: adenosine monophosphoric acid, CMP: cytidine monophosphoric acid, GMP: guanosine monophosphoric acid, UMP: uridine monophosphoric acid [29].

5. Other Applications

In principle, pellicular resins can always replace the ion exchangers presently used for analysis in ion exchange chromatography, when sufficiently sensitive detectors are available.   Then the advantage of rapid separation can be realized.   This is demonstrated by the chromatograms of uv absorbing components of cell extracts, shown in Figure 22.   The time required for such separations on Dowex-1 columns is 10 to 20 times longer and the number of detectable components is smaller.   In addition, the pellicular resin column is reusable.

High-performance liquid chromatography with pellicular resins is attractive, not only in biochemical research, but also in the analysis of a variety of nonvolatile substances, e.g., intermediates and products of the drug and dyestuff industry.   The speed of separation and the convenience of operation make possible the use of this technique for routine analysis. Figure 23 shows the separation of two isomeric acids in about 90 seconds

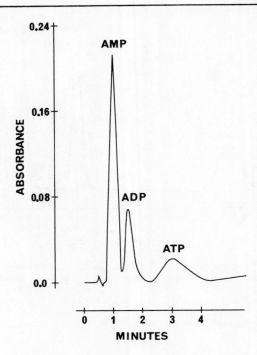

FIG. 17. Chromatogram of the adenosine mono-, di- and triphosphates. Column: pellicular strong anion exchanger, 44-53 μm 1 mm i.d., 300 cm. Eluent: 0.75M K_2H PO_4, pH 4.2. Inlet pressure: 2800 psi. Flow rate: 55 ml/h. Temperature: 80°C. Sample: 10 μg of each component; AMP: adenosine monophosphoric acid, ADP: adenosine diphosphoric acid, ATP: adenosine triphosphoric acid [13].

on an anion exchanger. Such high-speed analysis may be important in process control when gas chromatography cannot be used. The separation of substituted benzimidazoles is shown in Figure 24. The ion exchange capacity of the Zipax type cation exchanger used in this analysis was 3.5 μEq/g. The high efficiency, relatively low capacity, and nonaromatic character of the resin made it possible to obtain rapid separations without gradient elution.

V. OUTLOOK

Pellicular column materials are likely to continue playing a major role in high-performance liquid chromatography. Furthermore, the advancement

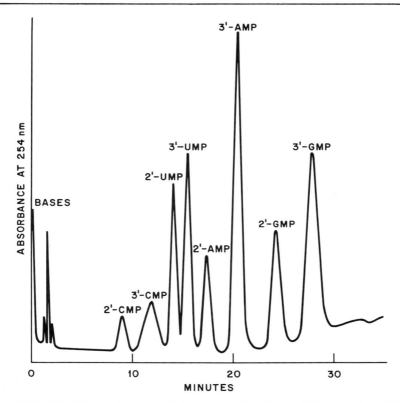

FIG. 18. Chromatogram of ribonucleosides 2'- and 3'-monophosphoric acids. Column: pellicular strong basic anion exchange resin, 44-53 μm, 1 mm i.d., 300 cm. Eluent: linear gradient from 0.01M $KH_2 PO_4$, pH 3.3 with 1.0M $KH_2 PO_4$. Inlet pressure: 2950 psi. Flow rate: 47 ml/h. Temperature: 75°C. Sample: 1 nmole of each isomer pairs. Symbols: See Figure 14. (From Horvath in F. Glick ed., Methods of Biochemical Analysis, to be published by John Wiley & Sons, Inc. in October, 1973. Preprinted by permission of the author and publisher.)

of this technique is expected to stimulate their future development in the following two directions. First, a variety of potentially efficient stationary phases, which do not give good column packing because of their poor mechanical properties in bulk, may be utilized in pellicular form. Examples of this are inorganic gels and resins which have low degree of crosslinking, and contain ionic or affinity groups. The versatility of functional polymers can, thus, be exploited to tailor stationary phases which possess desired sorption properties and give efficient and stable columns. This approach is particularly

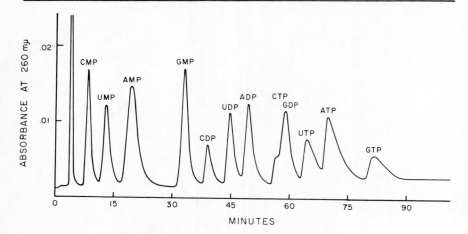

FIG. 19. Chromatogram of ribonucleosides mono-, di-, and triphosphoric acids. Column: pellicular strong anion exchanger, 44-53 μm, 1 mm i.d., 193 cm. Eluent: linear gradient of ammonium formate buffer, pH 4.35 at 25°C from 0.04M to 1.5M. Inlet pressure: 750 psi. Flow rate: 12 ml/h. Temperature: 71°C, Sample: 1.5-3.5 nmoles per component [28]

promising in biochemical separations where often a higher specificity is required than that of regular ion exchange resins, and the separation of large molecules demands a very open gel structure.

Second, pellicular resins might be prepared in the particle size range 10 to 20 μm to make columns which have a relatively high loading capacity, stability, and favorable handling characteristics, as well as a higher efficiency than obtained with conventional resins of the same particle dimensions. Of course, this development requires a further increase in the pressure capability of liquid chromatographic instrumentation. In reducing the particle diameter and shell thickness of pellicular materials we can conceive, in the limit, of submicron particles whose surface is covered with a film of chromatographically active molecules. Such superficial resins might give the ultimate column efficiency in liquid chromatography, if stable columns could be obtained without channeling in the packing. But their use may be limited by excessive pressure requirements.

The favorable mass transfer properties of the pellicular structure has already been exploited in high-performance liquid chromatography, with

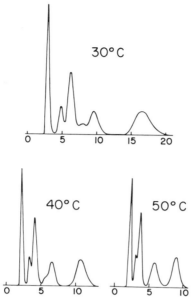

FIG. 20. Chromatograms of ribonucleoside 2'- and 3'monophosphoric acids at different temperatures. Elution order: UMP-s, GMP-s, CMP-s and AMP-s. Symbols: See Figure 14. Column: pellicular strong cation exchanger: 44-53 μm; 1 mm i.d., 152 cm. Eluent: 0.1M NH_4 H_2 PO_4, pH 2.5. Inlet pressure: 2000 psi. Flow rates: 14.8 ml/h (30°C), 18.7 ml/h (40°C), 19.3 ml/h (50°C). Time scales: min. Sample: 0.75 nmole of each isomer pair.

stationary phases other than ion exchange resins. Glass beads coated with thin porous layers of silica, alumina, polyamide, etc., as well as with crosslinked silicons containing functional groups, have been employed. The utilization of pellicular gels, however, goes beyond liquid chromatography. Noteworthy success has been achieved in solid phase peptide synthesis and protein immobilization. The Merrifield peptide synthesis employs a low crosslinked polystyrene (1-2% DVB) matrix as anchor for the first amino acid of the peptide chain, which is synthetized in subsequent steps by linking another amino acid to the anchored moiety in each step. By using the polystyrene gel in pellicular rather than in conventional form, the synthesis can be performed very conveniently in packed bed, much faster than usual,

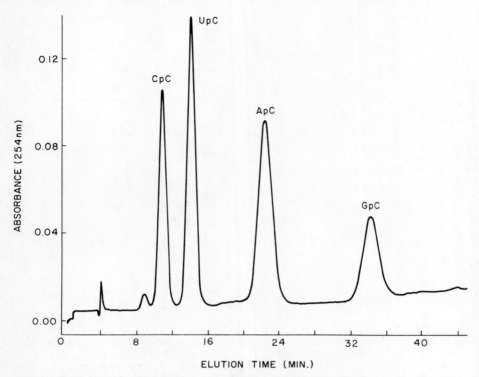

FIG. 21. Chromatogram of cytidine containing dinucleotides. Column: pellicular strong anion exchanger, 44-53 μm, 1 mm i.d., 300 cm. Eluent: linear $KH_2 PO_4$ gradient from 0.01M, pH 3.25 with 1.0M, pH 4.2 solution. Inlet pressure: 1350 psi. Flow rate: 18 ml/h. Temperature: 80°C. Sample: 2-4 nmole per component [13].

because all diffusion controlled processes such as removal of excess reagents and byproducts, as well as reaction rates which are otherwise diffusion controlled, can be accelerated. Columnar operation offers also a practicable way to scale up the process. These advantages engendered by the pellicular structure may be important in other solid phase syntheses, e.g., nucleic acid synthesis.

A variety of immobilized enzymes has been prepared in the author's laboratory in pellicular form. These heterogeneous catalysts could be efficiently used in packed columns unlike many colloidal or mucilaginous enzyme conjugates described in the literature. Again, polymer matrices which provide a favorable microenvironment for the immobilized enzyme, with respect to its stability and catalytic activity, but do not have the mechanical stability required in packed bed applications, could be utilized in pellicular form.

An extension of this concept leads logically to use of ion exchange resins, enzyme resins, etc., in tubular annulus configuration for specific applications such as automatic analyzers or extra-corporeal circulation systems in the clinical field. By coating the inner wall of plastic tubing with ion exchange resins and immobilized enzymes, open tubular ion exchange columns and heterogeneous enzyme reactors, respectively, have been obtained. The behavior and utilization of such systems is under investigation.

The large scale application of pellicular resins has not been explored yet. From the experience gained so far we can infer, however, that the short diffusion path and the possible use of soft gel layers are features which make their use in packed beds attractive for large scale separation processes, or for the other applications mentioned above.

ACKNOWLEDGMENTS

The author wishes to thank S. R. Lipsky for helpful discussions. The author's research work was supported by grants from the U. S. Public Health Service, No. RR00356 and GM16681, and from the National Aeronautics and Space Administration, No. NGL 07-004-008.

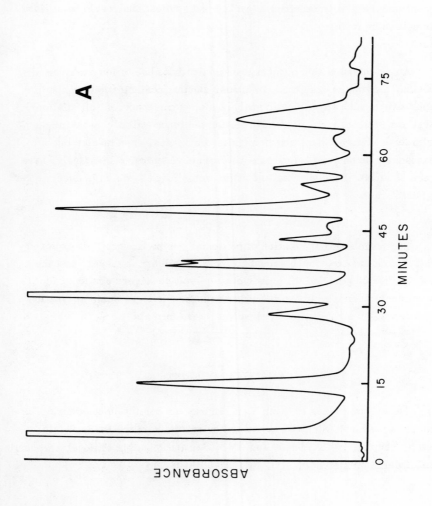

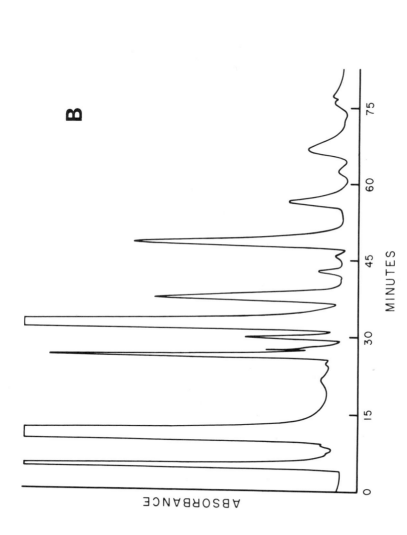

FIG. 22. Chromatograms of cellular extracts from mouse liver (A) and mouse brain (B) on strong pellicular anion exchange resin of polystyrene type using linear gradient elution with ammonium formate buffer, pH 4.35 [28].

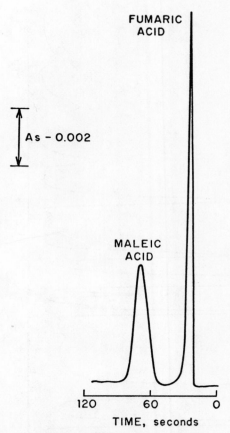

FIG. 23. Chromatogram of maleic and fumaric acid. Column: Zipax type anion exchange resin, 20-37 μm 2.1 mm i.d., 100 cm. Eluent: 0.01N HNO_3. Inlet pressure: 1900 psi: Flow rate: 163.8 ml/h. Temperature: 60°C [35].

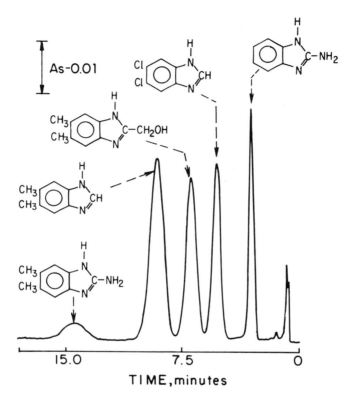

FIG. 24. Chromatogram of benzimidazole derivates. Column: Zipax type cation exchange resin, 20-37 micron; 2.1 mm i.d. 100 cm. Eluent: 0.025N tetramethylammonium nitrate-nitric acid, pH 1.74. Inlet pressure: 325 psi. Flow rate: 122.4 ml/h. Temperature: 60°C. Sample: 2 μg of each component [35].

REFERENCES

1. O. Samuelson, Z. Analyt. Chem., 116, 328 (1939).

2. W. C. Johnson, L. L. Quill and F. Daniels, Chem. Eng. News, 25, 2495 (1947).

3. W. E. Cohn and H. W. Kohn, J. Am. Chem. Soc., 70, 1986 (1948).

4. G. E. Moore and K. A. Kraus, J. Am. Chem. Soc., 74, 843 (1952).

5.   F. Helfferich, in Advances in Chromatography, J. C. Giddings and
      R. A. Keller, eds., Vol. I, Dekker, New York, 1965, pp. 3-60.

6.   S. Moore, D. H. Spackman and W. H. Stein, Anal. Chem., 30, 1185
      (1958).

7.   D. H. Spackman, W. H. Stein and S. Moore, Anal. Chem., 30, 1190
      (1958).

8.   P. B. Hamilton, in Advances in Chromatography, J. C. Giddings and
      R. A. Keller, eds., Vol. II, Dekker, New York, 1966, pp. 3-62.

9.   G. E. Boyd and B. A. Soldano, J. Am. Chem. Soc., 75, 6091 (1953).

10.   C. Ceserano and G. Pagnetti, Comit. Natl. Energia Nucl., RT/CH
      63, 4 (1963).

11.   C. D. Scott, J. E. Attril and N. G. Anderson, Proc. Soc. Exptl.
      Biol. Med., 125, 181 (1967).

12.   C. D. Scott, Clin. Chem., 14, 521 (1968).

12a. C. A. Burtis, private communication.

13.   C. A. Burtis, M. N. Munk and F. R. MacDonald, Clin. Chem.,
      16, 667 (1970).

14.   K. W. Pepper, J. Appl. Chem., 1, 124 (1951).

14a. K. W. Pepper, D. Reichenberg and D. K. Hale, J. Chem. Soc.,
      3129 (1952).

15.   D. E. Weiss, Australian, J. Appl. Sci., 4, 510 (1953).

16.   J. R. Parrish, Nature, 207, 402 (1965).

17.   M. Skafi and K. H. Lieser, Z. Anal. Chem., 249, 182 (1970).

18.   M. Skafi and K. H. Lieser, Z. Anal. Chem., 250, 306 (1970).

19.   M. Skafi and K. H. Lieser, Z. Anal. Chem., 251, 177 (1970).

19a. G. H. Fricke, D. Rosenthal and G. A. Welford, Anal. Chem., 43,
      648 (1971).

20.   N. K. Boardman, Biochim. Biophys. Acta, 18, 290 (1955).

21.   N. K. Boardman, J. Chromatog., 2, 388 (1959).

22.   N. K. Boardman, J. Chromatog., 2, 398 (1959).

23.   J. Feitelson and S. M. Partridge, Biochem. J., 64, 607 (1956).

24.   C. Horvath and S. R. Lipsky, Nature, 211, 748 (1966).

25. J. F. Weiss and A. D. Kelmers, Biochemistry, 6, 2507 (1967).

26. H. Flood, Z. Analyt. Chem., 120, 237 (1940).

27. K. Randerath, Thin Layer Chromatography, 2nd ed., Academic Press, New York, 1966, pp. 229-243.

28. C. Horvath, B. Preiss and S. R. Lipsky, Anal. Chem., 39, 1422 (1967).

29. J. J. Kirkland, J. Chromatog. Sci., 8, 72 (1970).

30. R. M. Wheaton and M. J. Hatch, in Ion Exchange (J. A. Marinsky, ed.), Vol. 2, Dekker, New York, 1969, pp. 191-197.

31. R. Kunin, in Ion Exchange Resins, 2nd ed., J. Wiley & Sons, Inc., New York, 1958, p. 100.

32. C. W. Carr, R. McClintock and K. Sollner, J. Electrochem. Soc., 109, 251 (1962).

33. J. J. Kirkland, U. S. Patent 3,488,922 (1970).

34. C. Horvath, Ph. D. Thesis, University of Frankfurt, Frankfurt, Germany, 1963.

35. J. J. Kirkland, J. Chromatog. Sci., 7, 361 (1969).

36. B. L. Karger, H. Engelhardt, K. Conroe and I. Halász, 8th Int. Symp. on Gas Chromatography, Dublin, Ireland, 1970.

37. I. Halász and P. Walkling, J. Chromatog. Sci., 7, 129 (1969).

38. B. L. Karger, K. Conroe and H. Engelhardt, J. Chromatog. Sci., 8, 243 (1970).

39. C. Horvath and S. R. Lipsky, Anal. Chem., 41, 1227 (1969).

40. F. Helfferich, Ion Exchange, McGraw Hill, New York, 1962, p. 91.

41. J. Incédy, Analytical Applications of Ion Exchangers, Pergamon Press, New York, 1966.

42. C. L. Burger, J. Chromat., 26, 334 (1967).

43. L. S. Ettre and A. Zlatkis, eds., The Practice of Gas Chromatography, Interscience, New York, 1967, pp. 210-211.

44. J. C. Giddings, Dynamics of Chromatography, Part I, "Principles and Theory," Dekker, New York, 1965, pp. 143-144.

45. C. Horvath and S. R. Lipsky, J. Chromatog. Sci., 7, 109 (1969).

46.   J. C. Giddings, Dynamics of Chromatography, Part I, "Principles and Theory," M. Dekker, New York, 1965, p. 47.

47.   J. H. Knox, Anal. Chem., 38, 253 (1966).

48.   E. E. Ebach and R. R. White, A. I. Ch. E. J., 4, 161 (1958).

49.   W. E. Brigham, P. W. Reed and J. N. Dew. Soc. Petrol. Engrs., 1, 1 (1961).

50.   D. S. Horne, J. H. Knox and L. McLaren, Separation Sci., 1, 531 (1966).

51.   C. D. Scott and N. E. Lee, J. Chromatog., 42, 263 (1969).

52.   T. K. Lakshmanan and S. Lieberman, Arch. Biochem. Biophys., 53, 258 (1954).

53.   G. Brooker, Anal. Chem., 42, 1108 (1970).

54.   P. R. Brown, J. Chromatog., 52, 257 (1970).

55.   W. P. Kennedy and J. C. Lee, J. Chromatog., 51, 203 (1970).

56.   H. W. Schmuckler, J. Chromatog. Sci., 8, 653 (1970).

57.   H. W. Schmuckler, J. Chromatog. Sci., 8, 581 (1970).

58.   S. N. Pennington, Anal. Chem., 43, 1701 (1971).

59.   M. Uziel, C. K. Koh and W. E. Cohn, Anal. Biochem., 25, 77 (1968).

AUTHOR INDEX

Numbers in parentheses are reference numbers and indicate that an author's work is referred to although his name is not cited in the text. Underlined numbers give the page on which the complete reference is listed.

SUBJECT INDEX

A

Acetate, use in element separation, 139

Acetone-hydrochloric acid, cation exchange separations in, 170-175

Acetylacetonate, use in element separation, 139

Alkali metals, ion exchange separation of, 155, 164, 170-171, 188-190

Alkaline earth metals, ion exchange separation of, 164-165, 170-171

Aluminum
ion exchange separation of, 165-166, 171
in rocks, 185, 188

Ammonium 12-molybdoarsenate, ion exchange properties, 88

Ammonium 12-molybdogermanate, ion exchange properties, 90

Ammonium 12-molybdosilicate, ion exchange properties, 88

Ammonium 12-tungstoarsenate, ion exchange properties, 88

Ammonium 12-tungstosilicate, ion exchange properties, 88

Ammonium 12-molybdophosphate (AMP), ion-exchange properties, 77-83

Antimonophosphoric acid, ion exchange properties, 71

Antimony, ion exchange separation of, 168, 173

Arsenic, ion exchange separation of, 168, 173

Arsenophosphoric acid, ion exchange properties, 71

Ammonium-12-tungstophosphate (ATP), ion-exchange properties, 83-87

B

Barium, ion exchange separation of, 141-142, 145, 151

Beryllium, ion exchange separation of, 140-143, 151

C

Cadmium, ion exchange separation of, 167-168, 172

Calcium
ion exchange separation of, 141-145, 151
in rocks, 182

Cerium arsenate ion exchangers, preparation and properties of, 65

Cerium phosphate ion exchangers, preparation and properties of, 63-65

Cesium 12-molybdophosphate, ion exchange properties, 89

Chelating agents, use in ion exchange separation of metals, 179-180

Chromium, ion exchange separation of, 166-167, 171

Chromium arsenate, ion exchange properties, 71

Other books of interest to you...

Because of your interest in our books, we have included the following catalog of books for your convenience.

Any of these books are available on an approval basis. This section has been reprinted in full from our *inorganic and organic chemistry* catalog.

If you wish to receive a complete catalog of MDI books, journals and encyclopedias, please write to us and we will be happy to send you one.

MARCEL DEKKER, INC.
95 Madison Avenue, New York, N.Y. 10016

inorganic and organic chemistry

AUGUSTINE   *Catalytic Hydrogenation*

(Techniques and Applications in Organic Synthesis Series)

by ROBERT L. AUGUSTINE, *Department of Chemistry, Seton Hall University, South Orange, New Jersey*

200 pages, illustrated. 1965

CONTENTS: Introduction • Apparatus and techniques • Catalysts and conditions • Hydrogenation of functional groups I • Hydrogenation of functional groups II • Hydrogenolysis.

AUGUSTINE   *Reduction*

(Techniques and Applications in Organic Synthesis Series)

edited by ROBERT L. AUGUSTINE, *Department of Chemistry, Seton Hall University, South Orange, New Jersey*

256 pages, illustrated. 1968

CONTENTS: Chemistry of mixed hydrides, *M. N. Rerick.* Dissolving metal reductions, *M. Smith.* Deoxygenation of carbonyl compounds, *W. Reusch.*

AUGUSTINE and TRECKER   *Oxidation*
In 2 Volumes

(Techniques and Applications in Organic Synthesis Series)

edited by ROBERT L. AUGUSTINE, *Department of Chemistry, Seton Hall University, South Orange, New Jersey,* and DAVID J. TRECKER, *Union Carbide Corporation, South Charleston, West Virginia.*

Vol. 1   edited by ROBERT L. AUGUSTINE
386 pages, illustrated. 1969

Vol. 2   edited by ROBERT L. AUGUSTINE and DAVID J. TRECKER
216 pages, illustrated. 1971

Provides concise and critical evaluations of important reactions in organic synthesis and makes available all aspects of oxidation. Serves as an easily accessible tool for the organic chemist.

CONTENTS:

Volume 1: Hydrocarbon oxidation using transition metal compounds, *D. G. Lee.* Oxidation of oxygen- and nitrogen-containing functional groups with transition metal compounds, *D. G. Lee.* Selenium dioxide oxidation, *E. N. Trachtenberg.* Glycol cleavage and related oxidations, *A. S. Perlin.* Peracid and peroxide oxidations, *S. N. Lewis.* Ozonization, *J. S. Belew.*

Volume 2: Sulfoxide-carbodiimide and related oxidations, *J. G. Moffatt.* Photosensitized oxygenations, *W. R. Adams.* Epoxidation of olefins by hydroperoxides, *R. Hiatt.* Metal ion-catalyzed oxidation of organic substrates with peroxides, *A. R. Doumaux, Jr.*

BAIZER   *Organic Electrochemistry:*
An Introduction and a Guide

edited by MANUEL M. BAIZER, *Monsanto Company, St. Louis, Missouri*

1,096 pages, illustrated. 1973

Provides in one volume for the first time a comprehensive guide to organic electrochemistry, written by organic chemists who have made notable contributions to the field. Explores the capabilities and limitations of organic electrochemistry: its principles, methods, problems; its utility in synthesis and in elucidation of mechanisms of organic reactions; and its fertility as a research area. Major emphasis is on the detailed explanation of the chemical events which accompany electron–transfer steps. Of utmost interest to all organic chemists, as well as research workers involved in electrochemistry.

CONTENTS: Introductory survey, *M. Baizer.* Basic concepts, *G. Cauquis.* Methods for the elucidation of organic electrochemical reactions, *G. Cauquis and V. Parker.* Relation between micro and macro phenomena, *P. Zuman.* Practical problems in electrolysis, *H. Lund and P. Iversen.* Cathodic reactions of hydrocarbons, *R. Dietz.* Electrochemical reduction of organic halides, *M. Rifi.* Cathodic reduction of nitro compounds, *H. Lund.* Saturated carbonyl compounds and derivatives, *L. Feoktistov and H. Lund.* α, β–unsaturated carbonyls, *M. Baizer.* Carboxylic acids and derivatives, *L. Eberson.* Onium compounds, *L. Horner.* Hydrocarbons, *L. Eberson.* Carboxylic acids, *L. Eberson.* Anodic oxidation of amines, *V. Parker.* **Anodic** oxidation of oxygen–containing compounds, *V. Parker*. Anodic oxidation of sulfur–containing compounds, *V. Parker*. Electrolysis of heterocyclic compounds, *H. Lund*. Organometallic syntheses, *H. Lehmkuhl*. Electrolytic reductive coupling, *M. Baizer*. Oxidative coupling, *K. Nyberg*. Cleavages, *L. Horner and H. Lund*. Anodic substitution, *L. Eberson*. Amalgam reductions, *H. Lund*. Electrogenerated reagents, *R. Dietz and H. Lund*. Use of the solvated electron, *H. Lund*. Comparison between electrochemical and analogous chemical reactions, *L. Eberson*. Stereochemistry of organic electrode processes, *L. Eberson and L. Horner*. Industrial electroorganic chemistry, *D. Danly*. Electrochemical polymerization, *G. Parravano*. Organic electrocatalysis, *M. Baizer*.

CARLIN Transition Metal Chemistry: A Series of Advances

edited by RICHARD L. CARLIN, *Department of Chemistry, University of Illinois at Chicago Circle*

Vol. 1 320 pages, illustrated. 1965
Vol. 2 360 pages, illustrated. 1966
Vol. 3 376 pages, illustrated. 1966
Vol. 4 368 pages, illustrated. 1968
Vol. 5 320 pages, illustrated. 1969
Vol. 6 344 pages, illustrated. 1970
Vol. 7 352 pages, illustrated. 1972

A series devoted to the science of the transition elements, one of the oldest and largest areas of research. Geared to research scientists, graduate students, and teachers of advanced inorganic chemistry.

CONTENTS:

Volume 1: Electronic structure and stereochemistry of cobalt(II), *R. L. Carlin*. Aqueous chemistry of chromium(III), *J. E. Earley and R. D. Cannon*. Hydride complexes of transition metals, *A. P. Ginsberg*. Electronic structures of square planar metal complexes, *H. B. Gray*.

Volume 2: Reactions of ligands coordinated with transition metals, *J. P. Collman*. Transition metal ions as reagents in metallo-enzymes, *A. E. Dennard and R. J. P. Williams*. Optical activity in inorganic and organic compounds, *A. D. Liehr*.

Volume 3: Electronic structures of some organometallic molecules, *D. A. Brown*. Equilibria of complexes in nonaqueous solvents, *L. I. Katzin*. Electron spin resonance of transition-metal complexes, *B. R. McGarvey*. Fluorescent lifetimes of trivalent rare earths, *G. E. Peterson*. Conformations of coordinated chelates, *A. M. Sargeson*.

Volume 4: Spectra of Re^{4+} in cubic crystal fields, *P. B. Dorain*. Paramagnetic relaxation in solutions, *W. B. Lewis and L. O. Morgan*. Nature of transition between high-spin and low-spin octahedral complexes of transition metals, *R. L. Martin and A. H. White*. Elec-

tronic structure and stereochemistry of nickel (II), *L. Sacconi*. Coordination compounds of unsaturated 1,2-dithiols and 1,2-dithioketones, *G. N. Schrauzer*.

Volume 5: Spectra of chromium(III) complexes, *L. S. Forster*. Copper complexes, *W. E. Hatfield and R. Whyman*. Metal-metal exchange interactions, *G. F. Kokoszka and G. Gordon*.

Volume 6: Theory of bridge bonding and the structure of binuclear coordination compounds, *B. Jezowska-Trzebiatowska and W. Wojciechowski*. Amine complexes of chromium (III), *C. S. Garner and D. A. House*.

Volume 7: Magnetic phase transitions at low temperatures, *J. E. Rives*. Preparation and properties of high valent first-row transition metal oxides and halides, *C. Rosenblum and S. L. Holt*. Magnetic anisotropy, *S. Mitra*.

CHAPMAN Organic Photochemistry

a series edited by ORVILLE L. CHAPMAN, *Department of Chemistry, Iowa State University, Ames*

Vol. 1 352 pages, illustrated. 1967
Vol. 2 248 pages, illustrated. 1969
Vol. 3 320 pages, illustrated. 1973

Presents a critical summary of organic photochemistry drawing together seemingly unrelated facts, summarizing progress, and clarifying problems.

CONTENTS:

Volume 1: Photochemical transformations of cyclohexadienones and related compounds, *P. J. Kropp*. Photochemical transformations of small-ring carbonyl compounds, *A. Padwa*. Photo-Fries reaction and related arrangements, *V. I. Stenberg*. Photochemistry of troponoid compounds, *D. J. Pasto*. Photochemistry of olefins, *G. Fonken*. Photocyclization of stilbenes, *F. Stermitz*. Photocycloaddition reactions, *O. L. Chapman and G. Lenz*.

Volume 2: Photosensitization by energy transfer, *N. J. Turro, J. C. Dalton, and D. S. Weiss*. Photodimerizations, *D. J. Trecker*. Photochemistry of heteroaromatic nitrogen compounds, *P. Beak and W. R. Messer*. Photochemical additions to multiple bonds, *D. Elad*.

Volume 3: The Cis-Trans photoisomerization of olefins, *J. Saltiel, J. D'Agostino, E. Megarity, L. Metts, K. Neuberger, M. Wrighton, and O. Zafiriou*. Photochemistry of three-membered heterocycles, *N. Bertoniere and G. Griffin*. Photochemistry of cyclic ketones, *O. Chapman and D. Weiss*.

CHINN Selection of Oxidants in Synthesis: Oxidation at the Carbon Atom

(Oxidation in Organic Chemistry Series, Volume 1)

by LELAND J. CHINN, *G. Searle and Co., Chicago*

204 pages, illustrated. 1971

(continued)

CHINN *(continued)*

Emphasizes stereoselectivity and the stereochemical aspects of the oxidative process. Useful to research chemists who are engaged in organic synthesis and graduate students and advanced undergraduate students in chemistry who are interested in the rationale behind the selection of an oxidizing agent for a particular transformation.

CONTENTS: Oxidation numbers • Formation of alcohols and ethers • Formation of alkyl hydroperoxides by autoxidation • Aldehydes and ketones from alcohols, halides, and amines • Formation of carboxylic acids from aldehydes • Generation of C=C or C–C bonds by dehydrogenation • Oxidation of olefinic double bonds • Oxidative cleavage of the C-C bond • Oxidation of alkyl groups to aldehydes • Oxidation of alcohols to acids and amines to amides • Oxidative cleavage of C–C and C=C bonds involving four electrons • Oxidation of methyl groups to carboxylic acids • Oxidative cleavage of C–C and C=C bonds involving six or more electrons.

COETZEE and RITCHIE
Solute-Solvent Interactions

edited by J. F. COETZEE, *Department of Chemistry, University of Pittsburgh, Pennsylvania and* CALVIN D. RITCHIE, *Department of Chemistry, State University of New York, Buffalo*

672 pages, illustrated. 1969

Directed mainly to research workers in all areas of chemistry, the book contains chapters written by research workers who are eminently prominent in their respective fields. Treats solvent effects in far greater depth than does any book published thus far.

CONTENTS: Heats and entropies of ionization, *J. W. Larson and L. G. Hepler.* Medium effects and pH in nonaqueous solvents, *R. G. Bates.* Acidity functions, *R. H. Boyd.* Interactions in dipolar aprotic solvents, *C. D. Ritchie.* Selective solvation of ions in mixed solvents, *H. Schneider.* Solvent isotope effect on thermodynamics of nonreacting solutes, *E. M. Arnett and D. R. McKelvey.* Solvent isotope effects for equilibria and reactions, *P. M. Laughton and R. E. Robertson.* Organoalkali compounds in ethers, *J. F. Garst.*

COOK   *Enamines: Synthesis, Structure, and Reactions*

edited by A. GILBERT COOK, *Department of Chemistry, Valparaiso University, Indiana*

528 pages, illustrated. 1969

Reviews and correlates in depth the synthetic, mechanistic, and physical properties of enamines.

CONTENTS: Structure and physical properties of enamines, *S. K. Malhotra.* Methods and mechanisms of enamine formation, *L. W. Haynes.* Hydrolysis of enamines, *E. J. Stamhuis.* Electrophilic substitutions and additions to enamines, *G. H. Alt.* Nucleophilic addition to iminium salts, *J. V. Paukstelis.* Cycloaddition reactions of enamines, *A. G. Cook.* Heterocyclic enamines, *O. Červinka.* Enamines in organic synthesis, *M. E. Kuehne.*

CRAGG   *Organoboranes in Organic Synthesis*

(Studies in Organic Chemistry Series, Volume 1)

by GORDON CRAGG, *Department of Chemistry, University of Cape Town, Rondebosch, South Africa :*

432 pages, illustrated. 1973

Illustrates the potential usefulness in organic synthesis of new methods for the synthesis of compounds containing a wide variety of functional groups, and examines in detail the preparation of organoboranes and their applications to the synthesis of the various classes of organic compounds. Of great value to chemists involved in synthetic, organic and organometallic research, as well as to teachers of organic chemistry.

CONTENTS: Organoboranes in organic synthesis • Synthesis of organoboranes • Hydroboration of alkenes • Oxidation of organoboranes • Hydroboration of functionalized alkenes • Hydroboration of dienes and polyenes • Hydroboration of alkynes • Synthesis of carbon chains and rings • Synthesis of functional derivatives via organoboranes • Reduction of functional groups.

DALEY and O'MALLEY   *Problems in Chemistry*

by HENRY O. DALEY, *Department of Chemistry, Bridgewater State College, Bridgewater, Massachusetts,* and ROBERT F. O'MALLEY, *Department of Chemistry, Boston College, Massachusetts*

in preparation. 1974

Provides the beginning chemistry student with a large number of problems which illustrate chemical principles. The problems are based, wherever possible, on experimental results obtained by chemists, and the references are cited.

DASENT   *Nonexistent Compounds: Compounds of Low Stability*

by W. E. DASENT, *Department of Chemistry, Victoria University of Wellington, New Zealand*

192 pages, illustrated. 1965

CONTENTS: General considerations • Compounds whose instability is a consequence of the restriction of first-row atoms (Li to F) to valence octet • Compounds whose instability is related to reluctance of certain atoms to undergo self-linkage or catenation • Compounds whose instability is a consequence of reluctance of atoms of second (and subsequent) rows to form multiple bonds involving $P\pi$-$P\pi$ overlap • Compounds whose instability has been attributed to operation of an "inert pair effect" • Compounds of elements of the first long period whose highest oxidation state is relatively unstable • Some compounds of the noble gases • Miscellaneous.

DENNEY Techniques and Methods of Organic and Organometallic Chemistry

edited by DONALD B. DENNEY, *School of Chemistry, Rutgers—The State University, New Brunswick, New Jersey*

248 pages, illustrated. 1969

Presents critical reviews of methods and techniques used in the laboratory. Is of interest to organic and organo-metallic research workers—organic and inorganic chemists—investigating the study of organic compounds.

CONTENTS: Ozonolysis of organic compounds, *R. W. Murray.* High-vacuum techniques, *A. C. Bond.* Applications of fused salts in organic chemistry, *J. E. Gordon.* Nonaqueous titrations for organic analysis, *C. A. Streuli.*

FLURRY Molecular Orbital Theories of Bonding in Organic Molecules

(Applied Quantum Chemistry Series, Volume 1)

by ROBERT L. FLURRY, JR., *Department of Chemistry, Louisiana State University, New Orleans*

244 pages, illustrated. 1968

CONTENTS: Introduction • Free electron theory • Simple LCAO theory • Perturbation methods • Solving LCAO equations • Group theory and symmetry orbitals • Atomic theory • Self-consistent molecular orbital methods • Sigma bonds • Applying the theories.

FONKEN and JOHNSON Chemical Oxidations with Microorganisms

(Oxidation in Organic Chemistry Series, Volume 2)

by GUNTHER S. FONKEN. and ROY A. JOHNSON, *The Upjohn Company, Kalamazoo, Michigan*

320 pages, illustrated. 1972

Presents organic chemists with an introduction to the many microbial oxidations of organic molecules that can be considered for use in the laboratory. Examines all major oxidative categories and several minor ones in a thorough manner. A highly useful work for organic chemists; undergraduate and graduate students in organic chemistry; industrial microbiologists and graduate students in microbiology; biochemists; and medicinal chemists working in the area of drug metabolism.

CONTENTS: Nonactivated carbon hydroxylation • Allylic oxygenations • Olefinic oxygenation • Aromatic ring hydroxylation • Aromatic ring opening • Microbiological Baeyer-Villiger oxidation • β-oxidation • Alkyl dehydrogenation • Alcohol dehydrogenation • Oxidation of amino to nitro • Oxidation of amino to hydroxyl • Sulfur oxygenation • Other microbial oxidations • Practical experimental methods.

HUYSER Methods in Free-Radical Chemistry

a series edited by EARL S. HUYSER, *Department of Chemistry, The University of Kansas, Lawrence*

Vol. 1 224 pages, illustrated. 1969
Vol. 2 256 pages, illustrated. 1969
Vol. 3 184 pages, illustrated. 1972
Vol. 4 in preparation. 1974

Written by authorities in various areas of free radical reactions, these volumes are of primary interest to the organic chemist.
CONTENTS:
Volume 1: Free-radical study by electron paramagnetic resonance, *L. Kevan.* Free radicals and photochemical reactions, *D. Neckers.* Free-radical chlorination of organic molecules, *M. L. Poutsma.*
Volume 2: Thiyl radicals, *R. M. Kellogg.* Free-radical brominations, *W. Thaler.*
Volume 3: Electrolytically generated radicals, *H.-G. Gilde.* One-electron reduction of aromatic cations, *M. Siskin.* Free-radical chlorinations via nitrogen cation radicals, *N. C. Deno.*

JACOBSON and CROSBY Naturally Occurring Insecticides

edited by MARTIN JACOBSON, *U. S. Department of Agriculture, Beltsville, Maryland* and DONALD G. CROSBY, *University of California, Davis*

600 pages, illustrated. 1971

A critical review on natural insecticides prompted by growing public alarm over the dangerous side effects of conventional pesticides and the prospects of many harmful

(continued)

JACOBSON and CROSBY (continued)

insects becoming resistant to the synthetic insecticides. Of value to entomologists, organic, analytical, and agricultural chemists, insect physiologists, and botanists.

CONTENTS: Pyrethroids, *M. Matsui and I. Yamamoto*. Rotenone and the rotenoids, *H. Fukami and M. Nakajima*. Nicotine and other tobacco alkaloids, *I. Schmeltz*. The unsaturated isobutylamides, *M. Jacobson*. Minor insecticides of plant origin, *D. Crosby*. Anthropod venoms as insecticides, *R. Beard*. Ant secretions and cantharidin, *G. Cavill and D. Clark*. Juvenile hormones, *W. Bowers*. The ecdysones, *D. Horn*. Bacillus thuringiensis as a microbial insecticide, *T. Angus*. Destruxins and piericidins, *S. Tamura and N. Takahashi*.

JONES *Inorganic Vibrational Spectroscopy*

by LLEWELLYN H. JONES, *Los Alamos Scientific Laboratory, University of California, Los Alamos, New Mexico*
Vol. 1 232 pages, illustrated. 1971

Presents a discussion of the use of vibrational spectroscopy to determine the strengths of chemical bonds, the bonding directional forces, and the interactions of one bond or bond angle with the others in a molecule. A great help to the inorganic chemist who is interested in the applications of vibrational spectroscopy or in evaluating other workers' results and interpretations.

CONTENTS: Force constants: Their interpretation and determination • Potential constants of some diatomic and triatomic molecules from observed data • Force constants of halide complexes • Metal cyanide complexes • Metal carbonyls.

KAPLAN *Bridged Free Radicals*

by LEONARD KAPLAN, *University of Chicago, Illinois*

504 pages, illustrated. 1972

Presents a comprehensive and critical examination of bridging in free radicals. Organized according to the structure of bridged free radicals in order to simplify finding specific information. Of particular importance to all graduate students and research scientists in organic and physical chemistry.

CONTENTS: Definitions • Silyl-substituted radicals • Germyl-substituted radicals • Stannyl-substituted radicals • Chloro-substituted radicals • Bromo-substituted radicals • Iodo-substituted radicals • Sulfur-substituted radicals • Cyano-substituted radicals • Vinyl-substituted radicals.

LAGOWSKI *Modern Inorganic Chemistry*

by JOSEPH J. LAGOWSKI, *University of Texas, Austin*
832 pages, illustrated. 1973

The most important textbook in the field to be published in the last decade.

Designed to give advanced undergraduate or first-year graduate students a working knowledge of the fundamentals of modern inorganic chemistry in those particular areas classically associated with the field. Acknowledges the close relationship between experiment and theory but separates these two aspects of chemistry in order to demonstrate that unity of experimental results is possible without the use of extensive theoretical arguments.

Modern Inorganic Chemistry is an invaluable teaching tool for all professors of chemistry.

CONTENTS: Atoms and their characteristics • Ionic compounds • Covalent compounds: Experimental observations • Covalent compounds: Theories of bonding • Representative elements: A brief survey • Hydrogen • Solvent properties of covalent hydrides • Alkali metals • Alkaline-earth metals • Group III Representative Elements • Group IV elements • Group V elements • Group VI elements • The halogens • The rare gases • The transition elements • Properties of transition-metal coordination compounds • Transition-metal complexes: Theoretical aspects • Organic derivates of the transition metals.

LAWLESS and SMITH *Inorganic High-Energy Oxidizers: Synthesis, Structures, and Properties*

by EDWARD W. LAWLESS and IVAN C. SMITH, *Midwest Research Institute, Kansas City, Missouri*

320 pages, illustrated. 1968

CONTENTS: Introduction • General characteristics of advanced oxidizers • Fluoronitrogen compounds • Fluorine and fluorohalogen compounds • Oxygen compounds.

LEDNICER *Contraception: The Chemical Control of Fertility*

edited by DANIEL LEDNICER, *The Upjohn Company, Kalamazoo, Michigan*

280 pages, illustrated. 1969

Provides the interested student with a critical review of the antifertility research and serves to acquaint the biologist and the chemist with the literature and methods in the field.

CONTENTS: The reproductive cycle in the female, *R. B. Jaffe, G. Peréz-Palacios, and G. B. Serra.* The biology of steroidal contraceptives, *R. A. Edgren.* The chemistry of steroidal contraceptives, *P. D. Klimstra and F. B. Colton.* The biology of nonsteroidal antifertility agents, *L. Lerner.* The chemistry of nonsteroidal antifertility agents, *D. Lednicer.* Assays and screens in antifertility research, *R. L. Elton.*

Part II: Synthesis and properties of the germanium-halogen and germanium-halogenoid bond, *J. Zuckerman.* Synthesis and properties of the tin-halogen and tin-halogenoid bond, *H. Clark and R. Puddephatt.* Synthesis and properties of the lead-halogen and lead-halogenoid bond, *S. Cook, F. Frey, and H. Shapiro.*

MacDIARMID *The Bond to Carbon*

In 2 Parts

(Organometallic Compounds of the Group IV Elements, Volume 1)

edited by ALAN G. MACDIARMID, *Department of Chemistry, University of Pennsylvania, Philadelphia*

Part I 624 pages, illustrated. 1968

Part II 280 pages, illustrated. 1968

CONTENTS:

Part I: Physical basis of the chemistry of the Group IV elements, *E. Ebsworth.* Synthesis and reactions of the silicon-carbon bond, *C. Eaborn and R. Bott.*

Part II: Synthesis and properties of the germanium-carbon bond, *F. Glockling and K. Hooton.* Synthesis and properties of the tin-carbon bond, *J. Luijten and G. van der Kerk.* Synthesis and properties of the lead-carbon bond, *L. Willemsens and G. van der Kerk.*

MacDIARMID *The Bond to Halogens and Halogenoids*

In 2 Parts

(Oranometallic Compounds of the Group IV Elements, Volume 2)

edited by ALAN G. MACDIARMID, *Department of Chemistry, University of Pennsylvania, Philadelphia*

Part I 392 pages, illustrated. 1972

Part II 248 pages, illustrated. 1972

Describes methods of synthesis of the group IV element-halogen bond and the group IV element-halogenoid bond, examines the chemical reactions in which these bonds are cleaved, and discusses the important physical and spectroscopic properties related to the presence of these bonds in a molecule. Valuable reading for research chemists and senior students of organometallic, organic, and inorganic chemistry.

CONTENTS:

Part I: Synthesis and properties of the silicon-halogen and silicon-halogenoid bond, *C. Van Dyke.*

MANHAS and BOSE *Synthesis of Penicillin, Cephalosporin C, and Analogs*

by MAGHAR S. MANHAS and AJAY K. BOSE, *Stevens Institute of Technology, Hoboken, New Jersey*

136 pages, illustrated. 1969

Begins with a brief history of penicillin synthesis, and continues with a detailed description of the spectral methods dealing with penam, cepham, and related systems which are prone to various rearrangements. Concludes with a discussion on the synthesis leading to penicillin, cephalosporin C, and their analogs.

CONTENTS: Introduction • Physical properties • Synthesis of penicillin and analogs • Synthesis of cephalosporin C and analogs.

MARCH *Problems in Advanced Organic Chemistry*

by JERRY MARCH, *Adelphi University, Garden City, New York*

432 pages, illustrated. 1971

Consists of over 800 problems, most of which are actual examples taken from recent literature, with references given for each. Answers to about one third of the problems are found at the end of the book; literature references are given for the remainder. Can accompany any textbook used for advanced courses in organic chemistry, or may stand alone when no text is available.

CONTENTS: **Problem Sets:** Bonding • Stereochemistry • Acidity, mechanisms, and reactivity • Aliphatic nucleophilic substitution • Aromatic electrophilic substitution • Aliphatic electrophilic substitution • Aromatic nucleophilic substitution • Free-radical substitution • Addition to carbon-carbon multiple bonds • Addition to carbon-hetero multiple bonds • Eliminations • Rearrangements • Oxidations and reductions • Additional problems in synthesis and mechanisms • Nomenclature • Literature • **Answers.**

MARINSKY   *Ion Exchange: A Series of Advances*

edited by JACOB A. MARINSKY, *Department of Chemistry, State University of New York, Buffalo*

Vol. 1   440 pages, illustrated. 1966
Vol. 2   256 pages, illustrated. 1969
Vol. 3   see MARINSKY and MARCUS for continuing volumes

". . . a brilliant work . . . The importance of this series lies in the vitality of its approach to the subject, together with the care with which hundreds of references are not simply collected, but are correlated, evaluated, and compared . . . throughout the books, a refreshing originality of approach is found . . ."—T. V. Arden, *Chemistry and Industry*

CONTENTS:

Volume 1: Transport processes in membranes, *S. R. Caplan and D. C. Mikulecky.* Ion-exchange kinetics, *F. Helfferich.* Ion-exchange studies of complex formation, *Y. Marcus.* Liquid ion exchangers, *E. Högfeldt.* Precise studies of ion-exchange systems using microscopy, *D. H. Freeman.* Heterogeneity and physical chemical properties of ion-exchange resins, *L. S. Goldring.* Ion-exchange selectivity, *D. Reichenberg.* Resin selectivity in dilute to concentrated aqueous solutions, *R. M. Diamond and D. C. Whitney.* Interpretation of ion-exchange phenomena, *J. A. Marinsky.*

Volume 2: Ion exchange in glasses, *R. H. Doremus.* Ion exchange in molten systems, *E. C. Freiling and M. H. Rowell.* Ion-exchange properties of zeolites, *H. S. Sherry.* Interactions between organic ions and ion-exchange resins, *J. Feitelson.* Partition chromatography of sugars, sugar alcohols, and sugar derivatives, *O. Samuelson.* Synthesis of ion-exchange resins, *R. M. Wheaton and M. J. Hatch.*

MARINSKY and MARCUS   *Ion Exchange and Solvent Extraction: A Series of Advances*

a series edited by JACOB A. MARINSKY, *Department of Chemistry, State University of New York, Buffalo,* and YIZHAK MARCUS, *Department of Inorganic and Analytical Chemistry, The Hebrew University, Jerusalem, Israel*

for earlier volumes see MARINSKY

Vol. 3   168 pages, illustrated. 1973
Vol. 4   264 pages, illustrated. 1973
Vol. 5   256 pages, illustrated. 1973
Vol. 6   in preparation. 1974

CONTENTS:

Volume 3: Extraction of metals by carboxylic acids, *D. Flett and M. Jaycock.* Solvent extraction with sulfonic acids, *G. Markovits and G. Choppin.* Nuclear magnetic resonance studies of organophosphorus extractants, *W. Stewart and T. Siddall, III.* Experience with the AKUFVE solvent extraction equipment, *J. Rydberg, H. Reinhardt, and J. Liljenzin.*

Volume 4: Ion exchange in nonaqueous and mixed solvents, *Y. Marcus.* Liquid exchange chromatography, *H. Walton.* Liquid ion exchange technology, *R. Kunin.* Electronic and ionic exchange properties, conductivity, and permselectivity of organic semiconductors and redox exchangers, *R. Buvet, M. Guillou, and L. Yu.* Equations for the evaluation of formation constants of complexed ion species in crosslinked and linear polyelectrolyte systems, *J. Marinsky.*

Volume 5: New inorganic ion exchangers, *A. Clearfield, G. Nancollas, and R. Blessing.* Application of ion exchange to element separation and analysis, *F. Strelow.* Pellicular ion exchange resins in chromatography, *C. Horvath.*

Volume 6: Carbon fiber structure, surface and surface treatments, *J. Larsen and T. Smith.* Isolation of drugs and related organic compounds by ion-pair extraction, *G. Schill.* The dynamics of liquid-liquid extraction processes, *G. Pollock and A. Johnson.* The application of the solubility parameter concept in liquid-liquid extraction, *H. Irving.*

MUETTERTIES   *Transition Metal Hydrides*

(The Hydrogen Series, Volume 1)

edited by EARL L. MUETTERTIES, *E. I. du Pont de Nemours & Company, Wilmington, Delaware*

360 pages, illustrated. 1971

The first book to answer the need for a systematic and definitive presentation of the chemistry of molecular transition metal hydrides. Of great value to inorganic and physical chemists, as well as to organic chemists seeking stereospecific syntheses.

CONTENTS: Physical properties of hydrogen, deuterium, and tritium, *E. L. Muetterties.* The transition metal-hydrogen interaction, *E. L. Muetterties.* Molecular structures of transition metal hydride complexes, *B. A. Frenz and J. A. Ibers.* Stereochemistry and stereochemical nonrigidity in transition metal hydrides, *J. P. Jesson.* Systematics of transition metal hydrides, *R. A. Schunn.* Role of transition metal hydrides in homogeneous catalysis, *C. A. Tolman.*

MUETTERTIES and KNOTH   *Polyhedral Boranes*

by EARL L. MUETTERTIES and WALTER H. KNOTH, *Central Research Department, Experimental Station, E. I. duPont de Nemours & Co., Wilmington, Delaware*

208 pages, illustrated. 1968

CONTENTS: Introduction • Structure and theory • Polyhedral rearrangements • Structure-reactivity correlation • Synthesis of polyhedral boranes • Chemistry • Nomenclature and numbering conventions • Recent developments.

OWEN Characterization of Organic Compounds by Chemical Methods: An Introductory Laboratory Textbook

by T. C. OWEN, *University of South Florida, Tampa*

256 pages, illustrated. 1969

CONTENTS: Introduction • Functional group organic chemistry • Equipment and techniques • Functional group identification • Selection and preparation of solid derivatives • Tables of physical properties.

RAO Xanthates and Related Compounds

by S. R. RAO, *Indian Institute of Technology, Delhi, India*

512 pages, illustrated. 1971

A comprehensive survey of all aspects of the basic chemistry of xanthates and the related compounds, dixanthogens. Directed to mineral flotation engineers and investigators, textile chemists, chemical analysts, and investigators in organo-sulfur chemistry. CONTENTS: Introduction • Methods of preparation and purification • General chemical properties and reactions • Methods of analysis of xanthates • Dixanthogens • Structural chemistry of xanthates and dixanthogens • Xanthates in mineral flotation • Analytical chemical applications • Xanthates in the cellulose industry • Miscellaneous applications of xanthates and dixanthogens.

RIFI and COVITZ Introduction to Organic Electrochemistry

(Techniques and Applications of Organic Synthesis Series)

by M. R. RIFI and F. H. COVITZ, *Union Carbide Corporation, Bound Brook, New Jersey*

424 pages, illustrated. 1973

Provides an up-to-date introduction to the field of organic electrochemistry. Discusses theoretical aspects and emphasizes the practical advantages of many experimental procedures and specific types of synthesis and cell designs. Primarily intended for organic chemists in academic or industrial environments who need the basic information to initiate a program in this field.

CONTENTS: Basic principles • Apparatus and techniques • Reduction of functional groups • Oxidation of functional groups • Electro-initiated polymerization • Electrocoating.

SAWYER Organotin Compounds

In 3 Volumes

edited by ALBERT SAWYER, *Department of Chemistry, University of New Hampshire, Durham*

Vol. 1 272 pages, illustrated. 1971
Vol. 2 389 pages, illustrated. 1971
Vol. 3 384 pages, illustrated. 1973

Provides contemporary, comprehensive coverage of the entire field of organotin chemistry, prepared by individuals who are well informed in their specialized areas. Of particular interest to organic, inorganic, polymer, surface, and physical chemists working in the field of organometallics and organotin chemistry.

CONTENTS:

Volume 1: Introduction, *G. van der Kerk and J. Luijten.* Organotin hydrides, *E. Kupchik.* Organotin halides, *G. van der Kelen, E. van den Berghe, and L. Verdonck.* Organotin compounds with Sn-O bonds: Organotin alkoxides, oxides, and related compounds, *A. Bloodworth and A. Davies.*

Volume 2: Organotin compounds with Sn-O bonds. Organotin carboxylates, salts, and complexes, *R. Okawara and M. Ohara.* Organotin compounds with Sn-S, Sn-Se, and Sn-Te bonds, *H. Schumann, I. Schumann-Ruidisch, and M. Schmidt.* Organotin compounds with Sn-N bonds, *K. Jones and M. F. Lappert.* Organotin compounds with Sn-P, Sn-As, Sn-Sb, and Sn-Bi bonds, *H. Schumann, I. Schumann-Ruidisch, and M. Schmidt.*

Volume 3: Organotin compounds with Sn-C bonds without Sn-Sn bonds, *M. Gielen and J. Nasielski.* Organotin compounds with Sn-Sn bonds, *A. K. Sawyer.* Organotin compounds with Sn-other metal bonds, *M. J. Newlands.* Applications and biological effects of organotin compounds, *J. G. A. Luijten.* Organotin polymers, *M. C. Henry and W. E. Davidsohn.* Analysis of organotin compounds, *C. R. Dillard.*

SCHRAUZER Transition Metals in Homogeneous Catalysis

edited by G. N. SCHRAUZER, *University of California, La Jolla*

428 pages, illustrated. 1972

The first book devoted entirely to homogeneous catalysis by transition metal complexes. Bridges the gap between academic teaching and industrial research in homogeneous catalysis.

(continued)

SCHRAUZER (continued)

CONTENTS: Catalysis: Fundamental aspects and scope, *G. Schrauzer*. Hydrogenation and dehydrogenation, *J. Kwiatek*. π-Allyl system in catalysis, *W. Keim*. Homogeneous metal catalyzed oxidation of organic compounds, *E. Stern*. Carbonylation, *D. Thompson and R. Whyman*. Catalysis of symmetry forbidden reactions, *F. Mango and J. Schachtschneider*. Electron-transfer catalysis, *R. Linck*.

SENNING Sulfur in Organic and Inorganic Chemistry

In 3 Volumes

edited by ALEXANDER SENNING, *Aarhus University, Denmark*

Vol. 1 400 pages, illustrated. 1971
Vol. 2 376 pages, illustrated. 1972
Vol. 3 480 pages, illustrated. 1972

Presents an integrated treatment of sulfur chemistry across the traditional lines of inorganic, organic, physical-chemical, and biochemical aspects of this field, and gives a critical and authoritative account of the principles found useful in the systemization of known facts and in the design of new research. Of prime importance to academic researchers in inorganic, organic, analytical, and physical chemistry, and biochemistry. Also of interest to industrial researchers working with drugs or pesticides and to graduate students.

CONTENTS:

Volume 1: Introduction, *A. Senning*. The sulfur-silicon bond, *A. Haas*. The sulfur-nitrogen bond, *H. W. Roesky*. The sulfur-phosphorus bond, *L. Almasi*. The sulfur-oxygen bond, *H. H. Szmant*. The sulfur-sulfur bond, *J. L. Kice*. The sulfur-fluorine bond, *S. P. von Halasz and O. Glemser*. The sulfur-chlorine bond, *C. R. Russ and I. B. Douglass*. The sulfur-bromine bond, *P. S. Magee*. The sulfur-iodine bond, *J. P. Danehy*.

Volume 2: The chemistry of atomic sulfur, *O. P. Strausz*. Diatomic species containing sulfur, *B. Meyer, D. Jensen, and T. Oommen*. Bond energy terms in the chemistry of sulfur, selenium, and tellurium, *D. A. Johnson*. Oxyacids of sulfur, *M. Schmidt*. Metabolic pathways of organic sulfur compounds, *G. A. Maw*. The pharmacology and toxicology of inorganic sulfur compounds, *B. Sörbo*. The mass spectra of sulfur compounds, *G. Schroll and S.-O. Lawesson*. Mixed sulfur halides, *F. Seel*. Commercially important sulfur compounds, *R. Leclercq*. Chromatographic techniques in sulfur chemistry, *E. R. Cole and R. F. Bayfield*.

Volume 3: Reactions of elemental sulfur with inorganic, organic, and metal-organic compounds, *H. Schumann*. Inorganic and organic polysulfides, *T. Pickering and A. V. Tobolsky*. The quantum chemistry of sulfur compounds, *J. Fabian*. Steric aspects of sulfur chemistry, *P. Laur*. NMR spectra of sulfur compounds,

C. Brown. Labeled sulfur compounds, *E. Blasius, W. Neumann, and H. Wagner*. Thionenethiol tautomerism, *R. Mayer*. The nomenclature of sulfur compounds and their selenium and tellurium analogs, *K. L. Loening*. Nucleophilicity of organic sulfur compounds, *M. J. Janssen*.

TARRANT Fluorine Chemistry Reviews

a series edited by PAUL TARRANT, *Department of Chemistry, University of Florida, Gainesville*

Vol. 1 430 pages, illustrated. 1967
Vol. 2 192 pages, illustrated. 1968
Vol. 3 160 pages, illustrated. 1969
Vol. 4 216 pages, illustrated. 1969
Vol. 5 200 pages, illustrated. 1971
Vol. 6 168 pages, illustrated. 1973

A series concerned with the theoretical and practical aspects of fluorine chemistry which provides complete coverage of current research in this rapidly expanding field. A valuable asset to all researchers involved in the field of fluorine chemistry.

CONTENTS:

Volume 1: Synthesis, compounding, and properties of nitroso rubbers, *M. C. Henry, C. G. Griffis, and E. C. Stump*. Electrochemical fluorination, *S. Nagase*. Fluoroketenes, *Yu. A. Cheburkov and I. L. Knunyants*. Hexafluoroacetone, *C. G. Krespan and J. J. Middleton*. Fluorocarbon toxicity and biological action, *J. W. Clayton, Jr*. Diels-Alder reactions of organic fluorine compounds, *D. R. A. Perry*. Methods for the introduction of hydrogen into fluorinated compounds, *F. J. Mettille and D. J. Burton*. Reactions involving fluoride ion and polyfluoroalkyl anions, *J. A. Young*.

Volume 2: Cycloaddition reaction of fluoroolefins, *W. H. Sharkey*. Reaction of halogenated cycloalkenes with nucleophiles, *J. D. Park, R. J. McMurtry, and J. H. Adams*. Ionization potentials and molecule-ion dissociation energies for diatomic metal halides, *J. W. Hastie and J. L. Margrave*. NMR spectra of nitrogen-fluorine compounds, *W. S. Brey, Jr. and J. B. Hynes*. ^{19}F chemical shifts and coupling constants of fluoroxy compounds, *C. J. Hoffman*.

Volume 3: Fluorine compounds in anesthesiology, *E. Larsen*. Reactions of fluoroolefins with electrophilic reagents, *B. Dyatkin, E. Mochalina, and I. Knunyants*. Fluoroalicyclic derivatives of metals and metalloids, *W. Cullen*. Phosphorus, arsenic, and antimony pentafluorophenyl compounds, *M. Fild and O. Glemser*.

Volume 4: Polyhaloalkyl derivatives of sulphur, *R. Dresdner and T. Hooper*. The chemistry of fluorinated acetylenes, *M. Bruce and W. Cullen*. The chemistry of aliphatic fluoronitrocarbons, *E. Bissell*.

Volume 5: Electron spin resonance of irradiated organic fluorine compounds, *M. Iwasaki*. The preparation and chemistry of fluorinated diazo compounds and diazirines, *C. G. Krespan and W. J. Middleton.* Fluorine-containing epoxides, *P. Tarrant, C. G. Allison, K. P. Barthold, and E. C. Stump, Jr.* The chemistry of fluoroalkyl radicals, *A. P. Stefani.*

Volume 6: The radiation chemistry of polyfluorinated organic compounds, *H. Sutcliffe and I McAlpine.* Fluoro-β-diketones and metal fluoro-β-diketonates, *P. Mushak, M. Glenn, and J. Savory.* NMR spectra and characteristic frequencies of compounds containing N-S-F bonds, *H. Horn.*

TAYLOR and BATTERSBY
Cyclopentanoid Terpene Derivatives

(Organic Substances of Natural Origin Series, Volume 2)

edited by W. I. TAYLOR, *International Flavors and Fragrances, Inc., Union Beach, New Jersey,* and A. R. BATTERSBY, *University Chemical Laboratory, University of Cambridge, England*

448 pages, illustrated. 1969

CONTENTS: The iridoid glycosides and similar substances, *J. M. Bobbitt and K.-P. Segebarth.* Picrotoxin, *C. J. Coscia.* Insect terpenoids and nepetalactone, *G. W. K. Cavill.* Monoterpene alkaloids, *W. C. Wildman, J. Le Men, and (in part) K. Wiesner.* Lower furanoterpenes, *T. Kubota.* Sesquiterpene alkaloids, *O. E. Edwards.*

TAYLOR and BATTERSBY   Oxidative
Coupling of Phenols

(Organic Substances of Natural Origin Series, Volume 1)

edited by W. I. TAYLOR, *International Flavors and Fragrances, Inc., Union Beach, New Jersey,* and A. R. BATTERSBY, *University Chemical Laboratory, University of Cambridge, England*

408 pages, illustrated. 1967

CONTENTS: Phenol coupling, *H. Musso.* Some natural products derived by phenol oxidation, *A. I. Scott.* Phenol oxidations in the alkaloid field, *A. R. Battersby.* Biochemical aspects of oxidative coupling of phenols, *B. R. Brown.* Aphid pigments, *D. W. Cameron and Lord Todd.* Lignin — a natural polymeric product of phenol oxidation, *J. M. Harkin.* Lignans and cyclolignans, *K. Weinges and R. Spänig.*

TAYLOR and FARNSWORTH   *Vinca Alkaloids*

edited by WILLIAM I. TAYLOR, *International Flavors and Fragrances, Union Beach, New Jersey* and NORMAN R. FARNSWORTH, *Department of Pharmacognosy and Pharmacology, University of Illinois, Chicago*

in preparation. 1974

Brings together in a single volume all the important aspects of *vinca* alkaloids. An excellent text for graduate students who are well grounded in organic chemistry, botany, or pharmacology, and a useful reference for established researchers.

CONTENTS: A synopsis of the genus *vinca* including its taxonomic and nomenclatural history, *W. Stearn.* The phytochemistry of *vinca* species, *N. Farnsworth.* The chemistry of the *vinca* alkaloids, *W. Taylor.* Chemotaxonomy of *vinca* species, *J. Trojánek, M. Novácek, and F. Stary.* The commercial cultivation of *vinca minor, K. Szász and G. Mark.* The pharmacology of *vinca* species and their alkaloids, *M. Hava.*

VIEHE   Chemistry of Acetylenes

edited by H. G. VIEHE, *Union Carbide European Research Associates, Brussels, Belgium*

1320 pages, illustrated. 1969

Presents for the first time in many years an up-to-date coverage of the chemistry of acetylene compounds. The material has been arranged in such an order as to develop and cover as many aspects of the field as possible. Of significant value to the entire chemical industry.

CONTENTS: **Part I: Theoretical:** Structure and physical properties of acetylenic compounds; the nature of the triple bond, *J. Dale.* **Part II: Syntheses:** Synthesis of acetylenes and polyacetylenes by elimination reactions, *G. Köbrich and P. Buck.* Synthesis of acetylenes and polyacetylenes by substitution reactions, *W. Ziegenbein.* **Part III: Reactions:** Ionic additions to acetylenes, *E. Winterfeldt.* Free radical additions to acetylenes, *M. Julia.* Partial catalytic hydrogenation of acetylenes, *H. Gutmann and H. Lindlar.* Propargylic rearrangements, *J. H. Wotiz.* Cyclic compounds from acetylenes, *R. Fuks and H. G. Viehe.* Coupling of acetylenes, *P. Cadiot and W. Chodkiewicz.* **Part IV: The Chemistry of Heterosubstituted Acetylenes:** 1-Halogenoacetylenes, *S. Delavarenne and H. G. Viehe.* Acetylenic ethers and thioethers, *L. Brandsma, H. J. T. Bos, and J. F. Arens.* Ynamines, *H. G. Viehe.* Acetylenic derivatives of groups IIIb, IVb, and Vb, *P. Cadiot and W. Chodkiewicz.* **Part V: Chemistry of Special Acetylenes:** Acetylenes from nature, *F. Bohlmann.* Cyclic acetylenes, *A. Krebs.* Dehydrobenzene, *R. W. Hoffmann.* Dehydrohetarenes, *H. J. den Hertog and H. C. van der Plas.*

───────OTHER BOOKS OF INTEREST───────

BOLKER *Natural and Synthetic*
Polymers: An Introduction

  by HENRY I. BOLKER, *Department of*
  Chemistry, McGill University, Montreal,
  Quebec
  in preparation. 1973

DURIG *Vibrational Spectra and*
Structure: A Series of Advances

  a series edited by JAMES R. DURIG, *Uni-*
  versity of South Carolina, Columbia
  Vol. 1 224 pages, illustrated. 1972
  Vol. 2 in preparation. 1973

MATAGA and KUBOTA *Molecular*
Interactions and Electronic Spectra

  by NOBORU MATAGA, *Osaka University,*
  Osaka, Japan and TANEKAZU KUBOTA,

Shionogi Research Laboratory, Osaka,
Japan
520 pages, illustrated. 1970

MUROV *Handbook of*
Photochemistry

  by STEVEN L. MUROV, *Department of*
  Chemistry, State University of New York
  at Stony Brook
  in preparation. 1973

VOGL and FURUKAWA
Polymerization of Heterocyclics

  edited by OTTO VOGL, *Department of*
  Polymer Science and Engineering, Univer-
  sity of Massachusetts, Amherst, and JUNJI
  FURUKAWA, *Department of Synthetic*
  Chemistry, Kyoto University, Japan
  216 pages, illustrated. 1973

───────────JOURNALS OF INTEREST───────

MOLECULAR PHOTOCHEMISTRY

  editor: DONALD VALENTINE, JR., *Hoffman-LaRoche, Inc., Nutley, New Jersey*

A periodical designed to encourage further discourse between photochemists and spectro-
scopists so that the symbiotic relationship between the two fields may be fruitfully
broadened. Mechanisms of photochemical reactions, primary processes, structure-reactivity
relationships, spectral-reactivity relationships, structures of molecules in excited states,
radiationless processes, and electronic energy transfer are discussed.

4 issues per volume

SYNTHESIS IN INORGANIC AND METAL-ORGANIC CHEMISTRY
An International Journal for Rapid Communication in Inorganic
and Metal-organic Synthetization

  editor: KURT MOEDRITZER, *Monsanto Company, St. Louis, Missouri*

Actively serves the practicing chemist by collecting new methods and techniques for
synthetization of compounds, preparation of new and known compounds, and general
procedures in organometallic and inorganic chemistry. It makes available for the first
time, preparations and procedures that have heretofore been hidden in graduate theses,
government reports, and personal communications.

4 issues per volume

SYNTHETIC COMMUNICATIONS

  editor: JAMES A. MARSHALL, *Northwestern University, Evanston, Illinois*

In recent years, the use of communications to provide a means for the rapid publication
of chemical data has increased markedly. Unfortunately, in those communications pertaining to synthetic organic chemistry, experimental details are usually omitted and
generally an extensive wait is needed before they become available. *Synthetic Communica-*
tions is a journal in which sufficient experimental detail is presented to permit the reaction
or sequence to be repeated by reasonably skilled laboratory workers. The journal assists
organic chemists the world over in attaining their goals.

6 issues per volume